Bache

Devoted Dads!

Bachelors' Babies

SECOND-TIME BRIDE
by
Lynne Graham

FAMILY SECRETS
by
Leigh Michaels

PART-TIME FATHER
by
Sharon Kendrick

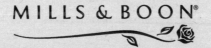

MILLS & BOON®

MILLS & BOON and MILLS & BOON with the Rose Device
are registered trademarks of the publisher.
Harlequin Mills & Boon Limited,
Eton House, 18-24 Paradise Road, Richmond, Surrey, TW9 1SR

BACHELORS' BABIES
© by Harlequin Enterprises II B.V., 2001

Second-Time Bride, Family Secrets and *Part-Time Father*
were first published in Great Britain by Harlequin Mills & Boon Limited
in separate, single volumes.

Second-Time Bride © Lynne Graham 1997
Family Secrets © Leigh Michaels 1994
Part-Time Father © Sharon Kendrick 1995

ISBN 0 263 82774 7

05-0601

Printed and bound in Spain
by Litografia Rosés S.A., Barcelona

Lynne Graham was born in Northern Ireland and has been a keen Mills & Boon® reader since her teens. She is very happily married with an understanding husband, who has learned to cook since she started to write! Her five children keep her on her toes. She has a very large Old English sheepdog, which knocks everything over, and two cats. When time allows, Lynne is a keen gardener.

Look out for:
DUARTE'S CHILD by Lynne Graham
in Modern Romance™, August 2001

SECOND-TIME BRIDE
by
LYNNE GRAHAM

CHAPTER ONE

TARA stood in the doorway, a daunting five feet nine inches of teenage truculence. 'Why do I have to go to Aunt Janet's?'

'Because that's what you do on Saturdays if I have to work.' Daisy shimmied her slender hips into a burgundy skirt while frantically trying to do up her blouse with her other hand, one anxious eye on her daughter, the other on the clock by the bedside. 'And if you're at Janet's I don't have to worry about you.'

'Yeah, so, like, it's not for *my* benefit, it's for *yours*.' Dark brown eyes rested accusingly on her much smaller parent.

'Look, can we have this out tonight?' Daisy begged, feverishly digging through the foot of her wardrobe for two matching shoes.

'I'm thirteen and I'm not stupid. I wouldn't drink or do drugs—'

'I should hope not,' Daisy muttered with a compulsive shudder.

'And I'm not like you were. I'm really sensible and mature for my age—'

'Why do I sometimes get the impression that I'm no giant in your opinion?'

'Mum, you're bound to be a worrier! You got taken in and rolled out by a major creep at seventeen and you've been paying for it ever since because you got stuck with me,' Tara reminded her ruefully. 'But I am not going to make the same mistake. Unless Mr Impossibly-

Rich-and-Handsome comes knocking on the door while
you're out, you're safe! I just want to go down to the
market with Susie and buy a new top. All the best things
will be gone if I have to wait until this afternoon—'

'I have *never* felt stuck with you!' Daisy protested.

'Mum...we haven't got time to get into that sort of
stuff. The market?' Tara pleaded.

Daisy hurried through the gilded glass doors of Elite
Estates exactly forty-five minutes later, breathless and
feeling harassed but trying not to look it. Her boss, Giles
Carter, had phoned first thing to inform her that the
virus doing the rounds of the agency had knocked out
the boy wonder on the sales team—Barry the Barracuda,
as Daisy thought of him in private. Her presence was
required to deal with Barry's latest new client on what
should have been a much cherished day off.

Daisy had worked ten years for Elite Estates and had
no illusions about management chauvinism. She was the
token woman on the sales staff. She had fought her way
up the office ranks with the greatest difficulty, disad-
vantaged by her sex, her lack of height and her youthful
appearance. It had taken hard sales figures to persuade
Giles to take her seriously but he still ensured that she
dealt only with the properties at the lowest end of the
market.

'Giles has phoned down for you twice,' Joyce on
Reception told her in a warning hiss. 'And boy, have
you got a treat in store...'

Daisy felt a cold chill down her back. Giles had never
given her a treat in his life. She always got the difficult
clients. 'It's not that old lady back again, is it? Mrs
Sykes?'

Joyce laughed. 'Didn't you notice the limousine
out front?'

Daisy had been in too much of a hurry to notice anything. Now she looked and saw the impressive long silver vehicle parked outside.

'The most utterly dreamy-looking guy I've ever seen got out of it,' Joyce sighed in a languishing undertone. 'Sadly, an utterly dreamy-looking blonde got out with him.'

A couple... Hopefully the type who still liked each other and respected each other's opinions. Daisy had had some nightmare experiences with twosomes who hadn't been able to agree on anything when it had come to the home of their dreams. Last-minute pull-outs on sales had been the result.

She knocked on the door of Giles's sumptuous office and walked straight in.

It was the woman she saw first. She was studying her watch with a little *moue* of annoyance, a fabulous mane of corn-gold hair partially concealing her features. A tall dark male was standing with his back turned to the door. He swung fluidly round as Daisy entered but she couldn't see his face in the sunlight flooding through the windows.

Giles gave her an exasperated look. 'I expected you sooner than this,' he complained ungraciously.

'Sorry,' Daisy said to the room at large. 'I hope you haven't been waiting too long.'

'Miss Thornton... this is Mr Leopardi and Miss Nina Franklin.' Giles introduced them in the oily voice he employed solely around wealthy clients.

Daisy froze. *Leopardi.* That name thudded into her brain like a sharp blow. Stunned, she stared at the large male presence now blocking out the sunlight. All she could focus on was a pale blue tie set against a slice of snowy white shirt bounded by the lapels of an exquis-

itely tailored charcoal-grey jacket. Numbly she tipped
her silver-fair head back and looked up at him. Disbelief
enclosed her in complete stasis. It *was* Alessio! The shock
of recognition was so intense that she couldn't move a
muscle. She simply stood there, all colour drained from
her triangular face, her polite smile sliding away into
nothingness. The hand she had begun to extend dropped
weakly back to her side again.

Helplessly she collided with deep-set dark eyes fixed
on her with an incredulous intensity that was as great
as her own. And then luxuriant black lashes swept low,
swiftly screening his gaze from her. She saw the tautness
of his facial muscles beneath the gold of his dark skin,
grasped the fierce control he was exerting and, with a
huge effort, dragged her shattered eyes from him,
fighting to regain her composure.

'Mr Leopardi...' she muttered in a wobbly undertone, and began to raise her hand again with all the
flair of a malfunctioning automaton.

Alessio ignored the gesture and spun on his heel to
address Giles. 'Is this woman the only employee you have
available?' he enquired harshly.

There was a sharp little silence.

'Miss Thornton is one of our most experienced
members of staff.' Giles fixed an ingratiating smile to
his full lips but his dismay was obvious. 'Perhaps you
think she seems a little on the young side but she's actually a good deal older than she looks!'

Daisy flushed to the hairline. The beautiful blonde
giggled. The thick silence pulsed like a wild thing in a
room that now felt suffocatingly airless. She focused on
Alessio's shoes—hand-stitched Italian loafers. She remembered him barefoot and in trainers. That was the

only thought in her mind but it speedily flowed on into another.

She remembered a teenage boy, *not* a full-grown adult male. She knew the adult only from pictures in newsprint that fractured her peace for days afterwards. But how much more disturbing it was to be faced with Alessio in the flesh…and without any warning whatsoever. Her tummy muscles were horribly cramped up. She felt sick, physically sick, and could not have opened her mouth had her life depended on it.

Giles cleared his throat uneasily. 'I'm afraid that there isn't anyone else available this morning. If it wasn't for *this—*' he frowned down at the clumsy plaster cast on his foot '—I would have been delighted to personally escort you round the Blairden property. As it is—'

'Alessio…if we don't get a move on, I'll be late for my booking,' the blonde complained petulantly, unfolding lithely from her chair to reveal a height very little short of Alessio's six feet three.

The woman was a model—a very well-known model, Daisy recognised belatedly, her dazed eyes scanning that impossibly perfect bone structure. She had seen that same face on countless magazine covers. And what had Giles said her name was? Like a sleepwalker, she moved forward and extended her hand. 'Miss Franklin…'

Manicured fingertips brushed hers only in passing. Bored green eyes flicked dismissively over her. The blonde slid her hand into Alessio's in a gesture of possessive intimacy and curved right round him to whisper something in his ear, her other hand moving caressingly up over his chest to curve finally to one broad shoulder.

Daisy went rigid and stared. Then abruptly she looked away, but every nerve in her body screamed as she did so. For a split second, as her own fingers had closed tightly in on themselves, she had been tempted to thrust their bodies apart. That insane urge shook her inside out.

'If you'll excuse me, I'll brief Miss Thornton.' Giles closed a taut hand round Daisy's elbow and practically pulled her out into the corridor.

His heavy features were flushed and angry. 'What's the silent act in aid of? No wonder the bloke wasn't impressed! Don't you know who he is?'

Daisy studied the wall opposite.

'The Leopardi Merchant Bank...that's who he is! I mean, you just stood there gawking at him! Hell's teeth, why does the richest client we've had in months have to come through the door the one and only day Barry's away sick?' Giles groaned in disbelief.

And it couldn't be happening to a nicer person, Daisy found herself thinking, because it was easier to think about that than to think of what had just happened. Of all the estate agencies in the London area, why had Alessio had to choose this one? Was it because of the grovelling service Giles offered to the well-heeled? Alessio was so rich that he would get that kind of service anywhere. Her temples pounded with sick tension.

'Hey...you're not coming down with this blasted virus *too*, are you?' Giles demanded, taking an almost comically fast step back from her.

'No...' Daisy finally found her voice again. 'I'm fine.'

'Then what's the matter with—?' Giles fell abruptly silent as the door behind her opened.

'Since we're in a hurry, Miss Thornton's services will be adequate,' Alessio asserted flatly.

Goose-flesh prickled along the nape of Daisy's neck. She didn't turn round even though she could see Giles regarding that scarcely civil oversight with a fresh look of incomprehension. *Adequate?* Her teeth clenched. Fierce resentment, backed by a rolling tide of humiliation she didn't want to admit to, flared through her taut length.

Thirteen years ago she had been unceremoniously dumped and she had done nothing to deserve Alessio's brutally dismissive reaction to her in front of her boss and his girlfriend. Was it embarrassment? Or was he, just like her, fighting off a distressing surge of adolescent memories? Don't kid yourself, Daisy, a more cynical voice urged. Even at nineteen, Alessio Leopardi didn't have a sensitive bone in his body...

Rigid-backed, Daisy descended the wrought-iron spiral staircase that ran down to the ground floor, and walked out through the crowded front office. Her legs felt as if they might fold beneath her at any moment. A deep trembling was beginning inside her. Shock was setting in hard. As she emerged out onto the pavement and began turning in the direction of the staff car park, Alessio drawled from behind her, 'We'll use the limo.'

'Of course,' she managed half under her breath.

'So tell us about this house,' Nina Franklin invited thinly as Daisy slid stiffly along the indicated seat opposite her.

Daisy's lips parted and closed again. She knew virtually nothing about the property in Blairden Square, not even if there were any offers on it. Since Giles had never allowed her to deal with what he termed the 'superior residences' on the agency books, she had had no reason to take any interest in them. Starter homes and apartments were generally her field. But had she been in her right mind she would have checked out the facts before she'd left the office.

A glossy brochure landed squarely on her lap. She jumped. Startled violet eyes switched to the male she had been rigorously avoiding looking at.

'Time to bone up,' Alessio said very drily, his expressive mouth as hard as iron.

'You're not very efficient, are you?' his companion remarked in cutting addition. 'High-powered sales routines are painful but total ignorance is something else again!'

Daisy had coloured but she tilted her chin. 'I'm afraid I haven't dealt with this particular property before—'

'It's a Georgian terrace,' Alessio slotted in gently. 'But don't worry about it. We can read too.'

Daisy bent her head, his smooth derision stinging like acid on her over-sensitive skin. Why was he treating her like this? Alessio was blunt but he had never been a boor. She didn't understand his apparent need to humiliate her. Surely he couldn't *still* be blaming her after all these years? And it was so ridiculous to be forced to pretend that they were strangers. Was that her fault...or his? He had made no attempt to acknowledge their previous relationship either. But then why should he have? Why should either of them want to? That relationship was all but lost in the mists of time, she told herself, until intelligence intervened. How could that long-ago summer ever be lost for her when she had Tara? Her stomach cramped again into even tighter knots.

The buzz of a mobile phone broke the tense silence. Daisy didn't lift her head. But she couldn't concentrate, couldn't even begin to study the brochure. It was as if her whole brain had gone into a state of suspended animation, as if the world had stopped dead the instant she'd glanced up and seen Alessio in Giles's office. No longer the long, lean youth she recalled but, if anything, even more heartbreakingly handsome...

He had level dark brows, cheekbones sharp enough to cut concrete, an aristocratic blade of a nose, lustrous tawny eyes and a head of glossy black hair, now ruthlessly suppressed into a smooth cut and infinitely shorter than she recalled. His hard-boned features were intensely male, his wide, beautifully shaped mouth pure sensual threat. He could smile and steal your heart with one scorching, teasing glance...but *that* had been the boy, not the man, Daisy reminded herself painfully.

She flinched as Nina Franklin gave an explosive little shriek of annoyance and thrust the mobile phone back into her capacious bag.

'I can't stay!' she told Alessio furiously. 'Joss needs me now. I could scream but how can I refuse? He's done me too many favours. You might as well let me out here. I can walk to the studio faster than you can get me there in this traffic! Look, I'll try to make it over to the house before you leave.'

'Relax...it's not important,' Alessio murmured soothingly.

'I could strangle Joss!' the blonde exclaimed resentfully, and then her green eyes landed on Daisy and hardened to accusing arrows of steel. 'If *you* had been on time, this wouldn't be happening!'

'Perhaps you would prefer to cancel and make a fresh appointment?' Daisy suggested with an eagerness she couldn't conceal.

'No, I'll keep this one,' Alessio drawled.

Stiff as a small statue, Daisy quite deliberately averted her gaze as the limousine stopped; the other woman slid out, but not without many regretful mutterings and an attempt at a lingering and physical goodbye that had car horns screeching in protest as the lights changed. *Of course* they were lovers. Daisy's fine features were clenched fiercely tight. The intimacy between them was blatant.

Viewing a house together... Were they getting married? Her stomach twisted as she pondered that idea for the first time. For some reason she suddenly felt as if somebody was jumping up and down on her lungs. The door slammed again, sealing her into unwanted isolation with Alessio, and Daisy stopped breathing altogether.

'It's been a day for unpleasant surprises,' Alessio commented grimly.

Daisy finally got up the courage to look at him again, her strained violet eyes unguarded. 'Is that why you felt that you had to take it out on me?'

'You are not one of my happier memories. What did you expect?' Hard eyes regarded her pale face without any perceptible emotion at all.

'I don't know...' Daisy whispered unevenly. 'I just never expected to see you again.'

'Look on this as a once-in-a-lifetime coincidence,' Alessio urged with chilling contempt. 'As greedy little bitches go, you're still top of the list in my experience! I would go some distance to avoid a repeat of this encounter.'

In the pin-dropping silence which ensued, Daisy turned bone-white. Her appalled gaze clung to his set dark features and the cold hostility stamped there. He made no attempt to hide the emotion. Shock rolled over her in a revitalised wave. He despised her; he *really* despised her! But why? Why should he feel like that? Hadn't she let him go free? Hadn't she given him back what he'd wanted and needed and what she should never have taken? Hadn't that single, unselfish action been sufficient to defuse his resentment?

'But it is some consolation to learn that you're now poor enough to be forced to earn a living,' Alessio acknowledged, his cold eyes resting on her like ice-picks in search of cruelly tender flesh.

'I don't understand what you're getting at...I've always worked for a living. And how can you call me a greedy bitch?' Daisy suddenly lashed back at him, shock splintering to give way to angry defensiveness.

Alessio emitted a sardonic laugh, his nostrils flaring. 'Isn't that what you are?'

'In what way was I greedy?' Daisy pressed in ever growing bewilderment. 'I took nothing from you or your family.'

'You call half a million pounds nothing?'

A furrow formed between her delicate brows. 'But I refused the money. Your father tried very hard to make me accept it but I refused.'

'You're a liar.' Alessio's eloquent mouth twisted with derision. 'My father was not the leading light in that deal. You made the demand. He paid up only because he was foolishly trying to protect me.'

'I didn't demand anything...and I didn't accept any money either!' Daisy protested heatedly.

Alessio dealt her a look of complete indifference that cut like a knife. 'I don't even know why I mentioned it. That pay-off was the tacky but merciful end to a very sordid little affair.'

Daisy bit the soft underside of her lower lip and tasted the acrid tang of her own blood. The pain steadied her a little. Alessio's father, Vittorio, had obviously lied. Clearly he had told his son that she *had* accepted the money. And why should that lie surprise her? The

Leopardi clan had loathed her on sight. His parents had tried hard to hide the fact when Alessio was around, but his twin sister, Bianca, had shown her hostility openly. Daisy stared into space, her whole being engulfed by a powerful wave of remembered pain and rejection.

In the swirling oblivion of that tide of memory she relived the heady scent of lush grass bruised by their lovemaking, the kiss of the Tuscan sun on her skin and the passionate weight and urgency of Alessio's lean body on hers. Broken dreams and lost innocence. Her eyes burned, her small frame tensing defensively. Why had nobody ever told her how much loving could hurt and destroy? By the time she had found out that reality, the damage had been done and her reward had been guilt and despair. A 'sordid little affair'? No, for her it had been so much more, and it was in the divergence of outlook that the seeds of disaster had been sown...

The clink of glass dredged her back from her dangerous passage into the past. Her lashes fluttered in confusion as Alessio leant lithely forward and slotted a brandy goblet between her nerveless fingers. 'You look like you are about to pass out.'

Faint colour feathered then into Daisy's drawn cheeks. She watched him help himself to a drink from the cabinet, every movement calm and precise. He did *not* look as though *he* was about to pass out. Although if he ever found out about Tara he might well make good the oversight. Hurriedly, she crushed that disturbing, foolish thought. Alessio had never wanted their baby.

At nineteen, Alessio had been able to think of an awful lot of things he wanted but they had not included a baby. So, knowing that, why on earth had she let him marry her? And yet the answer to that was so simple. She had honestly believed that he loved her... deep down inside...even though he hadn't been showing it any more. It was amazing what a besotted teenage girl could persuade herself to believe, she conceded painfully.

'And you are wearing odd shoes,' Alessio remarked in a curiously flat tone.

A feeling of unreality was starting to enclose Daisy but she also sensed that Alessio was not as in control as he wanted to appear. She surveyed her feet, saw one black court shoe, one navy. It didn't bother her. In the midst of a nightmare encounter, unmatched shoes were a triviality. She drained the brandy in one gulp. It sent fire chasing into the chilled pit of her stomach. She swallowed convulsively. 'I wasn't supposed to be working today. I came out in a hurry.'

'You've cut your hair.'

Daisy lifted an uncertain hand halfway to her shoulder-length bob of shining silver-blonde hair, connected with brilliant eyes and wondered why time seemed to be slowing up, why they were now having this curiously stilted conversation when barely a minute ago they had been arguing. 'Yes. It's easier to manage.'

Alessio was running that narrowed, gleaming gaze over her slight figure in a manner which made her feel incredibly hot and uncomfortable. A wolfish smile gradually curved his hard mouth as he lounged back with innate grace in the seat opposite. 'You don't seem to have much to say to me...'

She wasn't about to tell him that he was still gorgeous. Even as a teenager he had known that and had shamelessly utilised that spectacular combination of smouldering dark good looks and animal sex appeal to his own advantage. He had used it on Daisy—dug his own grave, really, when she thought about it. She had been agonisingly naïve and had fallen like a ton of bricks for him, defenceless against that polished seduction routine of his.

'You're still full of yourself,' Daisy told him helplessly.

A faint darkening of colour accentuated the slant of his chiselled cheekbones, his tawny eyes flaring with momentary disconcertion.

She loosed a sudden laugh, sharp in its lack of humour. 'But then why shouldn't you be?'

'What's that supposed to mean?'

'I think it means that you should get me out of this car before I say something we both regret,' Daisy admitted tightly, feeling all the volatile emotions she had buried so long ago rising up inside her without warning.

Alessio slung her a knowing look redolent of a male who knew women and prided himself on the fact. 'You never forget your first love.'

'Or what a bastard he was...' The assurance was out before Daisy could stop it.

Alessio's long, lithe frame tensed—a reaction which gave her a quite extraordinary surge of satisfaction. Shimmering eyes lanced into her with stark incredulity. 'How can you say that to me?'

'Because being married to you was the worst experience of my life,' Daisy informed him, throwing her head high.

'I beg your pardon?'

'And, believe me, I didn't require a financial bribe to persuade me into a quick exit! You were domineering, selfish and completely insensitive to what I was going through,' Daisy condemned in a shaking voice that steadily crept up in volume in spite of her attempt to control it. 'You left me at the mercy of your totally monstrous family and allowed them to treat me like dirt!

You stopped talking to me but that did not stop you *using* my body whenever you felt like it!'

Alessio was transfixed. There was no other word for his reaction. The Daisy he had married would never have criticised him. In those days, Daisy had crept around being quiet and apologetic while silently, miserably adoring him, no matter what treatment he handed out. Alessio had accepted the adoration as his right. She hadn't had the guts to stand up to him then, not when she had mistakenly blamed herself for the fact that he had *had* to marry her.

'In fact you went into a three-month-long sulk the same day that you married me! And the minute your obnoxious family saw how you were behaving they all jumped on the same bandwagon. I didn't just have one person making my life a living hell, I had a whole crowd!' she spelt out fiercely. 'And I don't care how any of you felt; I was only seventeen and I was pregnant and I did not deserve that kind of punishment!'

Daisy fell silent then. She was shattered, genuinely shattered by the bitterness that had surged up in her and overflowed. Until now she had not appreciated how deep her bitterness ran. But then she had not had an opportunity to vent those feelings before. Within forty-eight hours of her miscarriage, Vittorio Leopardi had presented her with divorce papers. And, sick to the heart from all that she had already undergone and Alessio's cruel indifference, she had signed without a word of argument.

'So, when you took the money and ran, you thought it was your due,' Alessio opined grittily.

She stole a dazed glance at him from beneath her feathery lashes. His darkly handsome features were fiercely taut. 'I ran but I didn't take any money,' she muttered wearily, and then wondered why she was still bothering to defend herself. When it came to a choice between her word and his father's, she had no doubt about whose Alessio would believe. And it wouldn't be hers.

'I despised you for what you did,' Alessio admitted with driven emphasis. 'And to listen now to you abusing my family makes me very angry.'

'I doubt if I'll lose any sleep over that.' Yet Daisy's heartbeat suffered a lurch when she met that anger brightening his hard gaze. Her chin came up, defying the sudden chill of her flesh. She had said her piece. She had waited thirteen years to say it and there wasn't a single word of it which she could honestly have taken back. How could he still behave as if he had been the only one wronged?

When she had discovered that her miscarriage had not been quite what it had appeared, she hadn't dreamt of bothering Alessio or his family with what would have been very bad news in their opinion. Indeed, still loving Alessio as she had, she had felt positively heroic protecting him from such an unwelcome announcement. He had wanted neither her nor their child, so she had taken care of the problem. She had kept her mouth shut, let the divorce proceed without interruption and brought her baby into the world alone. Alessio *owed her*! He had been able to get on with his life again, unhampered by all the many adult responsibilities that had become hers at far too young an age.

The limousine had stopped. She hadn't noticed. She gazed out at the elegant Georgian square and simply knew that she could not bear another single minute in Alessio's company. There was too much pain and confusion biting at her.

'I'm going to catch a cab back to the office and say you cancelled,' Daisy told him abruptly. 'Then you can come back on Monday if you like and see the house with someone else.'

'I don't think your boss would swallow that story.' Alessio's shrewd gaze lingered on her and his expressive mouth took on a curious quirk.

'I don't care!' Daisy stared back at him defiantly.

'So you *still* make stupid decisions on the spur of the moment.'

Colour ran up in a hot, betraying flush beneath her fine skin. She knew exactly what he was getting at. 'Shut up!' she hissed back.

'And you still blush like a furnace around me...in spite of your advanced years,' Alessio chided with lazy enjoyment at her embarrassment. 'And, in spite of *my* advanced years, you still turn me on hard and fast. Now isn't that fascinating?'

Daisy couldn't believe he had said that. The tip of her tongue stole out in a swift flick to moisten her lower lip. Involuntarily she connected with eyes that now blazed passionate gold, his ebony lashes low on his lingering scrutiny. The heavy silence stretched like a rubber band pulled too taut for safety.

'If this is your idea of a joke...' she began unevenly.

Alessio surveyed her with slumbrous intensity and a slow, devastating smile curved his mouth. 'Don't be pious. You're feeling the same thing I'm feeling right now.'

Her breath was trapped in her throat. Daisy could not tear her bemused eyes from the potent lure of his. And it was not an unfamiliar sensation that was creeping over her, she registered in dizzy disbelief; it was an old but never forgotten sensation of quite incredible excitement.

The whole atmosphere had a wild, electric charge. Her heartbeat was thundering in her eardrums, her whole body stretched and tight with every nerve-ending ready to leap.

'Curiosity and excitement,' Alessio enumerated with purring softness.

It was fatal to be so easily read but Daisy couldn't help herself. Slowly but surely she was sinking back to the level of maturity she had reached at the time of the party at which they had first met, and she remembered the sheer, terrifying *whoosh* of emotion and response which Alessio had evoked in her even at a distance of twenty feet. One look and she had been trembling, pitched on such a high of breathless, desperate yearning that she had felt slaughtered when he'd looked away again. 'Stop it...' she muttered shakily.

'I can't. I like to live dangerously now and again,' Alessio revealed huskily.

'I don't...' But her wretched body was not so scrupulous. She was devastated to feel her breasts, now full and heavy, surge against the lace barrier of her bra, the swollen nipples tightening into shameless, aching peaks.

'How would you feel about an afternoon of immoral, erotic rediscovery?' Alessio murmured thickly, his scorching golden eyes, as hot as flames, dancing over her heated skin. 'I'll take you to a hotel. For a few stolen hours, we leave the anger and the bitterness behind and relive the passion...'

Daisy was stunned, and on another level she was recalling the end of that long-ago party when Alessio had finally deigned to speak to her and make the smoothest pass she had ever encountered. She had been stunned then too by his sheer nerve. His brazen disregard of what she had naïvely seen as normal courting rituals had shocked her rigid. He had planted a drink in her hand and asked her to go to bed with him that night. She had slapped his face.

He had grinned. 'Tomorrow night?' he had asked with unconcealed amusement in his beautiful eyes, and she should have known then that it would take more than one slap to dent that ego.

'Daisy...' Alessio breathed.

This time she came back to the present with a sense of intense pain. Her violent eyes were starkly vulnerable; she veiled them. All of a sudden she felt horribly cold and lost. 'I don't want to relive the passion,' she told him tightly. 'Yes, you were quite incredible in bed but I wouldn't let you use me like that again. Once was enough. You're trying to put me down this time too. That's one advantage of being a grown-up: I can see the writing on the wall.'

The endless silence pulsed with fierce undertones.

'I *cannot* believe I am even having this conversation with you!' Alessio gritted with ferocious abruptness.

'I suppose it's comforting to know that you haven't changed. You're still a two-timing, oversexed, immoral rat,' Daisy muttered in a choky little voice, valiantly fighting off the threat of the tears damming up behind her burning eyes, ready to spill over.

'I am none of those things!' Alessio blistered back at her.

'Creep,' Daisy spat, making a dive to get out of the car. 'You really are one lousy creep to do this to me! Do you think I'm a whore or something? Do you think I don't know you're trying to humiliate me?'

A strong hand suddenly whipped out to capture one of hers, holding her back. 'It was an unfortunate impulse. I don't know what came over me. Call it temporary insanity if you like,' he growled savagely. 'I'm sorry!'

'Let go of me!'

He did, and Daisy wrenched open the door and almost fell out onto the pavement, sucking in a great gulp of fresh air as she did so. She was shaking like a leaf. She took a tottering step away from the limousine, her gait that of someone who had escaped a traumatic brush with death.

'And it's really pathetic to still be shooting the same lines at your age!' she slung back at him for good measure.

'*Dio*...will you keep your voice down?' Alessio roared at her, causing an elderly lady walking an apricot poodle to step off the pavement with a frown of well-bred disapproval and give the two of them a very wide berth.

Daisy stole a glance at Alessio, took in the shaken look of uncertainty currently clouding his normally sharp-as-paint gaze and grew in stature with the knowledge that he was handling their unexpected encounter no better than she was. Memories from their volatile teenage years and the effects of shock were driving a horse and cart through any effort they made to behave like civilised, intelligent adults.

'Look, do you want to see this house or don't you?' she asked stiffly.

'If you will control your tongue and stop hurling insults, I see no reason why we should not deal with this on a normal business footing,' Alessio drawled with icy control.

CHAPTER TWO

An hour and a half later, Daisy surveyed the elegant hall of the Georgian house for the hundredth time and wondered how much more time the owners would spend entertaining Alessio. Her presence had not been required to give the grand tour, oh, dear, no!

The Raschids had stayed in specially when they had learnt that Alessio Leopardi was coming to view their beautiful home. Mr Raschid was a diplomat and apparently had met Alessio at an embassy dinner last year. Eager to renew that acquaintance, the couple had lost no time in telling Daisy to wait in the hall, while assuring Alessio that they would give him a far more interesting tour than she could. Well, she *would* have been rather out of her depth in a three-way conversation taking place in Arabic.

Alessio hadn't looked at her again. Suddenly she had acquired all the invisibility of a lowly maid. And that was how it should be. Like the Raschids, he was a client, just another client, and clients, particularly very wealthy ones, frequently treated the agency staff as something slightly less than human. When she thought about it, their romance thirteen years ago had broken all the class and status rules—Alessio the adored only son of the Leopardi banking dynasty and Daisy the au pair working down the road from his family's palatial summer villa.

They had not one single thing in common. Alessio had grown up as part of a close-knit, supportive family circle but Daisy had lost both her parents by the time

25

she was six. Her elderly grandparents had brought her up. Her entire childhood had been filled with loss and death and sudden change. She had never had security. Illness and old age had taken everyone she cared about until her mother's sister had taken her turn of guardianship when Daisy was sixteen. A career teacher in her late thirties, Janet had encouraged her niece to be more independent than her own parents had allowed. But she had been dubious when Daisy had initially suggested spending the summer before her final year at school working as an au pair.

'I bet you land a ghastly family who treat you like a skivvy and expect you to slave for them day and night,' Janet had forecast worriedly.

In fact, Daisy had been very lucky. The agency had matched her up with a friendly, easygoing couple who owned a small villa in Tuscany and went there every summer with their children. The Morgans had given her plenty of time off and Liz Morgan had gone out of her way to see that Daisy met other young people. The very first week, Daisy had been invited to the party where she'd met Alessio.

He had roared up on a monster motorbike, sheathed in black jeans with a hole in one knee and a white T-shirt. Tousled, curly ebony hair had been blown back from his lean, vibrantly handsome features and an entire room of adolescent girls had gone weak at the knees with a collective gasp. What was more, his own sex had clustered round him with equal enthusiasm. Alessio had been hugely popular, the indisputable leader of the pack.

Even then he'd had an undeniable golden aura. One had had the feeling that even on a rainy day the sun would still shine exclusively around Alessio. He'd had the immense and boundless self-assurance of a being who had always led a charmed life. The angels had not been having forty winks when Alessio was born. Alessio had been young, beautiful, academically brilliant and rich. And Daisy's greatest attraction could only have been that she was different from the girls he was used to dating. The new face, the foreigner, who had to work to get a taste of the sun, had stood out from the familiar crowd.

But she hadn't known who he was then. His name had meant nothing to her. And even after being slapped Alessio had still trailed her all the way back to the Morgan villa on his motorbike when she had walked out on the party. Since losing face in public was every teenager's worst nightmare, she had been upset. The more she had told him to grow up and get lost, the more he had laughed. She had been convinced that he was sending her up for her shocked response to that proposition of his, embarrassingly aware that she had overreacted and that a smart verbal rejoinder would have been infinitely more adult.

'Anyone will give me a reference. I'm a really wonderful guy when you get to know me,' he told her, with a shimmering, teasing smile that made her vulnerable heart sing. 'And I'm delighted you're not the sort of girl who gives her all on a first date. Not that I would have said no, you understand...but the occasional negative response is probably better for my character.'

'You really like yourself, don't you?' she snapped.

'At least I don't lurk behind the furniture, scared to speak to people, and react like a startled rabbit when they speak to me,' he retorted, quick as a flash.

And she fled indoors, slunk up to her bedroom and cried herself to sleep. But Alessio showed up again early the next morning. Liz brought him into the kitchen where Daisy was clearing up the breakfast dishes. The whole time Alessio was with her the older woman hovered, staring at Alessio as if she couldn't quite believe he was real.

'I'll pick you up at seven...OK?' he said levelly, quite unconcerned by his audience. 'We'll go for a meal somewhere.'

'OK...'

'Smile,' he said, cheerfully ruffling the hair of the two-year-old girl clinging to his leg. 'She can smile at me...why can't you?'

'I wasn't expecting you.'

His mouth quirked. 'You're not supposed to admit things like that.'

Liz cornered her the instant he departed. 'Daisy, if I acted a little weird, put it down to me being shocked at the sight of a Leopardi entering my humble home.'

'Why?' Daisy frowned.

'We've been coming here every summer for ten years and I still can't get as much as nod of acknowledgement from the Leopardis! His parents are mega-rich—as well as their villa here they've got a huge mansion in Rome, where they live most of the time—and they are very exclusive in their friendships,' she explained uncomfortably. 'And Alessio has a reputation with girls that would turn any mother's hair white overnight. But he usually sticks with his own set. Please don't take this the wrong way, Daisy...but do you really think you can handle a young man like that? He's seen a lot more of life than you have.'

But Daisy didn't listen. Alessio did not seem remotely snobbish. And Alessio's unknown parents interested her not at all.

He rolled up in a low-slung scarlet sports car to take her out that evening. Daisy was impressed to death but

Liz grabbed her husband in horror as she peered out from behind the curtains. 'I don't believe it! They've bought a *teenager* a Ferrari! Are the Leopardis out of their minds?'

All the trappings of fantasy were there—the gorgeous guy who had miraculously picked her out of a wealth of beautiful, far more sophisticated girls, the fabulous car. That night they dined in a ritzy restaurant in Florence. Daisy was overpowered by her surroundings until Alessio reached across the table and twined her tense fingers soothingly in his, and then she quite happily surrendered to being overpowered by him instead.

On the drive back, he stopped the car, drew her confidently into his arms and kissed her. About ten seconds into that wildly exciting experience, he started teaching her *how* to kiss, laughing when she got embarrassed, laughing even harder when she tried to excuse her inexpert technique by pleading cultural differences. But surprisingly he didn't attempt to do anything more than kiss her. He was *so* different away from his friends. Romantic, tender, unexpectedly serious.

'Do you know I still haven't asked you what you're studying at college?' Alessio remarked carelessly at one point.

'History and English. I want to be an infant teacher,' she said shyly, and if he hadn't kissed her again she might have told him that she was already worrying that in a year's time she mightn't get good enough grades to make it onto the particular teacher-training course which her aunt had advised her to set her sights on.

'You wouldn't believe how relieved I am to hear that you're studying for your degree,' Alessio confided lazily. 'I was afraid you might still be at school.'

And she realised then that there had been a misunderstanding. She attended a sixth-form college for sixteen- to eighteen-year-olds, *not* a college of further education which would equip her with a degree. 'Would it have made a difference...if I had been?' she prompted uneasily.

'Of course it would have made a difference.' Alessio frowned down at her in surprise. 'I don't date schoolgirls. It may be only a matter of a couple of years but there's a huge gap in experience and maturity. You can't have an equal relationship on those terms. It would make me feel as if I had too much of an advantage and I wouldn't feel comfortable with that.'

And Daisy felt even less comfortable listening to him. She realised that Alessio would never have asked her out had he known what age she was. And that if she told him he had been given the wrong information he wouldn't want to see her again. So how could she admit to being only seventeen?

Choosing not to tell him the truth didn't feel like lying that night. It felt like a harmless pretence. She had not thought through what she was doing in allowing Alessio to believe that she was older than she was. It did not once cross her dizzy brain that there would come a time of reckoning and exposure...and that Alessio would be understandably outraged by her deception. By the end of that evening, she was walking on air and fathoms deep in love...

Daisy emerged from that unsettling recollection to find herself *still* taking up space in the Raschids' spacious hall. The sound of voices alerted her to the fact that she was about to have company again. She stood up just as the Raschids and Alessio appeared at the head of the staircase. Her uneasy eyes slid over him and lowered, but not before she'd seen his frown of surprise.

'I assumed you would have returned to the agency,' he admitted on the pavement outside. .

'My boss definitely wouldn't have liked that. Have you any queries?' Daisy prompted stiffly, ignoring the chauffeur, who had the door of the limousine open in readiness.

'Yes...were you sitting in that hall the entire time I was looking round the house?'

'No, I was swinging off the chandelier for light amusement! What do you think I was doing?'

'If I had known you were waiting, I wouldn't have spent so much time with the Raschids. Did you even get a cup of coffee?'

Daisy's head was pounding. She was at the end of her rope. 'Are you trying to tell me that you care?' she derided. 'One minute you're calling me a—*Alessio!*' she gasped incredulously as he dropped two determined hands to her tiny waist, swept her very efficiently off her feet and deposited her at supersonic speed in the limousine. 'Why the heck did you do that?' she demanded breathlessly as he swung in beside her.

'If we're about to have another argument, I prefer to stage it in privacy,' Alessio imparted drily. In the time he had been away from her, he had reinstated the kind of steely control that mocked her own turbulent confusion.

'Look, I don't want another argument. I only want to go home.'

'I'll take you there.'

Daisy froze. 'No, thanks.'

'Then I'll drop you back at the agency. It's on my route.'

'You're being all polite now,' she muttered, and it infuriated her that she sounded childish.

'We both overreacted earlier.' Shrewd, dauntingly dispassionate eyes rested on her hot cheeks. 'I'm prepared to admit that I threw the first stone. Calling you a greedy bitch for accepting a settlement on our divorce was inexcusable. You were entitled to that settlement. Unfortunately, after a very few minutes in your company, I regressed to being nineteen again. But I can't see why it has to continue like that. Thirteen years is a *very* long time.'

So why all of a sudden did it feel like the fast blink of an eyelid to her? Yet she had only to look at Alessio to know how much time had passed. He no longer smouldered like a volatile volcano. Alessio now had the ability to turn freezingly cool and civil. She moistened her dry lips. 'If you're interested in the house, you won't have to deal with me again. I was standing in for someone else today.'

'And you're not a great saleswoman around me.'

'I don't even know what kind of property you're looking for.'

'You didn't ask.'

'Not much point in asking now.' Daisy sat on the edge of the seat in the corner furthest away from him.

An uncomfortable silence followed.

'I wasn't lying when I said that I still find you attractive,' Alessio breathed grimly.

Daisy tensed, her head high, her neck aching with the stress of the position.

'Nor was I trying to put you down,' Alessio drawled with an audible edge of distaste. 'But some lustful urges are better suppressed.'

A lustful urge? In her mind's eye, she pictured a sleek wolf circling a dumb sheep. And with shrinking reluctance she recalled her own response to Alessio's sexual taunting in the car earlier. Thinking about that response devastated her. For a few terrifying seconds Alessio had somehow made her want him again. And, worst of all, Alessio *knew* what he had achieved. He had resurrected an intense sexual awareness that was stronger than anything she had ever expected to feel again and she hated him for doing that—hated him for forcing her to accept that he could still have that power over her.

But then mightn't her own wanton excitement have been an echo from the past? she reasoned frantically with herself. But yes, Alessio was right on one count— you never forgot your first love, most especially not when the relationship had ended in raw pain and disillusionment.

'I think it's wise that we don't see each other again,' Alessio said quietly. 'I have to admit that I was curious but my curiosity is now satisfied.'

A painful tide of heat climbed slowly up Daisy's slender throat. Dear heaven, he was actually warning her off! Concerned lest that confession of animal lust should have roused fresh expectations in her greedy, gold-digging little heart, he was smoothly striving to kill off any ambitious ideas she might be developing. So cold, so controlled, so unapologetically superior... Her teeth gritted. How *could* Alessio talk to her like this? Did he think he was irresistible? Did he fondly imagine that she was likely to chase after him and make a nuisance of herself?

'I wasn't even curious to begin with,' she lied.

'Naturally I was curious. The last time I saw you before today you were five months pregnant and still my wife.'

Her facial muscles locked hard. 'You didn't want a wife.'

'No, I have to confess that I didn't. I doubt if you will find many teenage boys who *do* want to get married,' Alessio responded grimly. 'I was no more prepared for that commitment than you were... but I did attempt to deal with the situation—'

'Yes, you were a real hero, weren't you?' Daisy broke in with a curling lip. 'You did the honourable thing. You *married* me! Your *mamma* wept and your *papà* overflowed with sympathy. Naturally no decent Italian girl would ever have got herself in such a condition!'

'They were upset!' Alessio growled.

'Do you think *I* wasn't upset? What do you think it was like for me, being treated like some brassy little slut who had set out to trap you?' Daisy condemned painfully. 'I wasn't allowed out the door in case someone saw me! I used to have nightmares about giving birth and then being buried alive in the garden!'

'Don't be ridiculous!' Alessio gritted fiercely.

'You mean your mother didn't share that little fantasy with you? She was hoping like hell that I would have the baby and then magically disappear, leaving the baby behind! She was always telling me that I was too young to cope with a child and how much *she* loved children...' Daisy shuddered. 'Talk about feeling threatened! Life with the Leopardis... it was like a Hammer horror movie!'

Scorching eyes landed on her in near-physical assault. 'You are making me very angry.'

Daisy shrugged and compressed her generous mouth. 'That's how I remember you—*angry*. No such thing as forgiveness from a Leopardi.'

'In the circumstances, I think I behaved reasonably well.'

Daisy treated him to a glance of naked contempt. 'By making the immense sacrifice of marrying me? Don't kid yourself, Alessio. You'd have done me a bigger favour had you dumped me and run the minute I told you I might be pregnant!'

'What the hell do you have to be so bitter about?' Alessio ground out, raking her with fiercely intent eyes. *You* walked out on *me*! And anyone listening to you would think it only happened last week!'

Daisy tried and failed to swallow. For an instant her confusion and dismay were openly etched on her fragile features and then she turned her head away and saw the familiar frontage of the estate agency with a sense of incredible relief. 'Being civilised isn't easy, is it?' she conceded tightly.

'I did love you,' Alessio murmured, his intonation harsh.

As the passenger door beside her swung open, Daisy spun back to him, violet eyes bright with incredulous scorn. 'Do you think I either want or need your lies *now*?'

'Don't let me keep you,' Alessio drawled with heavy irony, shooting her a chilling look of antipathy.

The agency was closed. Of course it was. It was after one. Daisy kept on walking, tight and sick inside. This was the very worst day of her life, absolutely the very worst... seeing Alessio again, all those tearing, miserable memories fighting their way up to the surface of her mind and driving her crazy. Mere minutes away from him, she found that she couldn't believe some of the things she had said to him. No wonder he had asked her

why she was so hostile! Thirteen years on and still ranting
as if the divorce had only become final yesterday!

Not that Alessio had reacted much better at first. But
Alessio had got a grip on himself fast. Alessio had stayed
in control. Scarcely a surprise, she allowed grudgingly.
Alessio had prided himself on never losing control of
his temper. For the entire three and a half months of
their marriage he had therefore smouldered in a silence
that was infinitely more accusing and threatening and
debilitating than any mere loss of temper. He had held
in all his emotions with rigid, terrifying discipline at a
time when Daisy had been desperate for any shred of
comfort, any hint of understanding, any crumb of forgiveness. And maybe that was why in the end she had
grown to hate her memory of him...

He had reduced her to the level of a tearful, pathetic
supplicant, utterly destroying her pride and self-esteem.
She had never had a great deal of confidence, but by
the time Alessio had finished with her she had had none
at all. And yet before their marriage, before everything
had gone wrong, Alessio had done wonders for her confidence. He had built her up, told her off for under-
valuing herself, frowned every time she cracked a joke
at her own expense. He had kept on telling her how
beautiful she was, how special, how happy she made *him*
feel. Was it surprising that she had fallen so deeply in
love with him? Or that when cruel reality had come in
the door and plunged them into a shotgun marriage their
whole relationship had fallen apart?

A fantastic boyfriend, a lousy husband. He had
married her purely for the sake of the baby she'd been
carrying. But the minute the wedding had taken place
the baby had become a taboo subject. He had never
mentioned her condition if he could avoid it. It had been

as if he was trying to pretend she wasn't pregnant. And then one night, when the curve of her stomach had become too pronounced for him to ignore, he had abruptly turned away from her, and for those final, wretched weeks he had moved into another bedroom. The ultimate rejection...he had severed even the tenuous bond of sex.

Within days, Bianca, his twin, had been smirking at her like the wicked witch. 'Fat is a total turn-off for Alessio. Only four months along and already you look like a dumpy little barrel on short legs. He wouldn't be seen dead with you in public. Now he doesn't want to sleep with you either. Can you blame him?'

No blow had been too low for Bianca. Daisy shivered in remembrance. That spiteful tongue had been a constant thorn in her flesh. Brother and sister had been very close. She had often pictured Alessio confiding in Bianca and had cringed at the suspicion that nothing that happened in their marriage was private. She had imagined Alessio describing her as a dumpy little barrel and had wept anguished tears in her lonely bed. Strange that it had occurred to none of them that the sudden increase in her girth was not solely the result of comfort eating but a sign that she was carrying two babies and not one...

Janet's house was only round the corner from her flat. Daisy headed for her aunt like a homing pigeon, praying that Tara was still at her friend's house, wondering if some sixth sense this morning had prompted her to give in to her daughter's pleas for a little more freedom.

Janet was on the phone when she came through the back door. 'Put on the kettle,' she mouthed, and went back to her call.

Daisy took off her suit jacket, caught a glimpse of herself in the little mirror on the kitchen wall and stared in horror. She rubbed at her cheeks, bit at her lips for colour but could still only focus on the stricken look in her eyes. She hoped she hadn't looked stricken to Alessio and then questioned why it should matter to her. Pride, she supposed. Why hadn't she managed to be cool and distant? Why had she had to rave at him the way she had?

'You're quiet. Tough morning?' Janet was drawing mugs out of a cupboard.

'I bumped into Alessio today—'

A mug hit the tiled floor and smashed into about twenty pieces.

'It affected me like that too,' Daisy confided unsteadily.

'Let's go into the lounge,' her aunt suggested tautly. 'We'll be more comfortable in there.'

Daisy couldn't stay still in any case. Her nerves seemed to be leaping up and down with jumping-bean energy. She folded her arms, paced the small room and briefly outlined the bare bones of that meeting. 'And just wait until you hear this bit... His lousy father told him I *took* the money he offered me!'

Her aunt's angular face was unusually tense. 'Alessio mentioned the money?'

'He wouldn't believe me when I said that I'd refused it!'

Janet's bright blue eyes were troubled, her sallow cheeks flushed. 'Because I accepted it on your behalf.'

Daisy stopped dead in her tracks. 'You did...what?'

Her aunt walked over to her desk and withdrew a slim file from a drawer. She handed it to Daisy. 'Try to understand. You weren't thinking about the future. I was worried sick about how you would manage with a baby if anything happened to me.'

Daisy studied the older woman in a complete daze.

'It's all in the file. A financial consultant helped me to set it up. Not a penny of that money has ever been brought into this country or touched. It's in a Swiss bank account,' Janet explained. 'But it's there for you and Tara should you ever need it.'

'Alessio was telling the truth?' Daisy mumbled thickly.

Her aunt sighed. 'His father came to see me while you were in hospital. He practically begged me to accept the money. He felt terrible about the way things had turned out—'

'Like heck he did!'

Janet's face set in stern lines. 'Vittorio was sincere, Daisy. He said that you were miserable and Alessio was equally miserable and that he had felt forced to interfere—'

'He couldn't wait to interfere!'

'I found it very hard not to tell him that he *still* had a grandchild on the way,' the older woman confessed wryly. 'But, just as his loyalties ultimately lay with his son, mine lay with you. I respected your wishes.'

'But to take the money...' Daisy was shattered by that revelation.

'I still believe I made the most sensible decision. You were very young at the time. You needed financial security—'

'I've managed fine all these years without Leopardi conscience money!'

'But you mightn't have done. A lot of things could have gone wrong,' Janet pointed out. 'And what about Tara? Don't you think that she is entitled to have something from her father's family?'

'I'll give it back!' Daisy swore, too upset to listen.

'Wait and ask your daughter how she feels about that when she's eighteen. I doubt very much that Tara will feel as you feel now. She does, after all, have Leopardi blood in her veins—'

'Do you think I don't know that?' Daisy asked defensively. 'Tara knows exactly who she is—'

'No, she knows who *you* want her to be. She's insatiably curious about her father.'

Daisy was finding herself under a surprise attack from a woman she both respected and loved and it was a deeply disturbing experience. 'Since when?'

'The older she gets, the more often she mentions him. She talks about him to me. She won't ask you about him because she doesn't want to upset you.'

'I have never ducked any of her questions. I've been totally honest with her.'

Janet grimaced. 'It's going to be very difficult for you but I think it's time for you to tell Alessio that he has a daughter—'

'Are you out of your mind?' Daisy gasped, thunderstruck.

'Some day Tara is likely to march into his office in the City and announce herself...and for *her* sake Alessio ought to be forewarned.'

'I can't believe you're saying this to me.'

'Do you intend to tell Tara that you met Alessio today?'

There was a sharp little sound from behind them. Both women jerked round. Tara was standing in the hall, wide-eyed and apparently frozen to the spot by what she had overheard. Then she surged forward, her pretty face suddenly full of wild excitement. 'You met my father...Mum, you were speaking to him? Really...genuinely...speaking to him? Did you tell him about me?' she demanded, as if that revelation might have just popped out in casual conversation.

Daisy was stunned by Tara's naked excitement, by the crucifying look of hope and expectation glowing in her eyes. She was being faced with a disorientatingly different side of the daughter she had believed she knew inside out. And, shorn of the world-weary teenage front, the innocence of the child had never shone through more clearly. Icy fingers clutched at Daisy's heart. Janet had been right. Tara *was* desperate to be acknowledged by Alessio but she had carefully hidden that uncomfortable truth from her mother. Only this morning she had carelessly referred to her father as a 'major creep'.

'No... I'm afraid I didn't,' Daisy said woodenly, traumatised by what she had seen in her daughter's face.

'Your mother didn't get the opportunity,' Janet chipped in heavily.

Tara's face shuttered as if she realised how much she had betrayed and then raw resentment flared in her pain-filled eyes. 'Just because he didn't want *you* doesn't mean he mightn't want to know *me*!' she condemned with a choked sob.

Daisy went white. Her daughter stared at her in appalled silence and then took off. The kitchen door slammed on her hurtling exit.

'Lord, all I've ever done,' Daisy whispered wretchedly, 'is try to protect her from being hurt.'

'As you were?' Janet squeezed her shoulder comfortingly. 'Doesn't it ever occur to you that Alessio could ave changed as much as you have? That the teenager who couldn't cope with the prospect of fatherhood is now an adult male of thirty-two? Are you telling me that he couldn't scrape through a single meeting with Tara? That could well be enough to satisfy her and if he won't

even agree to *that*...well, Tara will have to accept it.
You can't protect her by avoiding the issue.'

'I guess not...' Daisy's shaken voice trailed away
altogether.

Two sleepless nights had done nothing to improve Daisy's
outlook on life. All she could think about as she walked
into the Leopardi Merchant Bank was that in the space
of one morning Alessio had brought her whole world
down round her ears. And the pieces were still falling.
Tara was still very upset about what she had flung at
her mother in her distress. Quick-tempered and
passionate, Tara was also fiercely loyal and protective.
Nothing Daisy had so far said had eased her daughter's
regret at having hurled those angry, hurtful words.

So why *were* you hurt? Daisy was still asking herself.
There had to be something wrong with her that she could
still flinch from the reminder of Alessio's rejection this
long after the event. And how could she have been so
blind to her daughter's very real need to know that her
father had at least been made aware of her existence?
Had Tara even thought of what might come next? Had
she some naïve fantasy of Alessio welcoming her with
open arms and delight?

Or was that her own prejudice and pessimism talking
again? But Daisy could only remember Alessio's distaste when she'd been pregnant, his indifference to her
need for him when she had miscarried. That had been
the final bitter blow that had driven Daisy away.

Was there the remotest possibility that a male that
selfish could respond in an appropriate manner to a
painfully vulnerable teenage daughter whom he had
never wanted in the first place? Daisy acknowledged that
she *had* known what she was doing when she'd kept quiet

about Tara's existence. The risk of exposing her child to the same rejection that she herself had experienced had been too great.

Daisy got out of the lift on the top floor. If she had thought Giles's office was the last word in luxury, she was now learning her mistake. The sleek smoked-glass edifice which housed the Leopardi Merchant Bank was stunningly elegant in its contemporary decor. There were two women in the reception area. The older one moved forward. 'Miss Thornton? I'm Mr Leopardi's secretary. Could you come this way, please...?'

Daisy reddened. Alessio's secretary wore a marked look of strain—possibly the result of Daisy's steadfast determination not to be refused an appointment. Alessio was undoubtedly furious. After all, he had made it very clear that he did not wish to see her again. However, she didn't know where he lived so she had had no choice but to approach him at the bank.

Her heart pounding at the foot of her throat and reverberating in her eardrums, she walked dizzily into Alessio's office, a great big room with a great big glass desk and...Alessio standing there, suppressed dark fury and rigid restraint emanating from every lean, poised line of his tall, muscular body.

'What the hell are you doing here?' he demanded with icy precision.

Her head swam, her knees wobbled. She opened her mouth and closed it again. A quite sickening wave of dizziness overwhelmed her and the next thing she knew the blackness was folding in and her legs were crumpling beneath her.

CHAPTER THREE

DAISY surfaced from her faint very slowly. She focused on Alessio's dark features as he swam gradually into focus, and a dazed smile curved her soft mouth. He was cradling her in his arms, her slight body still limp, her head resting back against his forearm. It felt wonderful. Her violet eyes dreamy, she looked up at him... and melted, a honeyed languor stealing through her as she shifted and curled her toes in wanton anticipation.

'You have the most gorgeous eyes,' Alessio breathed in an abstracted undertone, drawing ever closer.

They were lost in his. Pools of passionate gold set between luxuriant black lashes even longer than her own. Daisy expelled a tiny sigh, the raw heat of his lean, hard body curling sensuously into her relaxed limbs. She curved instinctively closer and he lifted a hand almost jerkily and let long brown fingers thread into the fall of her hair, his thumb rubbing caressingly against her earlobe. Her heartbeat went crazy in the thrumming silence.

'Alessio...' she mumbled.

'*Piccola mia...*' The familiar endearment left him in an aching sigh.

Warm fingers cupped her cheekbone as he bent his dark head. He captured her moist lips in a devouring kiss and plundered them apart. From that first instant of contact, Daisy was electrified. The erotic flick of his tongue exploring the tender interior of her mouth made her jerk in shock and gasp. Lightning heat sizzled through her. Her hands came up to clutch at his thick hair, his broad shoulders, his powerful arms and clung. Every clamouring sense roared off in glorious rediscovery. He crushed her to him and she surrendered with enthusiasm. As she strained up to him in a fever of desire, excitement clawed at her throbbing body in a voracious surge.

With a driven groan, Alessio dragged his mouth from hers and stared down at her with stunned intensity. He snatched in a ragged breath and abruptly stood up, carrying her slim body with him. His strong face set like cement as he gazed into her passion-glazed eyes. Swinging lithely round, he simply opened his arms and let her drop from a height back down onto the sofa he had just vacated.

'Give me the *bad* news first!' Alessio raked down at her.

Daisy had landed in a mess of wildly tangled hair and inelegantly splayed limbs on the mercifully well-sprung sofa. She didn't know what had hit her. For an instant she didn't even know where she was but she knew that Alessio was there all right, standing over her like a hanging judge as she attempted to halt a seemingly unstoppable roll in the direction of his plush office carpet. A pair of strong hands caught her and impatiently flipped her back upright into the corner of the seat.

'"The bad news..."'? Daisy echoed. Momentarily, utter cowardice had her in its hold. She didn't *want* to be forced to think. Not about how time had cruelly slid back to entrap and humiliate her. Not about how excruciatingly pleasurable it had felt to be in Alessio's arms. Not about how dreadful it felt to be separated from him again. No, she definitely didn't want to think.

'You only faint when you're terrified! Do you think I don't remember that?' Alessio launched at her grimly. 'You drop in a pathetic little heap, then you open those big blue eyes and fix them on me and I have an uncontrollable urge to give way to my baser instincts. That's how you broke the news of your pregnancy!'

'*My* pregnancy?' Daisy questioned helplessly. 'I didn't get that way on my own!'

'There was nothing accidental about it,' Alessio condemned harshly.

Daisy froze, shattered by that particular accusation. Even thirteen years ago, it had not occurred to her that Alessio might believe that her pregnancy was anything other than an accident. That his family suspected her of such manipulative behaviour had been no surprise to her, but she had innocently assumed that at least Alessio did not share their suspicions. 'Are you really trying to accuse me of having deliberately set out to...?'

Alessio spread two brown hands in a frustrated movement of dismissal. 'We are not going to talk about this.'

'Now just you wait a minute,' Daisy objected, springing upright. 'You can't throw an accusation like that and then back off from it again!'

'Did you hear me? Leave yesterday's bad news where it belongs,' Alessio spelt out. 'We are not about to get into that again. We are not going to fight about ancient history like a couple of stupid kids!'

'Ancient history...yesterday's bad news...' How would Alessio react when she informed him that 'yesterday's bad news' was infinitely more current than he had had any cause to suspect? The fight went out of Daisy. She sank heavily back down on the sofa again. 'You want to know why I told your secretary I had to see you to discuss an urgent, confidential matter—'

'I think I'm ahead of you there.' Alessio surveyed her with innate cynicism, his lip curling. 'You're broke, aren't you? You're in debt.'

'I don't know where you get that idea.' But Daisy turned a guilty pink, unable to avoid thinking about that Swiss bank account filled with Leopardi money. Not just filled but positively *bursting* at the seams with Leopardi money, the original investment having grown greatly in the intervening years, according to Janet.

Alessio settled down on the matching leather sofa opposite. He looked incredibly formidable to her evasive eyes. He was wearing a superbly tailored navy pinstriped suit and a red silk tie. The expensive fabric skimmed wide shoulders and delineated long, powerful thighs. Hurriedly she tore her gaze from him but he stayed there in her mind's eye. So achingly handsome, from the top of his smooth, darkly beautiful head to the soles of his equally beautiful shoes. Her throat closed over. Her mind was a complete blank. Why couldn't he have started losing some of his hair or developed a bit of a businessman's paunch?

'Daisy, my time is at a premium. Since you forced this meeting by giving my secretary no opportunity to deny your demand, I had to cancel an important appointment to free a space for you—'

'A space on the sofa?' she bit out between gritted teeth.

'At this moment, I think the less said about that development the better.'

Bitter resentment tensed Daisy. Alessio... all heat and passion one moment, polar ice the next. Daisy had never had his trick of switching off, had never been able to understand how he could make mad, passionate love to her in the night and then turn away from her when she tried to talk. When her emotions were involved, she wore everything on the surface, could not hold her feelings back. But Alessio locked everything away and kept a ferociously tight hold on the key.

'To be frank, I'm not surprised that you have financial problems,' Alessio imparted coolly. 'I imagine the divorce settlement went a long time ago—'

'And why do you imagine that?'

'At that age you would have had no idea how to handle that amount of money. But I'm relieved that you are finally acknowledging that you did receive that settlement,' he drawled. 'It was very naïve of you to assume that I wouldn't know about it and that you could afford to lie.'

'I wasn't lying.'

'Being inventive with the truth...*again*?' Alessio asked very drily.

Daisy went pale and involuntarily glanced up, connecting with brilliant eyes alive with derision. 'I only ever told you one lie...*only* one. I let you think I was at university when I wasn't. You never actually asked me what age I was—'

'Semantics,' Alessio dismissed, unimpressed and not one whit more yielding or forgiving on the point than he had been in the past. 'I also thought we had reached an agreement, Daisy. The past is off limits. Let's strive to keep the temperature down. Perhaps I should speed up matters by admitting that because we were once married I do still feel some sense of responsibility towards you.'

Daisy stiffened and bridled. 'I don't want you feeling responsible for me and I am not here to ask you for a loan. But, while we're on the subject, let me assure you that I would die of starvation before I would ask you for help!'

'Then exactly what *are* you doing here?' Alessio enquired.

Daisy breathed in deep and dug into her slim handbag to extract a copy of Tara's birth certificate and a small photograph. Her slender hands were trembling, her stomach knotting up. She gripped the certificate. 'This is going to come as a big shock to you, Alessio... but I'm afraid that there isn't any easy way to do this—'

'Do what?' he broke in impatiently.

Daisy stood up on wobbly legs, her heart thumping as if she were tied to the rails in front of an express train. 'I think I'll just leave these with you and then maybe I could ring you tomorrow and see how you feel.'

Alessio had already vaulted upright. His dark features were taut. 'What the hell are you talking about?'

'After we split up, I discovered that I had been expecting twins... and although I had lost o-one of them,' Daisy stammered, a trickle of nervous perspiration running down between her breasts below her blouse, 'I didn't lose the other.'

Alessio stared down at her with fiercely narrowed eyes, a stark frown of bewilderment drawing his level black brows together. 'What are you trying to say?'

'I have a daughter of thirteen...*your* daughter,' she delivered with unconscious stress as she took an automatic step back from him.

'That's impossible.' The faintest tremor lent an uneven quality to Alessio's usually level diction and his accent had thickened. 'You had a miscarriage.'

'She was born three months after I left Italy. I was kept in hospital right up until her birth... in case I lost her too. She was a couple of weeks premature. You see,

I wasn't quite as pregnant as everyone assumed I was,'
Daisy muttered awkwardly in the thundering silence of
Alessio's total disbelief. 'The doctor in Rome got the
delivery date wrong because when he first saw me I was
bigger than he thought I should be, but that was because
I was carrying twins.'

'You had a miscarriage,' Alessio delivered in stubborn
repetition. 'And if at some subsequent stage you did give
birth to a baby which was premature it could not possibly
have been mine—'

'Tara was born in April.' Daisy's lips compressed
tremulously.

If Alessio had been capable of rational thought, his
intelligence would have told him that given the time
period concerned there was no way on earth that the
child could be anything other than his. But then Alessio
was not reasoning out anything right now. Alessio was
at a standstill, blocked from moving on by the barrier
of what he had believed to be concrete fact for thirteen
years.

'You lost the baby,' he said, his rich drawl oddly at-
tentuated and unevenly pitched.

Daisy couldn't stop staring at him. His strong bone
structure was fiercely prominent below his golden skin.
He was alarmingly pale. His astute eyes were curiously
dark and unfocused.

'I didn't lose Tara . . . I lost her twin,' Daisy whispered
shakily, her eyes aching. 'But when I left Rome I didn't
know that. What I did know was that you didn't want
me or the baby, and once the baby was no longer on the
way there was no reason for us to stay married. You
couldn't wait to get rid of me. You couldn't even bring
yourself to come and commiserate at the hospital be-

cause naturally you couldn't help being relieved that it was all over—'

'*Madre di Dio...*' Alessio breathed unsteadily, his lean hands suddenly clenching into powerful fists.

'And I don't blame you for that...not really,' Daisy admitted with innate honesty, her voice taut with the force of her own turbulent emotions. 'But I had had enough and the last thing I could have faced was breaking back into all your lives when you thought you were finally free of me and saying, Guess what? I'm *still* pregnant! It was easier to let you go on thinking that that was over, finished and done with, the way you all wanted it to be. So I really didn't want to have to come here this morning and spoil your day—'

'Spoil my day?' Alessio enunciated with visible difficulty.

Daisy stooped almost clumsily and dropped the certificate and the small photo on the low glass table between them. 'I would never have told you if it had been left solely up to me,' she revealed in a jerky undertone as she began backing away towards the door, her anxious violet gaze nailed to his low shimmering golden eyes. 'I know you're shocked and angry and undoubtedly thinking that you must have been cursed the night you first met me but please try to think of all this from Tara's point of view. She would like to meet you. She's not going to make a nuisance of herself or anything like that but she's curious—'

'Where the bloody hell do you think you're going?' In a sudden movement, Alessio sprang out of his statue-like stillness and strode after her.

'I've said all I've got to say for now!' Daisy confessed, and speeded up in her path to the door, wrenching it open when she got there and not bothering to look over her shoulder as she walked very fast down the corridor. She hit the call button on the lift and then looked.

'*Dio!* Get back here right now!' Alessio launched at her in a rage, from a distance of twenty feet.

Her heart leapt into her throat. She had a dazed impression of the receptionist's stunned incredulity and then she turned and fled, heading for the stairs instead. There was no point in assisting Alessio to spring an embarrassing scene in public. Obviously he was in deep shock, otherwise he wouldn't have shouted at her like that. He was also in a blaze of fury, and that was new—but not something Daisy planned to hang around and find out more about. She crashed through the last set of fire doors and raced down a wide set of stairs.

'I'll drag you up again by the hair if you don't get back here!' Alessio roared down at her from the flight above.

'I'm running away for your benefit, not my own!' Daisy hurled breathlessly back. 'If I don't, you'll say a lot of things that you'll be deeply ashamed of saying in a few hours' time!'

'You bitch!' Alessio grated as he continued his enraged pursuit.

'Don't you dare call me that!' Daisy paused to shout back. 'And by the way, it was *your* birth control that failed and not my *lack* of it! The dates prove that beyond doubt!'

Alessio spat something in Italian that sounded very aggressive. Daisy blenched. This was not a mood she knew him in—Alessio in an uncontrollable dark fury, doubtless made all the more dangerous by his lack of practice in expressing such feelings. It had not once crossed her mind that she might find herself being chased through the Leopardi Merchant Bank by a male who even at nineteen had prided himself on his self-control and superhuman cool. So he was furious—well, that was no surprise, was it? But that was no excuse to attack her!

Tara had been conceived in August, not July, which meant that Alessio was the one responsible. Of course, he had tried to push that responsibility off onto her, citing the very first time they had made love, when a slight misunderstanding had occurred and he had falsely assumed that she was protected from pregnancy. Even with Alessio in hot pursuit, Daisy was childishly delighted to have finally been able to throw that important fact in his teeth.

'Watch out! You're going to fall and break your neck!' Alessio blazed, sounding far too close for comfort.

In her attempt to speed up, Daisy missed her footing and lurched forward. She gasped as a powerful hand suddenly closed on the collar of her jacket to steady her and haul her back up a safe step. Whisking her round, Alessio imprisoned her between his hard, muscular length and the landing wall without noticing that her feet were no longer connected to solid ground.

'*Dio*...how dare you accuse me of being relieved when you lost our baby?' Alessio thundered down at her, glittering golden eyes splintering with violent anger, his hands anchored to her narrow ribcage to hold her entrapped. 'I went on a binge! I got so damned drunk, I nearly killed myself! I didn't have the guts to come to that hospital...I was too *ashamed* to face you! I didn't know what to say when it was too late to say it. "Sorry" wasn't likely to cover it when our baby was dead!'

As he slowly released her, she slid down the wall again and one of her shoes fell off but Daisy wasn't up to fumbling blindly for it. Keeping herself balanced on tiptoe on one side, she gaped up at him, violet eyes wide with astonishment at what he was telling her.

'I showed up three days later and you had gone,' Alessio added unsteadily, dense dark lashes screening his gaze from her, but not before she had seen the savage pain and guilt in the stormy depths of his darkened eyes. 'My father told me that if I put one foot onto a flight for London he would personally kill me! He said I'd done enough damage. But I didn't listen to him until Bianca told me about the money and convinced me that that was all you had wanted from the start—'

'I doubt you needed much persuasion.'

'You'd gone,' Alessio said again. 'You agreed to a divorce without even discussing it with me!'

'But that's what you wanted,' Daisy pointed out very shakily.

Aggressively taut, his strong face shuttered, Alessio took a step back from her. Her throat was working, her insides churning, but all she could think about was the fierce pain and remorse he had revealed—feelings that she had never once dreamt he might be experiencing in the aftermath of their breakup.

The noisy sound of a door swinging back on its hinges came from above them, followed by the echo of chattering female voices.

'Come back upstairs,' Alessio demanded harshly.

Daisy dug her foot back into her lost shoe and sidled away from him, terrified that she was about to break down in tears in front of him. Right now, she didn't think that she could cope with any more. And she had done what she had come to do. She had told him about Tara and he needed time to think about that. Did he appreciate that himself? Was that why he had concentrated on their past rather than on the revelation that he had a daughter? Or was the reality more that he had not yet been able even to begin to absorb that news?

'I'll phone you...t-tomorrow,' Daisy stammered sickly, gripping the handrail with a perspiring palm as she immediately began to head downwards again.

Alessio ground out a frustrated imprecation in his own language as the footsteps above grew louder and closer.

Daisy took advantage of the approaching company to flee, and she didn't glance back this time. Tears were blinding her as she reached the final flight of stairs. The heel of one of her shoes went skittering off the edge of a step and she fell heavily with a bitten-off gasp of fright. Briefly her body was numbed by the force of her fall. Then the pain came in a stomach-churning surge. Slowly, painfully she breathed in deep and picked herself up, straightened her rucked skirt with a trembling hand and limped out through the doors into the ground-floor foyer.

She caught a cab back to the agency. Her hip throbbed with the bruises she had inflicted on herself. But that physical discomfort was as nothing to the terrible pain and confusion tearing at her fast-crumbling composure. Using the rear entrance from the car park, she hobbled into the stark little room that the sales team used for coffee-breaks and collapsed down on an armchair.

You're like an accident around Alessio, she told herself wearily. But then even before she had met him her life had lurched from one disaster to the next. Why had she expected anything to change? She scolded herself for thinking like that. It was a loser's mindset which she had put behind her a long time ago. But somehow, when a real crisis loomed, it was hard to forget the childhood which had left her so desperately insecure, that insidious, confidence-zapping feeling that everything that went wrong was *always* her fault.

Yet that sun-drenched summer with Alessio had, ironically, been the happiest of her life. Feeling loved and wanted and needed had been an intoxicating new experience for Daisy. They had been inseparable and at the time that intensity had seemed mutual. Of course, in actuality, she conceded painfully, she had only been one more notch on Alessio's bedpost. A naïve pushover, always available, always willing, frankly asking to be slapped in the teeth, she thought now. What little common sense she had possessed had evaporated beneath the onslaught of Alessio's first smile.

The real reason why Alessio had not dated schoolgirls should have been obvious to her even then. He had been long past the stage of settling for a goodnight kiss at the end of a date. Daisy had been smoothly, gently but quite ruthlessly seduced by a teenager already expert in the field of sexual intimacy.

Of course, he had also talked with passionate conviction about how much he loved her and how he would fly over and see her at weekends after she went home, but then he *would* have said that, wouldn't he? Such assurances were par for the course. Daisy was convinced that if she hadn't got pregnant, if she had returned to London she would never have heard from Alessio Leopardi again. After all, he had already had a steady girlfriend at university, but Sophia had been abroad that summer...

Daisy swam back to the present, feeling utterly drained. She asked herself why she had been so devastated to hear Alessio admit that he had been too ashamed and upset to face her after her miscarriage. That he had got drunk, been ripped apart by guilt and an obvious inability to cope with either her feelings or his own. She had been shattered by the realisation that her image of Alessio had been inexplicably trapped in a time-warp.

At seventeen, she had looked up to him, depended on him, viewed him as an experienced and strong adult in comparison with herself. It had not occurred to her then that Alessio might have weaknesses of his own. Only now did she think he *was* only six years older than Tara is now; beneath the glossy, cool front he was only a kid too. But Daisy had made a hero of him because nothing less than a hero could have made her feel safe in the new and threatening world in which he and his family lived.

Tears had dampened her face. Daisy pressed unsteady hands to her wet cheeks. Telling Alessio about Tara had somehow brought all those painful feelings of inadequacy back again. But that was the past and far behind her now, she reminded herself. Taking a deep breath, she stood up again and set about eradicating the evidence that she had been crying.

Her phone was ringing when she reached her desk. She swept up the receiver a split second before Barry the Barracuda reached for it. He lounged back against her desk, curious brown eyes nailed to her, a faint smirk on his handsome mouth. 'You seem a little harassed ... anything wrong?'

Daisy shook her head, carefully avoiding his hotly appreciative appraisal. Even though she was as encouragingly warm as an ice sculpture around Barry, he had buckets of persistence. One minor pleasantry and Barry would be back to embarrassing the hell out of her by telling her what a good time an older woman could have with a younger man.

She put the receiver to her ear.

'Daisy?'

Her heart lurched violently against her breastbone. It was Alessio. 'What do you want?' she whispered.

'You ... *now*,' Alessio spelt out succinctly. 'I'm in the wine bar on the corner. You have five minutes to get here.'

The line went dead. Daisy straightened, deathly pale, and then reached for her bag again.

Alessio was in the darkest corner of the bar. As she walked towards him, he sprang fluidly upright and surveyed her with glittering eyes that were as hard as jet, his lean, powerful frame whip-taut with sizzling tension.

'I promised I'd ring you tomorrow,' Daisy reminded him defensively.

'I want to meet my daughter and I am not prepared to await your convenience,' Alessio gritted in a fierce undertone.

'She's at school.'

'Where?'

As she sat down, Daisy looked at him in appalled comprehension. 'You can't go there—'

'When does she get out?' Alessio growled.

'You're not thinking straight,' Daisy protested, shaken by the immediacy of his demand. 'Tara didn't even know I was coming to see you today.'

His eyes flared. *'Dio* ... you should be locked up! You breeze into the bank after thirteen years of silence and tell me I have a daughter! Then you walk out again and tell *me* I'm not thinking straight? What kind of a woman are you?'

A woman who had not enjoyed being forced to break the same 'bad news' twice in one lifetime, she thought.

'I still can't credit that you have done this to me,' Alessio confessed with barely suppressed savagery, driving not quite steady fingers through his luxuriant black hair and surveying her with more than a glimmering of stark incredulity. 'That you could be so bitter you would conceal the birth of my child from me—'

'I wasn't bitter then. I thought I was doing you a favour.'

'A *favour*?' Alessio queried in rampant disbelief.

A suffocating silence hummed.

'I believed you would be happier not knowing,' Daisy finally admitted.

'*Happier...?*'

'Obviously I was wrong,' Daisy conceded in a tense rush. I wish you would stop looking at me like that... like I belong in a lunatic asylum or something... I never had the slightest idea that you would feel like *this* about it!'

As Alessio got a grip on his seething emotions, chilling dark golden eyes closed in on her. 'It was a despicable act. Whatever mistakes I made, I did not deserve to be kept in ignorance of my daughter's existence. We were still married when she was born. Your silence was indefensible. Don't try to excuse it—'

'Maybe I could take this kind of talk better if you had once shown the slightest interest or concern for your child *before* she was born!' Daisy dared shakily, for there was something about the way Alessio was talking now which sent a compulsive shiver down her spine.

'I demonstrated my concern by marrying you. I did not once suggest any other means of dealing with our predicament. Nor, you may recall, did my family,' Alessio reminded her coldly.

'But you still didn't *want* the baby,' Daisy argued feverishly, desperate to hear him admit that fact.

Alessio sent her a look of derision. 'Why else did I marry you if not for our child's sake?'

Daisy snatched in a shaken breath, stunned by the whiplash effect of that one dauntingly simple question.

'I think I need a little time to come to terms with this *before* I meet my daughter.' Having made that charged acknowledgement from between clenched teeth of reluctance, Alessio abruptly thrust his glass away. 'Keep Tara home on Wednesday. I'll call around ten. I'll take her out somewhere. At this moment,' he asserted with icy conviction, 'I have nothing more to say to you.'

'You'll need the address.'

In the shattering, pulsing silence which followed, Daisy, employing his gold pen, scrawled her address on the back of the business card he presented to her.

Alessio stood up. 'If it is the last thing I do in this lifetime, I will punish you for this,' he swore half under his breath.

Daisy was left alone with an uncorked bottle of vintage wine and two untouched glasses. Her knees were knocking together under the table. For a weak moment, she was seriously tempted to try drowning her sorrows. Guilt and bewilderment were tearing her apart. Alessio was outraged and appalled by what she had done. And Daisy was in shock. Alessio, who had once blithely leapt in where angels feared to tread, was backing off for two days to take stock of the situation. Why did that frighten her even more?

CHAPTER FOUR

THE doorbell went in two short, impatient bursts. It was only twenty past nine.

'Do you think it's *him*?' Tara shrieked in panic from her bedroom. 'My hair's still wet!'

Daisy skimmed damp palms down her slender thighs, breathed in deep and opened the door. It was Alessio, strikingly elegant in a pearl-grey suit, pale blue silk shirt and tie.

'I thought you'd be at work.'

'I took the morning off,' Daisy told his tie.

'Does that mean you're planning to accompany us?' The ice in that rich dark drawl let her know how unwelcome an idea that was.

'No...but Tara's not ready yet. Would you like to come in?' Daisy enquired, her fingernails scoring purple crescents into her palms. His cold hostility bit deep.

'I'll wait in the car.'

Her tremulous mouth tautened. 'Alessio...please don't make this any more difficult than it already is.'

There was a sharp little silence.

He released his breath in a hiss and thrust the door shut. The fierce tension in Daisy's slight shoulders gave a little. She walked into the lounge. 'Would you like some coffee?'

He uttered a cool negative.

'She'll be a while. She's not even dressed yet. She was earlier, though. She got up at seven and trailed out her whole wardrobe. Then she decided she needed to wash her hair...' Conscious that she was babbling, Daisy compressed her lips and jerkily folded her arms. She no longer had any excuse to avoid looking at him.

Alessio's vibrantly handsome features were ferociously tense, his strong jawline harshly set. A frown drew his ebony brows together. He looked back at her with glittering golden eyes that chilled her to the marrow. 'What did I do that was so bad that you had to steal my child from me?'

Daisy's strained eyes burned and she spun away, not trusting herself to speak. An intimidating amount of bitter incomprehension had splintered through that demand.

'With that poor a start to our marriage, we were bound to have some problems,' Alessio continued harshly. 'But we had no arguments.'

Daisy almost smiled. To argue with someone you had to speak to them, didn't you? And doormats did not start arguments. Alessio had been able to stride about being mean, moody and silently macho without the smallest challenge from her corner. Indeed, Daisy had grown steadily more afraid of what she might hear if he did break that silence.

'I was never deliberately unkind to you,' Alessio asserted.

Daisy resisted an urge to mention his reconciliation with his former girlfriend, Sophia. Why dig up something so long buried? It would be demeaning and petty to confront him about that now. Teenage boys were not programmed for fidelity. And she didn't even know if he had been sleeping with the other girl or merely seeking out more entertaining company. She wanted to be fair. Their marriage had been over by then anyway.

Their relationship had really died the night when Alessio had turned away from her in bed. Thinking back to that devastating rejection, Daisy relived the anguish of a very insecure teenage girl who had been prepared to settle for sex if that was all she could have from the boy she loved. When Alessio had decided he didn't want or need the sex either, she felt utterly devalued and useless, instead of feeling relieved that so degrading a practice had ended. A couple of weeks after Alessio had moved out of their bedroom, Bianca had dropped the news about Sophia. Alessio's sister had enjoyed telling Daisy that her brother was seeing the other girl again.

'And, even though I then believed that you had chosen to become pregnant, I never once confronted you with that belief.' Alessio, Daisy registered, sounded very much as though he expected a burst of applause for such saint-like restraint.

'Why not?' she couldn't help asking.

'I assumed that you had done it so that you would not have to leave me at the end of the summer.'

Daisy reddened to the roots of her hair. She did it because she loved me...she just couldn't help herself. Trust Alessio to come up with an excuse for her that flattered him! But no wonder he had felt trapped; no wonder he had been so furiously angry with her throughout their short-lived marriage!

'And what would have been the point? Would it have changed anything? After all, I had already screwed up both our lives with spectacular efficiency,' Alessio derided, his wide, sensual mouth narrowing. 'I had failed my own expectations, bitterly disappointed and distressed my parents and got a very young girl pregnant. That was quite enough to be going on with, do you not think?'

Daisy cloaked her pained gaze. His every word tore at her and increased her confusion. It seemed inconceivable to her now, but back then she had never thought in any depth about the effect of their marriage on Alessio's relationship with his parents. Her adolescent outlook had been narrow and exclusive, centred solely on her own feelings and what was happening in *their* relationship. She had taken no account of all the other pressures on Alessio. Her belated acknowledgement of her own essential teenage selfishness dismayed her.

'And now I come here to meet a daughter who is a stranger,' Alessio breathed grimly. 'Have you any idea how that feels? A daughter whom I would have loved and cared for and protected has been living all this time within miles of the Leopardi bank in the City...and here she is in a grubby little flat you couldn't swing a cat in!'

Suddenly, Daisy wanted to cover her ears. 'I didn't think you would want her—'

'Is that what you have told her? Have you poisoned *her* mind against me as well?' Alessio dealt her a fierce look of condemnation. 'And still you do not tell me what I did to deserve such a punishment. So I wasn't *man* enough to make it to the hospital...but that was the one and only time I ever let you down!'

Daisy's knees wouldn't hold her up any more. She dropped down on the edge of an armchair. 'I'm sorry,' she mumbled thickly.

Alessio had stridden over to the window. He swung back to study her with bleak, darkened eyes, all emotion firmly back under lock and key. 'I can do without the tears. If my daughter sees them, no doubt I'll get the blame for that too, and I have no desire to make a first impression as some sort of big, nasty bully who makes her mother cry!'

Daisy gulped and scrabbled hurriedly for a tissue.

'As of now we can only look to the future and hope to do better this time around,' Alessio completed with hard, lingering emphasis, his screened eyes, with a sudden stormy flare of glinting gold, resting on her downbent silver head. 'Our daughter's needs *must* come first. We both owe her that consideration. I hope you appreciate that fact.'

Daisy was too choked up to speak. She was thinking about the pathetic little exercise book that Tara had produced from its hiding place on the top of her wardrobe. Some pictures of Alessio, carefully cut out of newspapers, had been glued into it. In her frantic excitement last night, Tara had bared her soul, hadn't been able to hold anything back. And Daisy had tossed and turned in her bed until dawn, coming to shamefaced terms with. the fact that she had never offered her daughter a photograph of her father. Yet she had a thirteen-year-old photograph of Alessio still lurking in her own purse. For the first time, it struck her that that was just a tad peculiar and rather hard to explain rationally.

'Excuse me,' she said, and made a dive for the door.

When she had managed to compose herself again, she popped her head round Tara's bedroom door. 'Are you ready yet?'

Tara was sitting on the edge of the bed, unusually still. Glossy streamers of black hair rippled as she turned her head, her anxious eyes so painfully like her father's that Daisy's heart skipped a startled beat. 'I'm terrified,' she whispered jerkily. 'I've thought about this for so long, but now it's really happening, now he's actually *here* . . . suppose he doesn't like me?'

Daisy recalled Alessio's restive, simmering tension. 'He's just as scared you won't like him.'

'Is he?' Tara scrambled up, bolstered by the assurance. 'Did he say so?'

'No, but it's written all over him,' Daisy managed with a wobbly smile.

'I guess this is hard for him too. Maybe he thinks I'm expecting Superdad or something.' Tara's eyes softened, her tender heart instantly touched. 'I mean, he won't know what to do or say either. I suppose it's easier for me really...I've always known about him.'

'Yes.' Daisy watched the carpet begin to blur under her aching gaze.

'And he must be dead keen, to arrive this early,' Tara decided.

'Yes—'

'I'm being really cruel staying in here and keeping him waiting,' Tara concluded with a sudden frown of discomfiture.

Having reached the conclusion that her father was more to be pitied than she was, Tara straightened her slim shoulders and stepped round her mother. 'It's OK...you don't need to come. I think I'd prefer to see him on my own first.'

Daisy flattened herself up against the wall and wrapped her arms round herself. Alessio wouldn't want an audience either. So why should she feel excluded? Her daughter was no longer a baby who needed her every step of the way and Tara had always had a strong streak of independence.

In the lounge they both spoke at the same time.

'You look like my sister...' she heard Alessio breathe raggedly.

'Do you still have your motorbike?' Tara asked in a rather squeaky rush.

Daisy pressed her fingers against her wobbly mouth, yanked herself off the wall which had been supporting her and fled into the kitchen. Where was all this truly slaughtering guilt coming from? she asked herself wretchedly. Did she have to accept that she'd been completely in the wrong to keep father and daughter apart?

But how easy it was for Alessio to heap all the blame on her! Thirteen years ago, he had not made a single attempt to share his real feelings with her. So, naturally, Daisy had made assumptions. His behaviour had led her to believe that she was making the right decision, but why had it not occurred to her that she might only be storing up trouble for the future? Yes, it was very easy for Alessio to condemn her now. Hindsight made everyone wise. He could say now that he would have loved and cared for his daughter, and how could she challenge him when he had never been put to the test?

And what was going to happen to her relationship with her daughter if Tara started thinking the same way? Did she deserve to be treated like some sort of unfeeling monster? But how much had she been protecting *herself* from further pain and humiliation when she'd chosen not to tell Alessio about Tara? Daisy dashed a hand over her streaming eyes. And what if Alessio proved to be a terrific father? Just to spite her, just to prove her wrong and himself right, Alessio would very probably break his neck to be Superdad and, the next thing she knew, Tara would bitterly resent having been denied her father all these years.

'Mum . . . we're away!' Tara called from the hall.

Before Daisy could respond, the front door slammed. From the lounge window she watched Tara walking admiringly all the way round the gleaming black Maserati that Alessio had evidently arrived in. She was chattering and laughing non-stop. She looked as if someone had lit a torch inside her. Alessio was visibly entranced by that glowing volubility. His absorption in his excited daughter was total.

And why not? Daisy thought painfully. In looks and personality, Tara was very much a Leopardi. Strong-willed, stubborn, outspoken and passionate, she was Alessio without the ice and self-control, Bianca without the spite and spoilt-rich-girl arrogance. Daisy would have had to be blind not to recognise that. And how much easier it must be for Alessio to relate to that laughing, talkative girl who bore so little resemblance to her mother. A cold, hard knot of fear clenched in Daisy's stomach as she gazed down at them. Breathing in deeply, she moved away from the window.

When she got back from work, Tara still wasn't home. It was after ten that evening when the bell went. Daisy went to the door, expecting it to be Tara but wondering why she hadn't used her key. Thirty seconds later, she knew why. Her daughter came through the door, smothering a yawn, with Alessio a mere step behind her. Caught unprepared, Daisy was appalled. She stood there barefoot, clad in a pair of old jeans and a T-shirt that had shrunk in the wash, while Alessio looked as infuriatingly immaculate and sleekly beautiful as he had done twelve hours earlier.

'I've had a fantastic day,' Tara confided, engulfing her small, stiff mother in a brief hug without even noticing her tension. 'But I'm really tired. 'Night, Dad.'

Dad? She said it so naturally, so easily that Daisy was shaken. As Tara vanished into her bedroom, she met Alessio's shrewd gaze and hurriedly cloaked her own.

'I'll take that cup of coffee now,' he drawled smoothly.

Daisy's cheeks coloured. For an instant, she had a dismaying image of herself hovering like a little girl obediently awaiting her instructions and Alessio taking control of the situation in his own good time. 'Coffee,' she said tightly, and marched into the kitchen, leaving him to find his own way into the lounge.

So Tara and her father had got on like a house on fire. She was pleased for them both—she *was*! A good relationship with Alessio could only benefit her daughter. Now that Tara had met him, the ice was broken and they could all settle down into the kind of detached sharing practised by thousands of divorced parents. Alessio and Tara would form a relationship in which Daisy would play little part.

Maybe she was a bit jealous of that, a bit scared... well, possibly very scared... that Tara might start preferring Alessio to her. But that was childish, wasn't it? Love stretched. Tara was perfectly capable of loving them both. And thirteen years had to count for something, hadn't they? Having rammed down her own insecurities, Daisy entered the lounge, determined to be mature and reasonable regardless of how Alessio chose to behave.

She was taken aback to find Tara down on her knees in front of the bookcase, extracting the last of a pile of photo albums, most of which were already stacked suggestively at Alessio's feet. She gave her mother an anxious look. 'You don't mind if Dad borrows these for a while, do you? I said he could.'

Thirteen years of Daisy's life were documented in those albums. Daisy felt that her privacy was being cruelly invaded and had to bite back words of dismayed refusal. Those were Tara's records too. What could be more natural than that her daughter should want to share that pictorial account of her childhood with her father?

'I'll look after them.' Alessio's faint smile was sardonic and Daisy registered the fact that he knew exactly how she felt.

Flushed and uncomfortable, she set a cup of coffee in front of him.

'We can go over them together after I come back from my school trip,' Tara told Alessio earnestly as she scrambled up again. ''Night, Mum...Dad.' She stopped in the doorway, grinned widely at both her parents and slowly shook her head in bemusement. 'It sounds so weird to say that, to have you both here...like a real family.'

Daisy shrank deeper into her armchair as the door closed. Why did Tara have to go out of her way to sound like a deprived child within Alessio's hearing? she thought in distress. A *real* family!

'Family...not a concept you ever knew a great deal about,' Alessio murmured. 'So in one uniquely selfish move you thought nothing of denying her her own family.'

Daisy thought of the family who had made her feel like a tarty little adventuress at her own wedding. Everyone had known she was pregnant. Bianca had made sure of that. And Alessio's mother had cried so much that people could have been forgiven for believing that she was attending her son's funeral. Taking the hint, the guests had stopped mouthing good wishes and had offered sympathy instead.

'It wasn't like that,' she countered.

'You know as well as I do that there would never have been a divorce if my father had known that you were still expecting a child. The subject would not even have been broached.'

Daisy thrust up her chin. 'Do we have to keep harping back to the past?'

Brilliant golden eyes rested on her. 'That past formed the present and will undoubtedly alter the future. Did you really think that I could meet my daughter and then walk away from her again? She's tremendous!' Alessio acknowledged, with a sudden surge of appreciative warmth that sharply disconcerted Daisy. 'Half-child, half-woman, and she slides from one to the other between one sentence and the next.'

Her tense mouth softened. 'Yes,' she conceded.

'She's funny and bright and very open...but do you know what I found hardest to take?' Alessio sprang upright and moved restlessly across the room before swinging fluidly back to her, his strong dark face taut. 'At first, it was like she was getting this one big chance to impress me and she was terrified that she might not make the grade. That's why she's exhausted. She's been living on her nerves all day.'

A lump ballooned in Daisy's throat. She focused studiously on her bare feet.

'I believe that I have set her fears at rest. I told her that I would have been there for her from the very beginning of her life had I been offered that opportunity.'

'I can see how popular I'm going to be,' Daisy muttered helplessly, but he wasn't telling her anything she hadn't expected. She was the fall guy in this newly formed triangle. Nothing would be allowed to come between Alessio and his desire to win his daughter's affection.

No excuses would be made for Daisy. He would emerge from the debris of their broken marriage shining white and squeaky clean. After all, Daisy hadn't given him a chance to be a father.

'On the contrary, you will be very popular, Daisy,' Alessio drawled in honeyed contradiction. 'You are about to play a leading role in fulfilling our daughter's painfully obvious desire for a *real* family.'

Her violet eyes were strained. 'I'm more than willing to meet you halfway for Tara's sake. You can see her whenever you like.'

'I expect much more than that from you.'

Daisy paled at that uncompromising assurance and curled her hands together on her lap. 'I know that you'll probably want to fly her over to Italy to meet the rest—'

'Of the cast of the horror movie you mentioned?'

Daisy reddened fiercely, finding that reference ungenerous when she was bending over backwards to be reasonable. 'You have to make allowances for the fact that I never knew that you would feel like this about Tara—'

'And you have to accept that now I've found her I'm not letting go of her again.'

'I am accepting that.'

'And that either you share on my terms or risk getting left behind,' Alessio extended drily.

Daisy struggled to work out what it was he wanted that she had not already offered. 'What are your terms?'

'Another home, two parents and complete security for my daughter.'

For a moment, Daisy looked back at him blankly. Then her sensitive stomach churned. *Two* parents? He could only be talking about marrying Nina Franklin. She vented a hiss of angry disbelief. 'You're planning to marry Nina and fight me for custody!'

'Give me one good reason why I would try to take an already insecure adolescent girl away from the mother she adores and give her a stepmother she would undoubtedly loathe,' Alessio invited with evident impatience.

'You said that if it took you a lifetime you would punish me!'

'Not at the cost of my daughter's happiness.'

Daisy's brain felt as if it was functioning at half its usual capacity. If Alessio was not talking about marrying Nina... But then he hadn't actually mentioned marriage specifically, had he? He had referred to another home and two parents. So what was he talking about? He simply couldn't be talking about what was currently crossing her mind. *That* would be sheer insanity.

'When did you last have a good night's sleep?' Alessio asked.

'I don't remember.'

'It shows. I feel as though I'm banging my head against a brick wall.

'We were talking about Tara.' Daisy was still shaken and embarrassed by the mad thought that had briefly occurred to her and she reached out for her cup of coffee with what she hoped was an air of cool, detached composure.

'I've already made the decision which will best serve all our needs.' Alessio studied her with brooding eyes, his wide, sensual mouth suddenly setting hard. 'We will get married again.'

As her fingers involuntarily loosened their grip on the cup and hot liquid splashed down her jeans, Daisy vented a startled shriek of pain and sprang up, pressing her palms against her burning thighs. Alessio dealt her a

split-second look of raw incredulity and then strode
forward. Snatching her unceremoniously up into his arms
and tumbling her down on the sofa, he proceeded to
unzip and peel down her jeans at speed.

'What are you doing?' Daisy screeched in horror, en-
deavouring without success to evade his determined
ministrations.

'I heard a scream,' Tara intervened. *Mum...?*

'Your mother has scalded herself. Where's the
bathroom?' Alessio countered.

Thirty seconds later, Daisy found herself standing in
the bath with Tara aiming the shower head at her bare
thighs to cool the smarting flesh with cold water. Tears
of mortification had now taken over from momentary
tears of pain. Alessio was rustling, tight-mouthed with
disapproval, through a first-aid box crammed with
cosmetics.

'You're really cool in a crisis,' Tara was saying ap-
preciatively to her father. As she took her attention off
what she was doing, the gushing water angled up to
drench Daisy's T-shirt as well. 'I did a first-aid course
last summer but I wouldn't have remembered what to
do so quickly.'

'I'm all right now,' Daisy murmured in desperation,
cringing with embarrassment.

'You need at least ten minutes of that treatment,'
Alessio overruled.

'At least ten minutes. He's right, Mum,' Tara added,
sounding like a little echo.

'It was a very minor scald. The coffee wasn't that hot.'
Daisy was trying somewhat hopelessly to tug the too
small T-shirt down over a pair of minuscule white pants
which were probably transparent now that they were wet.

'You screamed,' her daughter reminded her. 'You scared me!'

'Don't tell me Daisy hasn't done that to you before. She's accident-prone but wonderfully resilient,' Alessio put in reassuringly. 'She came off my motorbike twice without breaking anything.'

'Mum just hasn't got very good spatial awareness,' Tara told him informatively. 'Aunt Janet thinks it's because she was born weeks before she should have been. That's probably why she's so small and skinny as well. It was a real miracle that she survived. I mean *thirty* years ago a lot of premature babies died! I was only a couple of weeks early. It didn't harm me but Aunt Janet said that Mum's development was definitely affected—'

'I thought you were tired,' Daisy slotted into the flood of chatter, feeling older, smaller, skinnier, clumsier and less adequate than she had in years.

'Yes, you should go back to bed,' Alessio agreed, a slight tremor disturbing his smooth drawl. 'I can handle this.'

Daisy wondered if her legs were turning blue. They were numb. The bathroom was freezing cold too. But it was no use; she couldn't block out that shattering announcement one minute longer. 'We will get married again.' Though every rational thought denied that Alessio could have said that, she knew he had said it. And that unapologetic arrogance was at least familiar. Only the last time Alessio had told her that they were getting married Daisy had had no problem with being told rather than asked...

She had been weak with relief and, indeed, it hadn't been very long before she'd begun feeling incredibly happy that she was going to stay on in Italy as his wife and share as many of his waking and sleeping moments as she could possibly manage. Sadly, her sunny belief that Alessio would soon reach that same blissful state of acceptance hadn't lasted much beyond their wedding night, when she had had the poor taste to joke that she felt like Cinderella.

Alessio had looked at her for the very first time as if he could quite happily have strangled her. His wonderful sense of humour had vanished when he'd put that fatal ring on her finger and it had not reappeared. But had she then sown the first seed of his suspicion that she had been plotting all along to acquire a share of the Leopardi wealth? Daisy reflected that she could truthfully put her hand on her heart and assert that the very last thing that had ever been on her mind when Alessio had been making love to her was money...

Daisy emerged from an undeniably erotic reverie to find her T-shirt being whipped off. She emitted a strangled moan of protest just as her equally sodden bra was tugged down her arms. Alessio wrapped a towel round her bare, pouting breasts, met her outraged eyes and said tautly, 'You're cold and wet. I couldn't undress you in front of Tara. It would have embarrassed her.'

He sank down on the corner of the bath and directed the shower head at her shivering legs, and then his smooth dark head angled down and a lean hand settled on her hip to twist her round. 'Where the hell did you get those bruises?' he demanded thunderously.

'On the stairs at the bank.' Daisy was resigned to humiliation now but striving not to show that it mattered.

'Didn't I tell you to watch out?' Alessio gritted. 'Didn't I warn you?'

'Yes... you're *always* right,' Daisy muttered with a speaking lack of appreciation.

He switched off the water and minutely examined her goose-fleshed thighs for patches of scalded pink. 'Do you feel any heat anywhere?' he finally enquired.

'Are you joking?'

'It could have been a lot worse.' It was quite beyond Alessio to admit that he had overreacted.

He lifted her out of the bath and hunkered lithely down to pat her trembling legs as gently and carefully dry as if she were a baby. Daisy submitted, suddenly so choked up by tears that she was undyingly grateful that it was her skinny thighs that had all his attention. Below the discreet cover of the hip-length towel, her wet pants were tugged smoothly down. She didn't notice, for beneath the overhead light Alessio's black hair had the extraordinary iridescent sheen and lure of pure silk and involuntarily Daisy was entrapped by that compulsive view. She wanted to touch those gleaming strands so badly that her fingers tingled and she had to fold her arms tightly because, for a split second, she really didn't trust herself not to surrender to temptation.

It didn't even occur to her to wonder why Alessio was making her stand on one foot and then the other as the damp scrap of lingerie was deftly wafted away, for Daisy was by then in a hot-cheeked fever of self-loathing. Shame was flaming through her in punitive waves. She despised her physical weakness in Alessio's vicinity. What had been excusable at a sexually naïve and besotted seventeen was in no way allowable in a grown woman of thirty. Raw resentment suddenly filled her to overflowing. She couldn't understand how she could still be so disgustingly susceptible. One attack of Alessio ought to have conferred lifelong immunity.

And how dared he come into her home and upbraid her for *her* failings? He had given up on their relationship first, hadn't he? What possible future could he have envisaged for their marriage when he had already been consoling himself with Sophia? Why hadn't she faced him with that fact? But she knew why, didn't she? She couldn't have mentioned that final betrayal without revealing just how deeply she had been hurt by it. And, thirteen years on, she was too proud to expose herself to that extent.

Secure in the belief that she was ignorant of his extramarital activities, Alessio was aggressively determined to load her down with so much guilt that she wouldn't dare to fight back. And why had she not yet said a word about that insane proposition he had made? Marry Alessio again? Always honest with herself, Daisy could think of several things Alessio might be able to persuade her to do in a weak moment, but a second trip to hell and back was definitely not one of them.

'You should be in bed too,' Alessio said very quietly. 'You're exhausted.'

Banging his head against a brick wall . . . she reflected furiously. Just how much affronted dignity could one effectively portray standing naked in a towel with intimate items of apparel scattered round one's feet? Particularly one intimate item that she didn't even recall being removed! She could almost feel Alessio consciously tempering his powerful emotions to the constraints of the situation. If she hadn't been hurt, she knew he would have been laughing uproariously at what had happened. Instead he was practising tact. She hated him for that even more.

'Tell me you weren't crazy enough to say that we should get married again,' she begged, hugging the towel round herself as if it were a suit of armour.

'We'll discuss that tomorrow.'

'But there's nothing to discuss,' Daisy returned flatly. 'Don't be silly.'

'There *isn't*!' Stalking out of the bathroom, Daisy returned to the lounge and plonked herself down. Why was she now thinking that for the very first time Alessio had taken off her clothes and failed to make the smallest pass? she asked herself. Was there something wrong with her brain? Was she becoming obsessed with sex? He had been very impersonal about it, too, but teeth-clenchingly considerate. He had averted his attention from her naked body. Why had that only made her squirm more? Why did her ego suddenly feel as if it had been weekending in a concrete mixer?

'Daisy...' Alessio breathed tautly.

Daisy rigorously studied the wall to the left of him, and when he moved into that space found another section of wall. 'If you've got something you feel you *have* to say, say it now and get it over with. I have no intention of making myself available tomorrow.'

'Your towel's slipping...'

Her cheeks burning, Daisy snatched the towel higher over the embarrassingly full thrust of her breasts. She fixed accusing violet eyes on him. 'I want you to know that until this evening I truly believed that there was no sacrifice I would not make for my daughter's benefit. But there is one. I would give her every last drop of blood in my body, but I would throw myself under a bus before I would marry her father again!'

'You haven't even taken time to consider the idea,' Alessio returned very drily.

'Time? You think I need time? Are you out of your mind?' Daisy gasped with unhidden incredulity. 'I couldn't face being married to you again!'

A dark surge of blood had risen over Alessio's savagely high cheekbones. He breathed in deep.

'You always did have the sensitivity of a stone,' Daisy condemned shakily, her temper suddenly engulfed by a violent tide of debilitating memory. Slowly she shook her silver head. 'I would be a very wicked woman to deserve that much misery twice in one lifetime. Most people who sin have to die to go to hell but I got my punishment while I was still breathing.'

'That is not very funny, Daisy.'

'It wasn't meant to be.' Daisy stole a reluctant, fleeting glance at him.

Alessio was broodingly still, eyes of aristocratic ice fixed to her with chilling intensity. The temperature had dropped to freezing point.

'I wasn't trying to be rude. I was just being frank,' she protested, intimidated more than she wanted to admit by the chill in the air but determined that he should re-alise that he had suggested an act of sheer insanity which it would be a complete waste of time to discuss in any greater depth. 'I suppose you feel that if you're willing to make a huge sacrifice for Tara I should be too...and that most women would take one look at you and your bank balance and flatten you in the rush to the altar...but—'

'Not you,' Alessio slotted in grittily.

'Well, been there, done that...grateful to have got out alive,' Daisy said helplessly.

As the heavy silence stretched unbearably, she suddenly scrambled up again. Walking out fast into the hall, she prayed that he would take the hint and leave without argument. 'The next time you collect Tara, maybe you could just honk the horn...and I'd really appreciate it if you could keep any conversations you feel we must have to the phone—'

'When you bolt from reality, *piccola mia*, you literally streak. And it is done with such a complete lack of shame, it takes my breath away,' Alessio drawled with lethal emphasis.

Her face as hot as hell-fire, Daisy dragged open the front door. 'Goodbye, Alessio.'

CHAPTER FIVE

DAISY slammed the door, shot every bolt home and sagged, until she heard movement in Tara's bedroom. Creeping into her own room, she dropped the towel, grabbed up her nightdress, hauled it over her head and dived at supersonic speed into bed.

The door creaked open. 'Mum...?'

Daisy shut her eyes tight and played dead.

'I won't stay long...' Tara promised, making Daisy feel a total heel. 'I just can't sleep.'

Daisy surrendered. 'So what did you think of...Alessio?'

'He's terrific. We talked about just *everything*!' Tara bounced down on the end of the bed and stuck her feet in below the duvet. 'I even asked him about his girl-friend for you!'

'You did what?' Daisy moaned in horror.

'I knew you were dying to know if it was serious. Relax. We don't need to worry about her. Dad's finished with her.'

'Has he? It's none of my business,' Daisy said, but not quite quickly enough.

'Well, I thought it was very much *our* business,' Tara returned with a meaningful look. 'You should see the way women eye him up when you're out with him...it would frighten the life out of you! He's not going to be alone for long and you haven't got time to play hard to get if you want him back. You need to get in there quick!'

Daisy was aghast. 'Tara—'

'Mum, I *know* you still fancy him like mad! That's why you have that photo of him in your purse and read the *Financial Times* and look tragic when I mention him,' Tara reeled off with overflowing sympathy in her eyes. 'But don't worry—I didn't even drop a *hint* to him! I did ask him what he thought of you, though.'

Daisy rolled over and sank anguished teeth into the pillow.

'Well, I mean, if Dad didn't still fancy you even a bit, I thought *we* should know about it now. Mum, he's still single and he hasn't got anyone either! Don't you think that kind of means he's meant to be ours?' Tara pressed, as if she were talking about a stray dog in need of a loving home.

'No, I don't think that,' Daisy mumbled, but she had a terrifyingly inappropriate urge to giggle.

'Dad *said* you would never have got divorced if he'd known about me. He *said* he really loved you but he wasn't much good at being a husband when he was a teenager. He looked dead guilty too,' Tara revealed with a satisfaction she couldn't hide. 'I think you should have told him about me when I was born. If I'd been you, I wouldn't have let him go! It was his *duty* to be with us and he would have got used to being married eventually.'

That was definitely a self-centred Leopardi talking. Daisy's blood was now running cold in her veins. Tara had already decided that she didn't want Alessio as a part-time father and she was far too possessive to want to share him with any woman other than her mother. 'Very open,' Alessio had said of his daughter. Did that mean he had read Tara like a book? Very probably, Daisy conceded.

Alessio was as sharp as a knife. He was also a Leopardi, born to go from cradle to grave in the belief that he had a hotline to heaven and knew the wisest, smartest move in every situation. Had Tara let Alessio see exactly what she wanted from him? Had Alessio's blood run cold too? Had he then appreciated that Tara could be a real, manipulative handful? Was that why he had said they should remarry? If he was that impressionable, Tara would run rings round him.

Tara got off the bed and sent Daisy a cheeky grin. 'I know you're gasping to hear what he said. Dad thinks you're still gorgeous . . . and I think he'd be doing really well for himself getting a second chance with you—'

'It's not going to happen, Tara,' Daisy said as gently and firmly as she could.

'I don't see why not.' Her daughter looked distinctly smug and gave her mother a warm and approving appraisal. 'Lots of men go for you. Why shouldn't he?'

That revealing and explosive dialogue haunted Daisy throughout the next morning. She couldn't keep her mind on her work and found herself drifting off into thoughts of what life might have been like if she hadn't divorced Alessio. Would he have changed after she had had the baby? Would he have wanted her again then? Would he have dumped Sophia and become a faithful husband? Daisy looked out of the window in cynical search of a flying pig or a blue moon.

'You know, there's something different about you this week,' Barry commented, watching her doodle interlocking triangles on her pad. 'You're much more approachable.'

'Barry—'

'Have dinner with me tonight,' he urged, dropping down athletically into a crouch in front of her swivel chair so that they could meet eye to eye. 'I won't lay a finger on you...I promise!'

'Give over, Barry,' Daisy groaned.

'So I used to show off a little when I first started here but that was *three* years ago,' Barry stressed with a winning smile as he reached for her hands. 'I've grown up since then. I don't boast about my one-night stands any more. I know you're not impressed by how fast I drive my Porsche. I think I could even be faithful for you.'

Daisy studied him and experienced a very, very faint stab of remorse. Deep down inside, she had always known why she had loathed Barry on sight. In build, colouring and brash confidence, he reminded her just a little of Alessio as a teenager. Poor Barry. He had been chasing her for so long that it was a running office joke. 'Sorry—' she began.

'Daisy...'

Releasing her fingers, Barry vaulted upright. Daisy might have got whiplash if Alessio hadn't spun her chair round so fast that she saw whirling lights instead.

'Lunch,' Alessio drawled with definite aggression.

'I'm not hungry,' Daisy muttered out of the corner of her mouth as she turned her chair back to her desk. 'Go away...'

'Mr Leopardi?' Barry cleared his throat after a lengthy pause. 'We spoke on the phone last week—'

'You may inform your superior that Miss Thornton won't be returning to work here,' Alessio interposed, smooth as glass. 'She'll be far too busy roasting in the fires of eternity as my wife.'

'Your...your *wife*?' Barry spluttered incredulously.

Ignoring him, Alessio lifted Daisy's slim handbag from the desk and studied it with scepticism. 'Where's all the rest of the junk?'

'Junk?' Daisy's voice fractured as she rose jerkily upright, unable to believe that he had made such an announcement in front of the entire office.

'Daisy, you couldn't get through one day with a purse this tiny. This is for show. Somewhere else there has to be a holding tank for the hundred and one things you have to keep within reach. *Ah...*' With unhidden satisfaction, Alessio reached below the desk and lifted the large, battered leather holdall he had espied. 'Yours? How often do you feed the purse? Hourly? Half-hourly?'

'I'll be back after lunch, Barry,' Daisy said frigidly, striving to regain control of the situation but quite shattered by the manner in which Alessio was behaving. Barry simply gaped at her.

'You won't be,' Alessio drawled, running at speed through the drawers of her desk, extracting a small teddy bear, a single shoe, three fat romantic novels, two hairbrushes and several packets of tights. He stuffed the lot into the leather holdall. 'Have you a coat? One? Two?'

'I'll see to that.' Joyce giggled into the resounding silence and crossed the room to a cupboard, to emerge with two umbrellas, a coat, a jacket and a pair of red stiletto-heeled ankle-boots which had sent Barry into such paroxysms of lust that Daisy had stopped wearing them out of pity.

'I'll be back,' Daisy said defiantly.

'You're not the Terminator,' Alessio dropped in with gentle satire as he curved a hand round her elbow and marched her out into the fresh air, Joyce following in their wake. 'Didn't the toy boy ever figure out how to derail you? Take you by surprise and you're as helpless as a tortoise turned on its back, *cara*.'

'Was it love at first sight?' Joyce prompted with dreamily intent eyes as she passed Daisy's possessions over to the chauffeur.

'Is that when you feel like you've been run over by a tank?' Alessio enquired with a deeply reflective air. 'That magical but gut-wrenching moment when you realise that nothing is ever going to be the same again? It was more like having a very large rock dropped on me from a height. The earth may have moved but I wasn't fast enough on my feet.'

Daisy studied him in disbelief.

'I suppose men feel they have to fight it,' Joyce sighed philosophically. 'But you didn't fight for long, did you?'

'I don't think you want the answer to that one,' Alessio murmured, pressing Daisy into the limousine and tossing her bag in after her.

'How could you embarrass me like that?' Daisy demanded as the car drew away from the kerb. 'How am I supposed to explain all that nonsense you talked?'

'You won't have to. When I said you weren't setting foot in there again I was not joking. I have already acquired a special licence. We can get married on Saturday morning before Tara goes off on her school trip to France,' Alessio explained with immovable calm.

Her lashes fluttered over incredulous violet eyes. 'A special licence? S-Saturday?' she stammered. 'Are you crazy? We're divorced and staying that way!'

'Are you prepared to lose Tara?' Astute golden eyes rested on her enquiringly.

Daisy stiffened. 'Are you threatening me?'

'It was a warning. I'm telling you what may well happen if we *don't* get married and present a united front,' Alessio pronounced with deflating cool. 'You chose to bring Tara up outside the society in which she belongs and her life is now about to change out of all recognition. She is not in any way prepared for that transformation and my family will try to spoil her as much as they spoiled me.'

Daisy dropped her head in surprise at that admission.

'Everything Tara wants, she will receive. You couldn't possibly compete from a distance, any more than you can continue to deny who she is. She's a Leopardi and one day she will be an extremely wealthy young woman. She will have to make major adjustments.'

'I could help her—'

'How could you help if you weren't there? And how quick would you be to blame me if anything went wrong? Tara will need more backup than I can give her. She will need her mother's full support. When she realises how much she has missed out on, you won't find it easy to stay in control when she's abroad and you're still here in London,' Alessio pointed out drily.

He had spelt out realities about Tara's future that Daisy did not want to hear. Her daughter would indeed find the Leopardi lifestyle shockingly seductive. Her grandparents would undoubtedly greet her with open arms. Tara was, after all, one of *them*. All that money and attention might turn the head of even the most stable adult, so what effect might they have on an impressionable teenager? She remembered the Ferrari, Alessio's eighteenth-birthday present, and her stomach turned over sickly.

'You're talking as if Tara's likely to be spending a lot of time in Italy.'

'You won't have much choice about that, Daisy. My father is moving into semi-retirement. While he will retain a consultative position within the bank, I'm taking over our main office in Rome next month,' Alessio imparted. 'I'll only be back in London on business trips after that—'

'But you were looking for a house *here*,' Daisy said involuntarily, struggling to conceal her growing dismay at what he was telling her.

'I was viewing the house on my parents' behalf, not my own. They're looking for a base in London.'

A base, Daisy reflected dizzily. Only a Leopardi could refer to a house that big and expensive as a base. She surveyed Alessio with dazed eyes. It was a welcome escape from the daunting facts he was hammering her with. He looked gorgeous—undeniably and infuriatingly gorgeous. No sleepless shadows beneath *his* eyes and, remarkably, not even a hint of yesterday's strain. His superbly tailored charcoal-grey suit was a spectacular showcase for his lean, vibrantly male physique, but even so Daisy found that she was experiencing a deep craving to see him in a pair of faded, tight jeans again...

Daisy stopped herself dead, guiltily squashing that train of thought. Why should she get all worked up about the fact that Alessio still attracted her? Wasn't that immature and narrow-minded? It was only her hormones which were at fault—natural female promptings accentuated by silly, sentimental memories. Alessio was incredibly sexy...that was all. Her body was tempted but her intelligence was safely in control.

'So you must see that if I am to establish a relationship of any depth with my daughter she will be travelling to Rome on a very regular basis.'

'Hmmm...' Daisy sighed absently, wondering if he remembered the time she had tried to take his jeans off with her teeth...seriously hoping that he didn't.

'I think that you owe both Tara and me the chance to make something out of this mess.'

Daisy nodded and wished she had sat beside him instead of opposite.

'I also want to give Tara what *she* wants, and I would have to be extraordinarily stupid not to know what she wants after yesterday.'

With enormous effort, Daisy fought to reinstate rational concentration and lifted exasperated eyes to his. 'That's what this is all about, isn't it? You let Tara tie you up in knots, didn't you?'

Disorientatingly, Alessio's gleaming dark gaze flared with spontaneous amusement. 'Not at all. When she asked me very loudly in the middle of a crowded restaurant whether I thought I could still fancy her mum, I took it beautifully.'

The challenging slant of Daisy's chin wavered as she slowly turned a beetroot shade, horror-striking into her bones.

'It was only half past twelve but I was already waiting for the question,' Alessio confessed lazily. 'Tara has no subtlety. She can't wait for anything either. She just jumps right in and splashes everyone around her. Thirty-two years' experience of Bianca stood me in good stead.'

Daisy was mortified. 'So you guessed what she was trying to do.'

'She was like a suicide bomber forcing herself out on a diplomatic mission. She told me how she had always thought that you and I had a lot in common with Romeo and Juliet.'

Daisy went from mortification to sheer agony. 'Oh, no—'

'How divorce destroys children's lives: that was phase two. She backed that up with several hair-raising horror stories about schoolfriends. I lunched to the accompaniment of tales about spiteful stepmothers and abusive stepfathers. By the time the dessert cart came my appetite was flagging but Tara was putting away enough fuel to stoke a steam engine,' Alessio recalled wryly. 'I was allowed a break until mid-afternoon before she embarked on the problems suffered by children from broken homes.'

'I'm *really* sorry,' Daisy said feelingly.

'She took me step by painful step through subjects such as low self-esteem and abysmal academic achievement—'

'She's top of her class!' Daisy gasped.

'I suspected that. Nobody that determined to make me feel guilty could possibly be lacking in intelligence. And by the end of my indoctrination session the picture was crystal-clear. Tara worships the ground you walk on. You have also attained martyr status while still alive,' Alessio murmured with sardonic eyes. 'The divorce was fifty per cent my fault and fifty per cent the fault of the in-laws from hell. My evil, scheming parents, who sounded remarkably like a twentieth-century resurrection of the Borgias, may not have succeeded in driving you to suicide but then that is only a tribute to the strength of your character.'

Daisy gulped. 'Teenagers can be very melodramatic.'

'There were moments yesterday when I could have shaken you until your teeth rattled in your head,' Alessio confided. 'But the bottom line is that Tara is consumed by a desire to see us reconciled.'

'It's an understandable dream for her to have,' Daisy conceded grudgingly.

'But I want to give my daughter that dream,' Alessio returned with dangerous softness. The limousine had stopped and the chauffeur walked round the car to open Daisy's door for her. Tight-mouthed, Daisy slid out. 'Where on earth are we going?'

'My apartment.'

Inside the lift, she breathed in deep. 'Alessio... I love Tara very much and I understand that, the way you're feeling right now, you'd try to give her the moon if she asked for it, but I don't want—'

'What you want doesn't come into this.'

Daisy's generous mouth fell wide open.

'Haven't you had everything *your* way for long enough?'

Daisy froze in shock.

'When the going go too rough, you walked out on our marriage without hesitation,' Alessio delivered with aggressive bite. 'I got no choice then and I got even less choice when it came to my rights as a parent. You didn't compromise your wants and wishes until Tara gave you a guilty conscience. If she had had no interest in her absent father, I would probably never have learnt that I had a daughter. *Dio*... I feel I've earned the right to make some demands of my own!'

Daisy was devastated by that condemnation. Clearly, Alessio saw her as an utterly selfish individual who had caused unlimited damage. But she was being unfairly judged by adult standards. In marrying her at nineteen, Alessio had acknowledged that their child's needs should come first. It had been a fine and noble ideal but he had not carried through with the reality that their marriage would have to work to make that possible.

His penthouse apartment was breathtaking. Inquisitively she glanced through open doorways, taking in glimpses of richly polished wooden floors, magnificent rugs and

gleaming antiques. In an elegant dining-room, the first
course of their meal already awaited them. A silent man-
servant pushed her chair in, shook out her linen napkin
and poured the wine before leaving them. Daisy emptied
her glass fast. Over the rim, she collided with Alessio's
broodingly intense dark gaze and the silence pulsed and
pounded like the quiet before the storm.

Alessio expelled his breath in an impatient hiss. 'When
we met again, I admit that I was very hostile.' His strong
jawline squared. 'But that was self-defence. All the
memories came back and I only allowed myself to
recognise two reactions—lust and anger.'

In the past, Daisy had had a large personal acquaintance with both emotions, although, admittedly,
Alessio had never before acknowledged the existence of
either. She surveyed her empty glass with a sinking heart.
She wondered what it would take to satisfy the Leopardi
need for blood and retribution. When would Alessio take
account of his own sins of omission?

'But there was a lot of pain and bitterness in there
too.'

Daisy experienced enough of a surge of interest and
surprise to look up and pay closer attention.

Alessio's gaze was screened to a mere glimmer of gold.
'I was amazed that I could still remember those feelings,'
he admitted tautly. 'But then my ego was very fragile at
the time and you do hold the distinction of being the
only woman who ever ditched me for a large injection
of cash.'

Daisy's breath caught in her throat as she belatedly
recalled that she had not yet explained about that money.
'I—'

Alessio shifted a lean, autocratic hand to silence her.
'But that sordid reality does not release me from what

is patently my duty of care and responsibility towards my daughter. Nor do your personal feelings release you from that same obligation.'

Sordid reality? In the midst of reflecting that it might well have done Alessio a great deal of good to believe that he had been ditched in return for a large injection of cash, Daisy was sidetracked by his horrific use of that word 'duty'. Her daughter had used it last night and it had given her mother a distinctly nasty turn. Leopardis were heavily into buzz words of the 'duty' and 'honour' variety. Employing such terms, they braced themselves to do masochistic things and then took revenge by punishing the unfortunate being who had forced them into those sacrifices.

That was the story of their first marriage in a nutshell, Daisy conceded with an involuntary shudder. Alessio had been punishing her for *his* sacrifice. She was not crazy enough to give him a second bite at the same apple. Tara would thank neither one of them for involving her in the misery of an unhappy marriage. If Alessio wanted a sacrifice, he was not going to find one in Daisy. Whatever he might think, Daisy knew she was not good martyr material.

'Daisy...' Alessio breathed in a charged undertone. 'Are you listening to me?'

Like a mouse slowly raising its gaze to risk the hypnotic and deadly enchantment of a snake, Daisy lifted her head. 'Sorry?' she said very tautly.

Anger glittered in his incisive scrutiny. 'No doubt it will surprise you, but I am accustomed to attention when I am speaking.'

Daisy was not at all surprised. Alessio had the most gorgeous dark, seductive drawl. That rich voice sent tiny, delicious quivers down her spine. He also had the most

incredibly beautiful eyes and the most fabulous bone
structure, she acknowledged, fully concentrating on what
really mattered . . . her *own* vulnerability. She could not
remarry a man whom she had once loved so much and
who had hurt her so terribly. It would be a suicidally
stupid act. And she might have a bad habit of learning
most of her lessons the hard way but nobody could ever
say that she made the same mistake twice!

'But then I am accustomed to dealing with individuals
with some *small* measure of concentration,' Alessio
added softly.

'This has been a very traumatic week for me,' Daisy
muttered evasively.

'Really?' Alessio prompted dangerously, causing her
anxious eyes to shoot back to his strong dark face.

'Yes, really.'

'How *could* it have been traumatic?' Alessio thundered in sudden, seething frustration. 'You're on another
bloody planet! You might be here in body but you're
certainly not here in spirit!'

Daisy reddened with discomfiture. 'I just lost the
thread of the conversation for a—'

'What conversation?' Alessio derided. 'You've hardly
opened your mouth since we got out of the lift! Barely
a word has crossed your lips—'

'I was *listening*,' she protested.

'No, you weren't,' Alessio gritted with a flash of strong
white teeth. '*Dio*, how this takes me back! You avoid
things that you don't like.'

'I didn't get very far with you, did I?'

Daisy was thinking about the mountain of recriminations that had already come her way. Not a lot to talk
about there that she could see. There had been her denial
of his parental rights. Fact. Her acceptance of cash in

return for him—what other people called a divorce settlement but still fact, since she was technically in possession of that cash. Then there had been the lust and anger bit, followed by the pain and bitterness bit, neither of which had impressed her as being the conversational opener of the year. Alessio took account of only his own feelings and Daisy had not been tempted to reveal what *she* had suffered in the aftermath of their marriage...

Agonies, sheer appalling agonies, she recalled strickenly. She had been like one of those dreadfully clingy vines suddenly torn loose from its only support. Without Alessio, her world had collapsed. Day and night had fused into a progression of endless, miserable hours. If they hadn't kept on remorselessly shovelling food into her in the hospital she wouldn't have survived to tell the tale. But that was not a tale she was about to tell *him*. Wasn't it better that he should believe that she had cheerfully grabbed the money and run? Alessio thought she had departed with a big, brazen, gold-digging bang. Why share the news that she had been one very damp squib?

'Daisy,' Alessio murmured grittily.

But Daisy was still being crushed by the weight of her memories. She had even missed the silences—those volatile, terrifyingly moody silences which had driven her into doormat mode on the least said, soonest mended principle. And yet now she couldn't shut him up, she thought in bewilderment. It was as if he had a mission to talk her to death. Couldn't he understand that she had nothing more to say to him on the subject of remarriage? At least nothing that would not be conducive to further conflict...and Daisy did not like conflict, unless she already had an escape route worked out.

'That's *it*!' Alessio enunciated with grim emphasis.

Daisy flinched as he thrust back his chair and sprang upright. 'Can I go back to work now?' she asked in a small and not very hopeful voice.

Alessio spread his lean brown hands wide in a frustrated arc. His smouldering golden gaze sizzled across the room and landed on her quailing figure like forked lightning. 'No, you may not go back to work!'

'There's no need to shout—'

'It's shout or strangle you!'

Daisy stood up. 'I was listening.'

'How much did you take in?'

'Were you expecting me to take notes?' Daisy demanded defensively.

In the act of leaving the room, Alessio stopped dead, his broad shoulders rigid. The atmosphere was electric.

'Hang on every word the way I used to?' Daisy continued with unconcealed rancour.

'Even then your mind wandered places I could never follow,' Alessio acknowledged gruffly without turning his head. 'We are very different people.'

For some peculiar reason that reminder distressed her, yet it was an undeniable truth. Alessio was an extrovert, but he didn't show his emotions—not the private ones anyway—and he was always in control. Daisy was an introvert, but love had smashed her barriers and she had poured out on Alessio all the fierce emotion and affection that no one else had ever wanted from her. *She* had been dangerously out of control. Afterwards, she had promised herself that she would never bare herself to another human being like that again. And, with the single exception of her daughter, she had kept that promise.

'Yes...' she acknowledged unevenly, and just in case he might be thinking of that humiliating inequality she added, 'You're organised and practical and sensible. You don't lose things or forget things or...or fall over or off things.' Sucking in a shaky breath, Daisy pinned her lips shut with an effort, her eyes suddenly smarting with tears. At seventeen she had been dumb enough to think that those differences meant that they complemented each other.

'Exasperatingly efficient but with not much in the way of imagination?' Alessio queried silkily. 'Possibly I am about to surprise you.'

'Surprise me?' Daisy questioned.

He swung back another door and stood back for her to precede him. Her fine brows knit as she walked through and glanced round a room obviously used as an office. She cleared her throat uncertainly. 'Why have you brought me in here?'

His strong dark face hardened. 'I didn't want to have to do this, Daisy.'

Goose-flesh prickled at the sensitive nape of her neck. 'Do what?'

'It was not my intention to use undue pressure.'

'Undue pressure?' Daisy queried slightly shrilly, already calculating the distance she was from the door, her fertile imagination running riot.

'I have employed every means of rational persuasion within my power.'

'Tara...' Daisy sighed limply.

Alessio lifted a thick document from the desk and held it out to her.

Daisy tensed even more. 'What's that?'

'A deed of purchase for Elite Estates. I have bought the agency.'

The taut silence thrummed in her eardrums.

Her brow slowly furrowed. 'That's not possible. Old Mr Dickson would never sell. It was his first business, and he may not take much of a direct interest these days but—'

'The agency is not very profitable given the current state of the property market,' Alessio returned levelly. 'Lewis Dickson couldn't close with my offer fast enough.'

'But what would you want with a London estate company?' Daisy looked at him in perplexity. 'You *couldn't* have bought the agency!' she argued with sudden conviction. 'Giles would have known if there was anything like that in the wind.'

'Carter is only an employee.'

'But he manages Elite Estates—'

'That does not grant him automatic access to his employer's decisions, and discretion was part of the deal.'

Alessio had bought the agency? Daisy studied the document, intricate legal terms blurring beneath her searching gaze until she finally picked out sentences that had a frightening ring of reality. 'I just don't understand why...' she muttered in a daze.

'I *could* make a very tidy profit on the deal. The agency is sitting on a prime site with a great deal of expensive space wasted on that car park. It's ripe for redevelopment.'

'Redevelopment?' Daisy repeated sickly. 'Are you talking about closing the agency down?'

Glittering eyes rested intently on her. 'That's up to you.'

'*Me?*' Daisy gasped. 'What's it got to do with me?'

'The fate of your former colleagues is in your hands,' Alessio delivered softly. 'If you marry me, the agency will continue to do business. If you don't marry me, I will be consoled by a large profit but the agency will cease trading.'

A brittle laugh of disbelief was torn from Daisy. 'You're not serious!'

'Never before has so much ridden on the back of one little deal,' Alessio responded with complete cool.

'But...but *you* wouldn't do that sort of thing...make it personal like that,' Daisy reasoned unsteadily. 'That would be unethical.'

Alessio's eyes met her expectant gaze in a head-on collision. 'Blackmail *is* unethical.'

Daisy tried and failed to swallow at that unashamed acknowledgement. 'You're saying that if I don't marry you you'll put people out of work and it will be my fault. Why... why do you think that will influence me?'

Alessio's gaze wandered over her, taking in her stark white face, the horror in her expressive eyes, and the hold she had on the desk to stay upright. His lush dark lashes lowered and his shapely mouth quirked. 'I know you.'

'You don't know me. If you're the new owner of Elite Estates, it's got nothing to do with me!' Casting aside the document, Daisy turned her back on him, her stomach twisting. She was reeling with shock but struggling desperately hard to hide it.

'Daisy, you couldn't sleep knowing that you were responsible for *one* person losing their job.'

Daisy flinched from that confident assurance, inwardly counting up the ten other people who formed the agency staff. In recent times, many estate agencies had cut back on employees. It would be very difficult, if not impossible for some of her colleagues to find work elsewhere. Four of the men had families to support. One woman was a single parent like herself, another had a husband who had recently lost his own job. The sudden loss of their pay cheques and their security would devastate all their lives.

'Daisy...you feed stray animals. You weep over soppy movies. You worry that plants feel pain,' Alessio enumerated softly. 'That bleeding-heart sensitivity may not have extended to me thirteen years ago but you are definitely not one of the world's most ruthless women.'

'I hate you,' Daisy mumbled strickenly, her slight shoulders rigid with strain.

'You hate spiders...but have you ever stepped on one?'

'Don't be snide.'

'I was being realistic on your behalf.'

'I am a very realistic person but I never, ever thought that you would do anything like this,' Daisy confessed chokily. 'I always thought that aside from all the flaws you couldn't help or were just born with...well, that you did at least *try* to be a basically decent human being...and even if you weren't very good at it at least the trying had to count for something. To find out that you're not even *trying* any more... Well, words just fail me...'

They appeared to fail Alessio as well because the silence stretched and thrummed for enervating and endless seconds. Then a strangled little hiss of air escaped him and all of a sudden he went off into a bout of coughing.

'I hope you choke,' Daisy said thinly while she toyed wildly with the idea of telling Tara about his threat. Her daughter would be appalled. Didn't Alessio appreciate that? If Daisy talked, Tara's trust in her father would be destroyed. But such an act would damage and hurt her daughter most of all, wouldn't it? Tara had so many hopes and expectations already centred on Alessio.

Acknowledging defeat, Daisy sagged like a beaten but bitterly resentful rag doll down into an armchair.

'You've won...'

Alessio swung back to her.

'I'll marry you,' she whispered jerkily. 'But I want you to know that you are making a very big mistake.'

Alessio was very still, not a muscle moving in his darkly handsome face. 'I don't think so.'

'We will be utterly miserable together,' Daisy forecast.

'That's a risk I'm prepared to take.'

'Tara will be miserable too,' Daisy stressed.

'Not if I have anything to do with it.'

'She just won't believe that we're getting married again this fast.'

'No?' Alessio queried silkily. 'I wonder who it was who first filled her head with all that stuff about Romeo and Juliet?'

Daisy flinched and looked hunted.

'Because, oddly enough, she's a very practical girl,' Alessio continued smoothly. 'I wouldn't have said that she had a natural bent for throbbing melodrama. None of my family have. In fact the *only* person I have ever known who could turn a broken cup into a stirring six-act tragedy is—'

'So we're getting married on Saturday, are we?' Daisy broke in feverishly fast.

'But we'll still be lagging a long way behind the example set by Shakespeare's star-crossed lovers.' Alessio contrived to look simultaneously soulful and sardonic. '*They* got hitched within twenty-four hours.'

Two spots of scarlet now burned over Daisy's cheekbones. 'I wouldn't know. I've never read *Romeo and Juliet*,' she said, crossing two sets of fingers the way she always did when she lied.

'I'm reading it line by line. So far, it has been a most enlightening experience.'

Daisy's soft mouth compressed and she tilted her chin. 'This will be a marriage of convenience, right?' she prompted snappishly.

'Mutual convenience,' Alessio agreed silkily. 'What else?'

CHAPTER SIX

JANET and Tara chattered cheerfully the whole way to the register office. It was just as well. Daisy was not in a chatty mood. Her wedding day. Her second wedding day. She tried hard to concentrate on positive thoughts. She was not in love with Alessio, nor did she have any illusions about this marriage. Alessio had made no attempt to pretend that it would be anything more than a convenient arrangement for Tara's benefit.

And Tara was ecstatic, Daisy reminded herself. Indeed her daughter had decided that her father was madly romantic and impetuous and that her mother was one incredibly lucky woman. But then Tara had been so absorbed in the end of the school term, packing for her French trip and contemplating the new life awaiting her in Italy on her return that she was currently suffering from a severe case of over-excitement.

Janet had remarked that Daisy had never been remarkable for her caution in Alessio's radius. As a thought for the day, it had not been inspiring. And when her aunt had had the insensitivity to point out that, after all, she had always had this *thing* about Alessio and that it would be pointless to interfere when the two of them had always acted *crazy* around each other Daisy had almost choked on her sense of injustice.

This time around, she had withstood Alessio with the heroic self-denial of a chocaholic on a strict diet. When he had asked her to marry him again, it had been like a shot of aversion therapy. No blissful dream of drifting down the aisle to the tune of a heavenly chorus had afflicted her. She had felt *ill*, hadn't she? She had not been tempted. But Alessio had employed blackmail. Alessio had defeated her only with cold-blooded threats and intimidation.

And Daisy had been truly shattered by that development. Now she asked herself why. All that inquisitive reading of the financial papers over the years had taught Daisy that Alessio was not a pussy-cat in the business world. Indeed, he was downright ruthless. In the world of international finance, the name of Leopardi was feared as much as it was respected. But the idealistic teenager whom Daisy remembered would never have sunk to using such brutal tactics in a personal relationship.

But then there was no *personal* relationship between them, Daisy acknowledged painfully. Before Alessio had learnt that she had his daughter, he had made it very clear that he wanted nothing more to do with his ex-wife. The sofa encounter had just been the knee-jerk response of an innately sexual predator. It had meant nothing. In fact, Alessio had been eager to believe that she was in his office to scrounge money, because he would have happily *paid* her to go away and lose herself again! So how could she feel anything but bitter and humiliated at the prospect of becoming his wife a second time?

'You're awfully quiet, Mum,' Tara finally observed as Daisy clambered shakily out of the limousine which Alessio had sent to pick the three of them up.

'Wedding-day nerves,' Janet commented lightly.

Tara frowned at her mother. 'I wish you hadn't worn that black suit.'

'It's smart,' Daisy muttered.

'But you look like a pencil going to a funeral.'

A pencil, Daisy reflected wretchedly. She had barely eaten and slept for a week now and it showed. Alessio strolled towards them and her haunted eyes trailed over him in wondering disbelief. He exuded vibrant energy in surplus waves, his eyes diamond-bright, a brilliant smile curving his relaxed mouth. In an exquisitely tailored cream suit that accentuated his golden skin and black hair, he looked as if he had strayed off a Hollywood movie set. Daisy averted her attention again, menaced by the strength and resilience of the enemy.

'As you can see, Mum is just overwhelmed,' Tara burbled. 'It's nerves...not cold feet or anything like that!'

'So you didn't try to make a last-minute break for it through the bathroom window?' Alessio murmured softly to Daisy.

Daisy sidled off one foot onto the other because, oddly enough, there *had* been an insane moment when Tara had been hammering on the door and telling her that the limo had arrived when she had considered using the fire escape. Alessio curved what felt like an imprisoning arm of steel round her slender back. Daisy went rigid. The scent of him so close flared her nostrils. Clean and warm and very male but, worst of all, agonisingly familiar. Her senses remembered him. In a pitch-dark room, she could have picked Alessio out of a hundred men. The knowledge absolutely terrified her.

The marriage ceremony was brief. A tide of sick dizziness ran over her as a slender platinum wedding ring was threaded over her knuckle.

'Signora Leopardi...' Alessio carried her ice-cold fingers smoothly to his lips and kissed them.

The return of that name churned up Daisy's stomach. Tugging free of his light hold, she rubbed her trembling fingers against her skirt. Her wavering smile, kept in valiant place for Tara, died away altogether.

Alessio swept them off to an early lunch at the Ritz. He ate a hearty meal, whereas his bride couldn't manage a single lettuce leaf. He cracked jokes with Janet and teased Tara. No, there was nothing remotely sensitive about Alessio, Daisy reflected. When Alessio triumphed, he was never tempted to a show of mock humility. No, indeed. He radiated glowing satisfaction and that burning, wolfish smile flashed out with unnerving frequency. When a Leopardi was on top, all was bliss in the Leopardi world.

Repelled by that brazen lack of remorse, Daisy escaped to the cloakroom and, finding a comfortable chair, sat there for a while with the attitude of an earthquake victim waiting for the tidal wave that would surely follow. When she finally emerged again, she was startled to find Alessio waiting outside for her.

'I thought you might have done a runner,' he confided with complete calm. 'Lucky for you that you didn't. I would have called the police—'

'The *police*?' Daisy repeated in horror.

'When your sense of tragedy overpowers you, you are very likely to fall under a bus. *Dio*, in the state you're in right now, it would be like letting a rampaging toddler loose in rush-hour traffic!' Alessio said with rueful amusement. 'I have known people who have faced death with greater fortitude than you faced our wedding with today, but it has been a memorable experience for which I thank you from the bottom of my heart. I have been entranced from the minute you tottered into the register office in unrelieved black. Every lachrymose sigh, every sensitive shudder has held me mesmerised.'

Hot pink invading her extreme pallor, Daisy straightened her slight shoulders. 'Excuse me?'

'Oh, don't stop drooping,' Alessio pleaded, studying her with dancing golden eyes. 'It makes me feel so wonderfully medieval and macho.'

'I was not *drooping*!' Daisy bit out in outrage.

'And you look so incredibly feminine and fragile when you do it, I get this really erotic buzz,' Alessio drawled with thickened emphasis, his golden eyes flashing over her with a sudden, startling smoulder of raw sexual appreciation.

Shocked to the core by the unexpectedness of that assertion, Daisy connected with that explicit look and jerked as if she had been struck by lightning. Instantaneous heat surged up inside her, making her slender thighs clench. Suddenly it was alarmingly difficult to breathe and her heart was pounding insanely fast. Horrified, she dropped her head, breaking that dangerous visual contact while she struggled to still her racing pulses and conceal the response he had so effortlessly evoked.

'That remark was inappropriate,' Daisy managed to say in what she hoped was a lofty tone of disapproval. 'This is a marriage of convenience.'

'Convenience.' The repetition deep and audibly appreciative, Alessio caught her hand smoothly in his to lead her in the direction of Tara and Janet, who stood across the foyer. 'How do you define convenience, or haven't you got around to that yet?'

'Separate bedrooms,' Daisy said in breathless clarification. 'I should think that was obvious.'

'Barry was *so* sweet last night,' Tara was proclaiming loudly as they drew level. 'I felt really sorry for him. He even brought Mum flowers.'

Alessio stilled. 'Barry?'

Spinning around, Tara flushed and threw her father a startled look.

Daisy stiffened. 'He called in to see me... and wish me well.'

Out of her daughter's hearing, Barry had congratulated Daisy on being such a fast mover and had then implied that she owed him a favour for her good fortune as Alessio had, after all, been his client. 'Maybe you would like to marry him instead,' Daisy had said. Barry had roared with laughter and soon revealed the true motivation behind his visit. That very morning, Giles had told Barry that Alessio now owned Elite Estates. Barry, very much in barracuda guise, had called round to remind Daisy that she had always thought Giles Carter was a sexist pig. He had gone on to suggest that young, aggressive blood in management would bear much more profitable fruit.

They dropped Tara off with her luggage at the school. She hurtled onto the waiting coach to join her friends and waved frantically through the back window.

'She's scared that one kid on that coach will fail to see the limousine,' Daisy groaned in embarrassment.

'She's happy,' Alessio countered. 'That's all that matters.'

A few minutes later, the limo drew up outside Janet's house. Her aunt smiled widely at them both, her eyes brimming with wry amusement, her indifference to the tense atmosphere profound. 'Have a wonderful honeymoon!' she urged with immovable good cheer.

'What honeymoon?' Daisy bleated as the door thudded shut.

'We're flying straight to Italy,' Alessio informed her. 'Janet packed a few things for you.'

'What do *we* need with a honeymoon?'

'I think we need one very, very badly.'

'I thought I would be moving into your apartment until Tara got back—'

'But you hadn't packed for that eventuality either, had you?' Alessio murmured drily.

The uncomfortable silence lasted all the way to the airport and onto the Leopardi private jet. After take-off, the steward served them with champagne and offered them the flight crew's best wishes.

'Have you told your family about this yet?' Daisy asked Alessio abruptly.

'Of course.'

'I suppose it hit them harder than a crisis on Wall Street.'

'They would have liked to have attended the wedding.'

Daisy turned as pale as death and helped herself to some more champagne with an unsteady hand. 'And I thought the day couldn't have got any worse...'

'There would have been no recriminations,' Alessio asserted.

Daisy sat forward, dragged from her lethargy by a horrible thought. 'We're not going back to live with them, are we?'

Alessio expelled his breath in a hiss. 'Of course not!'

Daisy sank back, weak with relief.

'But they were extremely shocked to learn that I am the father of a teenage daughter,' Alessio admitted tautly. 'They feel very guilty.'

Daisy wasn't listening. She had already switched off. One Leopardi at a time was enough for her to deal with. 'This has been the very worst week of my life,' she complained, looking back on a mindless blur of sleepless nights, abandoned meals and thumping tension headaches.

'Last Saturday, I met you again. It destroyed my weekend,' Alessio volunteered with velvet-smooth emphasis. 'On Monday, you told me I was a father. I spent the night walking the floor. Tuesday was dominated by an almost overwhelming desire to seek you out and strangle you. I consoled myself by buying the estate agency. Wednesday, I met my daughter. I cooled down and started to laugh again. Thursday, I had to play games of entrapment. Friday, I prayed that Tara would prevent you from buying a one-way ticket to somewhere like the Bermuda Triangle. But today we got married and the games are over. I can now finally relax.'

Outraged by that assessment, Daisy studied his darkly handsome face and long, lithe, undeniably indolent sprawl. 'How can you call what you did to me a game? You *blackmailed* me!'

Alessio surveyed her, his bright gaze a sliver of gleaming gold below luxuriant ebony lashes. 'Stress is not for you, *piccola mia*. I thrive on it. You don't. If I hadn't gone for the special licence and the blackmail you might well have starved yourself into a lasting decline before I got you to the altar. You've already lost a lot of weight.' His lean features were surprisingly taut.

The complete exhaustion which Daisy had been fighting off all week was relentlessly gaining on her. It was becoming an effort to think straight. An enormous yawn crept up on her while she wondered why he was going on about her weight.

'And let me assure you that you will not be staging a continuing decline under any roof of mine. The next meal that is put in front of you you will eat,' Alessio spelt out as he sprang lithely upright. 'Now I think you should get some rest.'

Daisy regarded the ring on her finger with a heart that sank, and then looked up. 'You're trying to manage me. I don't like being managed. I don't like being married either,' she added helplessly.

'We have only been married for five hours.' A slow, teasing smile curved Alessio's sensual mouth as he gazed down at her.

It was the most genuine smile that Alessio had given her over the past week but Daisy was even more chilled by the charismatic approach. Tara smiled just the same way when she was after something—usually something that cost two arms and a leg. 'Five hours feels like long enough.'

'When a challenge comes knocking on the front door, you're already halfway out the back, aren't you? You're faster on your feet than a greyhound!' Alessio censured her grimly as he bent down and without the smallest warning scooped her bodily out of her seat. 'You've done that from the first night we met, right through our marriage and out of it again, and you were still doing it this week when you bolted from the bank. But there'll be no escape *this* time, I assure you.'

'What do you think you're doing?' she gasped, unnerved by his behaviour.

'What I should have done an hour ago. You're suffering from sleep deprivation.' Alessio laid her down on the bed in the cabin. 'Trying to talk to you now is like trying to talk to a drunk. I am getting nowhere fast. And it's all my own fault. *Mea culpa.* I employed every device

I could to nail you. I leant on your conscience. I crowded you. Your weaknesses were my strengths. I admit it. Does that make you feel better?'

Dumbstruck, Daisy stared up at him.

Alessio sank down on the edge of the mattress and calmly took off her shoes. 'One bad week and we're married. What's one bad week?'

'It was fourteen the last time...hell on earth—'

'It was not hell on earth. *Dio*, give me strength!' Alessio growled, searing her with exasperated eyes. 'So we had a few problems...OK? But it wasn't all my fault. You changed. All of a sudden you were creeping about like Little Orphan Annie, looking all wounded and pathetic.'

'You stopped talking to me.'

'I wasn't talking to anyone.'

'You could have talked to me.'

'You couldn't have handled it. You were blissfully oblivious to the fact that life as I knew it had gone down the tubes.' A wry smile twisted his well-shaped mouth and then faded again. 'Superficial things that shouldn't have mattered to me *did* matter then. My friends thought it was hilarious when you ended up pregnant. In fact, they thought it was the funniest thing they had ever heard. Alessio had finally got caught.'

Daisy winced and paled. 'I didn't know that.'

'And anything *but* marriage would have been cool in my circle. I wasn't very good at laughing at myself at nineteen. One day I was a social lion, the next a hermit...and then on top of that I had Vittorio trying to act the heavy father for the first time at the wrong time...you weeping over me, my mother weeping over me, Bianca weeping over me. You're right,' Alessio suddenly breathed, with the faintly dazed air of one making

a long-unacknowledged admission. 'It *was* sheer bloody
hell.'

Daisy flipped over and looked at the wall. Her eyes
stung, her mouth quivered. He was finally agreeing that
their first marriage had been a nightmare. She felt astonishingly ungrateful for that agreement. Why was it
that she should now recall odd little moments when the
sheer hell seemed worth it? She was being very perverse.
And at seventeen she must have been appallingly self-
centred not to appreciate that Alessio might be suffering
just as much as she was, if not more...

As she lay there, Daisy saw the past slowly rearrange
itself along less familiar but perhaps more realistic lines,
and it was not a pleasant experience. Alessio might have
changed towards her but hadn't she also changed towards him? The sunny romantic he had shared that
summer with had turned into a weepy wet blanket. She
had been a complete pain. Wasn't it time she admitted
that? Out of her own emotional depth and feeling painfully insecure, she had needed the kind of constant re-
assurance that no teenage boy would have been capable
of giving her.

Alessio had not been deliberately punishing her. He
had been getting by the only way he could. He had even
tried to protect her by keeping quiet about his own
problems. His friends laughing at him... Daisy shrank
from that image, remembering with aching clarity just
how proud Alessio had been then. It must have taken
real guts to marry her in the face of that cruel adolescent
mockery. His friends would have been far more impressed if he had given her the money for a termination
and put her on the next flight back to London. She
swallowed back the thickness ballooning in her throat.

And if Alessio had blamed *her* for just about every-thing that had gone wrong between them, hadn't she been guilty of doing the exact same thing to him? When had she ever looked back and acknowledged that she had made mistakes too? She had dug her head into the sand and hoped and prayed that their problems would magically melt away. Paralysed by the fear that she was losing him, she had done nothing constructive either, she reflected with growing discomfiture.

'Alessio...?' Daisy whispered thickly, and then, frowning, she turned her head.

But Alessio had already gone, leaving her alone. Just as quickly the past lost the power to hold her. It was the present which was tearing her apart. Alessio could freely admit to having forced her back into marriage and yet his conscience remained clear. In his view, she had com-mitted a far greater sin in denying him all knowledge of his child. And as Tara's mother she was merely a useful adjunct to Alessio's desire to have full custody of his daughter. As a woman, as a wife, she didn't count.

With that depressing thought, Daisy fell asleep.

A hand on her shoulder shook her half-awake. Daisy focused blearily on the photo album lodged mere inches in front of her face.

'Who is that?' Alessio enquired, a lean finger indi-cating the male standing beside her and a three-year-old Tara in one of the photos.

Daisy made an effort to concentrate. 'That was George—'

'And this character?' Alessio flipped over a page.

Daisy focused uncertainly on another male face. 'Daniel...I think.'

Another page turned. A giant yawn crept up on her as she peered at the handsome blond man whom Alessio was now indicating. She looked blank. 'I don't remember him—'

'You don't remember him? I'm not surprised!' Alessio blistered down at her, making her jump in shock. 'Tara gave me six albums. Every one of them is full of strange men! You could run an international dating agency out of the male contingent in your photographs!'

Daisy gazed up at him with wide, drowsy eyes filled with incomprehension.

'Tara told me that you didn't date, that you hardly ever went out...'

Daisy's sleepy eyes opened even wider. She was shocked that her daughter could have told such a whopper. She had always enjoyed a reasonably healthy social life.

With a not quite steady hand, Alessio snapped the offending album shut. 'I suspected a certain amount of exaggeration on that point.' Scorching golden eyes raked her small, sleep-flushed face accusingly. 'But I had *no idea* what she was covering up! What about the toy boy?'

'Toy boy?' Daisy repeated dazedly, hanging on every explosive word that emerged from between his bloodless, compressed lips.

'He was the latest, wasn't he?' Alessio surveyed her with sudden, icy derision, anger reined in as his expressive mouth clenched as hard as a vice. '*Dio*...you've been sleeping around ever since you divorced me!'

As the door slammed on his exit, Daisy's jaw dropped. Sleeping around? Was he crazy? Sex had just about wrecked her life at seventeen and she had learnt that lesson well. Casual intimacy was not for her. She might have had no shortage of male company over the years

but she had never fallen in love again—hadn't wanted
to either, she acknowledged honestly—and it had always
seemed easier to end relationships when they'd demanded more than she'd been prepared to give.

Janet, she reflected drowsily, might say that she had
a fear of commitment that amounted to paranoia, but
she herself thought that she had been very sensible. No
man had caused her grief in thirteen years. She was proud
of that record and not at all proud of the fact that she
had been a mass of painful and grieving nerve-endings
from the instant that Alessio had come back into her
life.

Daisy shifted in voluptuous relaxation. The bed was very
comfortable. Memory slowly stirred. A slight frown-line
divided her brows. She had the oddest recollection of a
meal being thrust under her nose when being forced to
stay awake had felt like the cruellest torture. She had
pleaded for the mercy of a bed.

And had Alessio really said, 'If you don't eat, you
don't sleep,' and cut up a steak into tiny, bite-sized pieces
while her head had sunk back down on the supporting
heel of her hand and her eyelids had kept on closing no
matter how hard she tried to keep them open? He had
been so damnably domineering, but the chocolate gateau
which had come next had melted in her mouth and for
the first time in a week her stomach had felt settled instead of queasily empty.

They were in Italy... and Alessio was smouldering
again but, unhappily, *not* in silence, she thought as she
recalled that scene with the photo album. At nineteen,
Alessio had told her that a boy who slept around was
only gaining necessary masculine experience but that a
girl who slept around was a tart. That might not be fair

but that was life, he had informed her cheerfully. But Alessio could not find it within himself to be quite so cheerful now about the idea that he might have *married* a tart.

Daisy might have told the reassuring truth had she been asked, but she hadn't been asked. Alessio was not prone to demanding direct answers on sensitive subjects. He was naturally devious. Being sneaky had put him into the hands of his equally sneaky daughter. Tara, bless her scheming and shrewd little Leopardi brain, had worked out exactly what her father wanted to hear and had given it to him in spades. Daisy felt no pity for Alessio. Her sex life... or indeed her lack of a sex life... was none of his business.

But, for her daughter's sake, she had to make the best of this crazy marriage, she told herself staunchly. Thankfully, she was *not* the sort of female who made a six-act tragedy out of a broken cup, contrary to Alessio's opinion. She lifted her feathery lashes and then froze. A stricken gasp was torn from her. All languor banished, Daisy jackknifed upright, her horrified gaze flying round the eerily familiar contours of the spacious room.

Vacating the bed in a flying leap, she wrenched back the curtains with impatient hands and looked out in disbelief at the formal gardens spread out below. Box-shaped parterres adorned with statures and fountains and huge planted stone urns ran up to the edges of a magnificent oak wood. Beyond the trees stretched the rolling verdure of the Tuscan hills.

The very first time Daisy had seen that magnificent view, she had been under the naïve impression that she was having a guided tour of the palatial Leopardi summer home. Alessio's parents had generally been in residence only at weekends. Daisy had been hugely intimidated by her luxurious surroundings. Having got her off balance, Alessio had easily overcome her shy, uncertain protests by smoothly locking his mouth to hers in heated persuasion and sweeping her off to bed to deprive her of her virginity...

But not before assiduously assuring her that he would not go one step further than she wanted him to, that she had only to say no and he would immediately stop. Daisy hadn't been capable of vocalising a single word in the flood of passion which had followed. Alessio would naturally have worked that fact out beforehand. Even as a teenager, he had been ruthlessly well acquainted with her every weakness.

Daisy finally spun from the window and back into the present, trembling with outrage and discomfiture. How dared Alessio bring her back to the family villa in Tuscany? How could any man be so insensitive that he didn't appreciate that this was the very last place she would want to revisit? This was where they had fallen in love, where they had played adult games of passion, blithely risking consequences that neither of them had been equipped to deal with.

She was standing beneath the shower in the adjoining bathroom before it occurred to her that thirteen years ago that bedroom had been *his* bedroom. Of course it wouldn't still be his, she thought, scolding herself furiously for the fact that her impressionable heart had just skipped an entire beat. Instead of being clenched by horror, she had been clenched by excitement, she conceded with deep chagrin. But she would never allow herself to succumb to the potent lure of Alessio's all-pervasive sexuality again. A healthy distance and detachment would provide the only safe and sensible foundation for a marriage of convenience.

Daisy turned off the shower and towelled herself dry. Then, throwing the towel aside, she padded back into the bedroom. She was heading for the dressing room, where she hoped to find some clothing, when a light knock on the door momentarily froze her to the spot. She wasn't wearing a stitch! As the doorhandle began turning, she gave a frantic, unavailing pull at the securely lodged sheet on the bed and then dived with a strangled groan under the massive bed to conceal herself. The rattle of china broke the silence. Daisy waited to see a pair of maid's feet approaching but instead she saw male feet...unmistakably Alessio's feet—bare, brown, beautifully shaped.

'Daisy...?' he called.

She held her breath and turned puce with mortification. Things like this did not happen to other people; why did they continually happen to her? Especially around Alessio, who would greet a hurricane in the middle of the night with a stopwatch. He checked the bathroom, the dressing room, muttered something in Italian.

Daisy couldn't stand the suspense any longer. She cleared her throat. 'I'm under the bed. For heaven's sake, go away!' she hissed in furious conclusion.

'So...you are hiding under the bed,' Alessio drawled after a lengthy pause, a slight tremor disturbing his diction.

'I thought you were the maid.'

'I know you used to feel a little self-conscious around the staff, *piccola mia*...but don't you think this is rather excessive?'

'If you must know, I haven't got any clothes on!' Daisy blitzed back.

'Oh, I'm well aware of that,' Alessio assured her huskily. 'I was standing below the trees earlier when you hauled open the curtains and stood there in all your unclothed glory for an entire ten minutes.'

'You *timed* me?' Daisy could barely frame the scandalised demand.

'I may not wax lyrical about sunrises or spout romantic speeches under balconies but I was deeply appreciative of that particular view. I also congratulated myself on my foresight that the domestic staff come in at only discreet hours of the day. We are presently the only people in the house—and isn't it fortunate that I included the gardeners in that embargo? I don't think I'm narrow-minded but I'm remarkably selfish. If you had even unwittingly flashed your attractions for anyone else, I would have wrung your neck!'

'Get out of here, Alessio!' Daisy exploded, fit to be tied.

'But I haven't enjoyed myself this much in years,' Alessio said with intense appreciation. 'Why? I have learnt to cherish and value eccentricity and I am rejoicing in the sure knowledge that my wife is unique. I am certain that I am the only man in Italy who had to force-feed his bride on their wedding night, put her to bed alone and then hold a conversation with her while she hid naked under the bed the next day.'

'*Push off!*' Daisy screeched, unimpressed. 'I'm not coming out until you go away!'

Alessio set down a tray on the carpet. 'Look,' he invited in a lazily seductive undertone. 'Your favourite hot chocolate topped with whipped cream. Disgustingly rich and sweet. Every undiscriminating taste bud you possess has to be watering...'

'I don't want it!' Daisy hauled wildly at the sheet hanging over the bed. It still wouldn't budge. Her teeth ground together. Then she espied something cotton lying in a heap on the floor on the other side of the bed and rolled over to stretch out her hand and retrieve it.

'Even when you are concentrating sufficiently to know what's happening around you...which admittedly isn't all that often...you still fascinate me,' Alessio mused reflectively, stretching out long, denim-clad legs as he sank down in an armchair. 'Any other woman would have got *into* the bed to conceal herself but you crawled under it.'

Feverishly engaged in trying to button the shirt, Daisy's fingers slowed to a clumsy fumble as she focused on those legs. She emerged from below the bed, silver hair wildly mussed, her violet eyes as bright as jewels in her triangular face. Treating her to a shimmering smile of blinding brilliance, Alessio sprang fluidly upright, a disturbing distraction in faded tight jeans and a white polo shirt.

Transfixed by that heart-stopping smile, her mind a dizzy blank, Daisy was now wholly absorbed by the jeans. Her mouth ran dry. She moistened her lips, her breath catching in her throat. Denim faithfully followed every superbly virile line of his lean hips and long, powerful thighs. Her magnetised attention strayed to the distinctively masculine bulge at his crotch and something almost painful twisted low in her stomach, colour slowly creeping up her slender throat in a burning wave.

'Do the jeans still make your socks sizzle even when you're not wearing any?' Alessio enquired with purring emphasis as he reached down a strong hand and tugged her upright. '*Dio*, I should have ransacked my wardrobe in London. To hell with sartorial elegance! Clearly I missed out on a critical coup.'

'Rubbish!' But Daisy was convinced that even her toes were turning shocking pink and could not credit that she had gawped at him like that. How could she have? How *could* she have? Her face burned hotter than ever.

'And you are walking a tightrope in that shirt. Tara is not in a bedroom next door. You have no safety net. When you fall... I'll catch you.'

His narrowed gaze was a hot sliver of stark gold, semi-concealed by the lush crescent of his lashes. In the humming stillness, her fingers flew up to the pulse flickering madly at the base of her throat and pressed against it; she frowned as she tore her gaze free and finally registered that she was wearing one of *his* shirts.

'Where did you sleep last night?' Daisy demanded starkly.

'In the dressing room... like a gentleman.'

Her brows knit as she pondered that admission. 'Was there only one bedroom prepared for us?'

'You haven't buttoned my shirt up properly,' Alessio murmured as if she hadn't spoken, and that deep, low-pitched observation made her knees wobble. 'Don't worry about it. I have every intention of taking it off again.'

Her startled eyes whipped back up to his. 'But we're not going to *do* things like that!' Daisy gasped.

'You do have some very peculiar ideas about marriage, *piccola mia*.'

'You only married me to get custody of Tara... it's nothing more than a convenient arrangement!'

'Convenient—available, ready-made, handy,' Alessio defined softly, savouring the words, his brilliant golden eyes smouldering over her with unconcealed anticipation.

'Forget it!' Daisy said furiously, drawing herself up to her full five feet. 'I am not a fast-food outlet...'

Alessio flashed her a megawatt smile of wolfish challenge. 'And I am no celibate. I'm an unreconstructed, very old-fashioned guy. My wife shares my bed. That is not an issue up for negotiation today, tomorrow or any other day. You will not qualify for a separate bedroom should there be fifty guest rooms under the marital roof!'

CHAPTER SEVEN

DAISY was stunned by the sheer challenging cool of that brazen assurance. 'You know that I won't agree to that,' she stated tightly.

Alessio elevated a winged ebony brow. 'No?'

'No. Sharing a bedroom or a bed is out of the question. And I'd like you to leave so that I can get dressed,' Daisy informed him in speedy conclusion.

'Daisy—'

'There's the door. Use it,' Daisy advised, tilting her chin. 'This is not the average marriage. I was forced into it against my better judgement.'

'But whichever way you look at it we're *still* married. And without the passion this marriage hasn't got a hope in hell. In fact right now it's the only damned thing we've got going for us,' Alessio returned very drily. 'So why would you try to deny us that one positive element?'

Unprepared for that raw candour, Daisy lost every scrap of her animation and colour. In demanding a room of her own, she had only been trying to protect herself. She was terrified of putting herself in a position where Alessio could hurt her again. And she could not imagine making love with Alessio without an awful lot of vulnerable feelings becoming involved and putting her at risk.

'I will not allow you to sabotage this marriage before it even gets a fighting chance,' Alessio asserted with stark impatience. 'Just for once in your life you are going to stand your ground and make a real effort.'

Daisy snatched in a shaky breath. 'You have no right to speak to me like that.'

His starkly handsome features were set concrete-hard. Icy eyes held hers with an innate force of will. 'It was a warning. No matter how bad things get, you are staying this time. We have Tara to think about now—'

'Yes...but—'

'And it was a miracle that I didn't drop dead with shock when *you* attacked *me* last week!' Alessio continued with raw emphasis, his lip curling at the memory. 'It took you thirteen years to work up the courage to tell me why you walked out and you slung it all at me as if you were telling me things I already knew!'

Daisy stiffened. 'I—'

'But not one word did you say to me at the time!' Blazing golden eyes raked over her small, still figure. His wide mouth clenched hard, fierce tension splintering from every taut angle of his lean, poised length.

'So, believe it or not, the divorce hit *me* very hard! *I wasn't prepared for it* and *I certainly didn't see it coming.* I loved you and I genuinely believed that you loved me...and then I found out different, didn't I, Daisy?'

That devastatingly candid admission hung there, quivering in the rushing silence.

Daisy was frozen to the spot, plunged at shattering speed into emotional turmoil. Even that day at the bank, she had not considered the staggering idea that Alessio might *not* have wanted the divorce. 'You're just saying that now to make me feel bad,' she censured him in a faltering undertone. 'You're lying.'

Alessio strode forward. '*Dio*, I—'

Pale and taut, Daisy whirled away from him. 'You're trying to twist everything and act as if I left for no good reason when you know very well that there was nothing left to stay for! You had already moved out of our bedroom!'

Alessio tugged her back to him, his strong hands closing round her slim forearms to imprison her. His dark features were rigid and his eyes held something that looked remarkably like bewilderment. His long fingers tightened on her slender arms and then loosened before slowly dropping from her. His ebony brows drew together, black lashes lowering as he frowned down at her. 'Only because I couldn't sleep in the same bed and hope to keep my hands off you.'

'That doesn't make sense—'

'Doesn't it? The most embarrassing time of my life,' Alessio confided with a rueful twist of his eloquent mouth, 'has to be the day my father cornered me to say that he sincerely hoped that I wasn't still making sexual demands on my wife because pregnant women didn't find lovemaking comfortable after the first couple of months.'

Daisy's jaw dropped.

'I was *seriously* embarrassed,' Alessio admitted with a grim half-smile of remembrance. 'And I wanted to ask you whether I had been hurting you but I couldn't quite work up the courage. My demands in that department had, after all, been pretty voracious—'

'I thought you didn't want me any more,' Daisy interrupted, in a complete daze. 'You never hurt me.'

'Didn't I?'

She shook her head in an urgent negative, her shining silver-blonde hair flying round her flushed cheekbones, her violet eyes welded to his.

'That was why I felt so guilty when you lost the baby,' Alessio confessed harshly. 'I thought that all those passionate encounters might have contributed to that—'

'No!' Daisy protested in a pained whisper, her gaze soft with distress as she drew instinctively closer to him and smoothed her fingers down his arm in a comforting motion. 'That was just something that happened. The doctor had assured me that there was no reason why we shouldn't be making love—'

'How the hell could you have believed that I didn't want you any more?' Alessio broke in with a blatant lack of understanding.

'That's how it seemed. You never touched me again,' she muttered uncomfortably.

'Daisy, I couldn't *trust* myself to touch you! I didn't have any self-control around you and I was very frustrated,' he breathed feelingly. 'Celibacy felt like another punishment. I was a selfish little jerk.'

'No, you weren't,' Daisy said shakily, devastated by what he had told her but undeniably touched too. Her heart skipped a beat as her eyes connected with his vibrant golden gaze. A tiny muscle somewhere deep down inside her pulled tight and her lower limbs turned weak as insidious heat curled in the pit of her stomach. 'But you didn't have to be so extreme...' She swallowed and the tip of her tongue stole out to moisten her full lower lip. 'We could have done—'

'Other things to ease my raging libido?' Alessio slotted in huskily as he reached out and folded both arms round her to ease her up against him, his burnished gaze nailed with magnetic attention to the voluptuous curve of her pink mouth. 'Having made my magnificent gesture of self-sacrifice, I was in full martyr mode, and I was far too proud to come back and ask for favours.'

'It...it wouldn't have been a favour...'

'No?' Alessio prompted thickly.

'I always liked making you lose control…it was almost as exciting as losing it myself,' Daisy confided abstractedly, in severe shock and unable as yet to emerge from it. In one bitter bout of confidence, Alessio had yanked the ground from beneath her feet. All those years ago, he had not turned away from her in deliberate rejection. No, indeed. Incredible as it seemed to her, Alessio had still been seething with unabated lust for her dumpy little barrel of a body, and that thought knocked Daisy sideways and over.

'*Please*…don't say things like that,' Alessio groaned, and with lean, strong hands he gradually drew her up the poised length of his taut, muscular body, letting her find out for herself why he was trembling as she came into head-spinning contact with the bold, hard jut of his aroused masculinity.

Held level with the scorching blaze of his eyes, Daisy hadn't a single thought in her entire head. Every wanton skin cell in her body was busy limbering up at the starting line and Alessio did not disappoint her. He took her mouth with a wild, hot hunger. Excitement hit her in a violent shock wave of response. In an instant, she closed her arms round him, sent her fingers delving blissfully into his luxuriant hair and only uttered an encouraging moan when he sent his hands travelling down over her hips and clamped them to her slim thighs to hold her in place.

That single kiss blazed into fiery heat. Her head spun. Her heart raced. The passion she had damped down and suppressed for too long exploded in a shower of multi-coloured fireworks and blew her away. With a muffled growl of raw satisfaction, Alessio hungrily probed her mouth with a wickedly erotic precision that imitated a far more primal possession.

He set her down and flipped her round, his seeking
mouth delving in marauding exploration of the soft,
sensitive skin between her neck and her shoulder, discovering pulse points she had forgotten existed. Daisy
extended her throat in an ecstasy of shivering pleasure
and automatically snaked her hips back into the hard,
thrusting heat of him, feeling him shudder in urgent
sexual response to that helpless provocation.

He brought his hands slowly, caressingly up over the
straining thrust of her breasts, their swollen fullness
pushing against the smooth cotton of the shirt. As his
thumbs brushed and circled over the aching prominence
of her nipples, all Daisy's breath escaped at once. Damp
heat surged between her trembling thighs and her legs
buckled. Twisting her round, Alessio lifted her against
him to bring her down on the bed, locking her mouth
urgently beneath his again.

'You said I was incredible in bed,' Alessio breathed
raggedly, blazing golden eyes holding her entrapped as
he sat up and peeled off his shirt. 'It wasn't true. We
were incredible *together...*'

As a muscular golden brown expanse of chest high-
lighted by a triangle of curling black hair filled her vision,
Daisy started melting from outside in, languorous
weakness enclosing every limb. Alessio leant over her,
releasing the buttons on the shirt then spreading the edges
apart with deft fingers, to gaze down at the pouting swell
of her pale breasts with explicit appreciation.

As their eyes collided again and meshed, Daisy
quivered in sensual shock. He lowered his dark head and
his mouth engulfed an achingly tender pink nipple,
making her jerk and moan in unconscious supplication
as her fingers tangled with his hair and then clutched
blindly at his shoulders. The sensuous glide of his teeth

was followed by the soothing sweep of his tongue. Her breath escaped in torturous bursts, her whole body burning up.

Somewhere irritatingly close a telephone shrilled and she frowned. Alessio cursed with what breath remained to him. Two more rings and a vicious burst of Italian was dragged from him. With the abruptness of violent frustration, he lifted himself away from her and lunged a seeking hand down to retrieve a mobile phone.

Then, unexpectedly, Alessio froze, dark blood highlighting the hard slant of his cheekbones while Daisy watched him in growing fascination.

'Hi,' he murmured with surprising warmth. '*Sì...Sì*...wonderful...terrific...great... Would you like to speak to your mother?'

'Tara?' Daisy mouthed, her embarrassment as instinctive as it would have been had their daughter walked in and surprised them in bed together.

Alessio extended the phone without a word.

'How are you guys getting on?' Tara chattered. 'I knew you'd be worried sick about me because this is the first time I've been away.'

'Yes—'

'Isn't Dad romantic taking you back to where you first met?' Tara gushed. 'I bet you were really knocked flat by that.'

'Yes—'

'Well, I'm fine and I'm having a whale of a time, so I hope you won't mind me not ringing again...' Her daughter's voice dropped very low before she continued, 'Sorry, but it looks really naff having to phone home.'

Seconds later, Daisy returned the phone to Alessio. He tossed it aside. A gulf of silence stretched and Daisy's brow furrowed when Alessio made no move to pull her back into his arms. Her still heated body tautened and flushed with guilty acknowledgement of her own lingering and intense arousal.

'I thought my memories might have been coloured by adolescent fantasy but they weren't.' His dark, deep voice flat with a curious lack of expression, Alessio cast her a sudden chillingly cold glance from below spiky black lashes, his brilliant dark gaze bleak and hard. Springing lithely off the bed, he reached for his shirt. 'You really *are* dynamite in bed...but I think I'll take a rain check.'

Daisy's face flamed with shock and humiliation. That rejection slashed like a winter wind across her exposed flesh. She tugged the sheet over herself, her fingers bone-white as she clenched them beneath its cover. 'What's the matter with you?' she heard herself whisper strickenly.

Alessio swung back to her, his dramatically handsome features taut. His wide, sensual mouth twisted. 'I'm still very angry with you. Every time I remember that you took my daughter away from me, it makes me want to smash things. But I'll get over that. It's irrational to expect more from you than you are capable of giving and it's impossible to turn the clock back.'

Ill-prepared for that level of frankness, Daisy flinched. He had hidden that anger so well from her that she had been fooled. Now, when her every defence was down he condemned her with that reminder, throwing her into guilty confusion. 'You're not being fair.'

Alessio's screened gaze closed in on her and lingered in cool appraisal, his detachment somehow making her even more painfully aware of her nudity beneath the sheet. 'On the contrary, I am being very fair. You're a remarkably good mother. You're gorgeous and sexy and great in bed.'

Daisy bent her head, burning pink invading her cheeks afresh. But not so sexy and not so great that he couldn't still walk away, she thought, in an agony of mortification and self-loathing.

'That you should also be a little greedy and emotionally shallow is no big deal,' Alessio added grimly.

Her head flew up. 'I am not greedy... and I am not shallow!'

'Daisy, you have the staying power of a butterfly.'

'That's not true!'

'It's not important.' In the thundering silence, Alessio shrugged with an air of arrogant finality. 'If it wasn't for Tara, we wouldn't be here now.'

'I don't need you to tell me that.' He was only confirming what she had already known, what she had inexplicably allowed herself to forget over the past half-hour. Yet the reminder made Daisy feel incredibly empty and degraded. The intimacy she had foolishly believed they had recaptured had only been an illusion, born of her own stupid sentimentality and sexual hunger. She hated herself for that weakness. She wanted to lie down and die, but not in front of *him*.

Without warning, Alessio strode over to the door and flung it wide, an impatient frown drawing his black brows together. 'I think we have a visitor.'

'A visitor?' Daisy repeated in bewilderment.

A female voice echoed through the upper reaches of the villa, the distant tap-tap of stiletto heels sounding on the marble staircase, telegraphing their wearer's impatience.

'Bianca,' Alessio breathed, already moving out into the corridor to intercept his sister.

Daisy paled. 'But how on earth did she get in?' she gasped. 'Through a window on a broomstick?'

Alessio froze, his dark head whipping round, the smooth planes of his strong profile hardened by a flash of angry incredulity.

Daisy turned crimson as she realised what she had said.

'Grow up, Daisy,' Alessio advised with withering bite. 'You may be stuck in a time-warp but the rest of us have moved on. If you can't behave like an adult and be civil, I suggest that you stay up here!'

'I—'

But the door closed with a final thud. With a groan of frustration, Daisy flung herself back against the pillows. Smart move, Daisy. Alienate him more by attacking his twin. Alessio had no idea how much abuse she had once had to take from his sister. Daisy hadn't told tales. And it was too late now to redress the balance. She would only sound like a sulky child harbouring a grudge. And really Bianca was the least of her problems, she told herself painfully as she threw back the sheet and got up.

For only now did she truly appreciate the depth of Alessio's bitterness. In angry impatience, he had taken her beliefs and shaken them inside out, shattering her view of the past. Alessio had not been grateful to be released from their shotgun marriage. Alessio had been equally devastated by their divorce. He had actually thought *he* was the one being dumped.

That picture dredged a shaky laugh from Daisy but it also made her think. Bianca's assurance all those years ago that within months of their wedding her brother was already involved with his former girlfriend again no longer seemed credible. Had her sister-in-law lied about Sophia and that supposed reconciliation in a cruelly clever play on Daisy's insecurity?

Whatever—Daisy gave her head an impatient shake—naturally Alessio was still seething at the fact that after walking out on their marriage she had chosen to deny him all knowledge of his daughter. Alessio thought she was a greedy, shallow woman who could not be trusted. Although, with cool Leopardi calculation, he had not shared that news with her until *after* the wedding. Daisy shivered, suddenly cold with apprehension about what the future might hold. She had still fallen into his arms, her every defence destroyed, a physical hunger that terrified her betraying her with humiliating ease.

Ten minutes later, she descended the sweeping staircase, her battered confidence bolstered by the elegant pale blue dress she wore. Inside she was still a mess of see-sawing emotions and conflict but she had no intention of entertaining Bianca with a miserable face.

The front doors in the hall were wide open. On the last step of the stairs, Daisy froze. Alessio was standing outside with a blonde draped round him. Daisy blinked and looked again, unable to credit the evidence of her own eyes. Slender brown arms were linked round Alessio's throat as the woman laughed up at him, her flawless profile and the flowing mane of her corn-gold hair instantly recognisable to Daisy...

Her heart gave a sickening lurch as she was plunged into shock. Nina Franklin. What was *she* doing here? And why had Alessio led her to believe that the visitor was his sister? A stifled moan of distress trapped in her throat, Daisy reeled off the stairs before she could be seen and fled into the drawing room.

CHAPTER EIGHT

'SOMEHOW you don't look quite as smug as I expected,' a languidly amused female voice remarked.

Startled, Daisy spun round, breathless and bewildered. In shock, she focused on Alessio's sister. Bianca was standing by the window, a tall, rake-thin brunette in an enviably simple white shift-dress that screeched its designer cut. 'Bianca...?' she muttered dazedly, her brain refusing to function.

The only image stamped inside her head was that of Nina with her arms linked round Alessio, laughing and smiling with confident intimacy, certainly not reacting as any woman might have been expected to react when her lover had broken off their relationship and almost immediately married another woman. That disturbing image still twisted like a fiendish knife in Daisy's shrinking flesh.

Bianca strolled forward, a mocking smile pinned to her lips. 'Yes, I have to admit that much as I despise you, Daisy, I also have to admire your sheer nerve. You are holding a real live Leopardi as a hostage to fortune.'

In an uncertain gesture, Daisy pushed back damp tendrils of silver-fair hair from her brow. 'I don't know what you're talking about.'

'Tara...your miracle ticket back into the family circle!' Bianca vented a scornful laugh. 'But I wouldn't get too comfortable if I were you. Alessio may have married you to get custody of his daughter but I don't think he's planning to hang on to *both* of you—'

'What are you trying to say?' Daisy cut in tautly, fighting to get a grip on her wits again.

'So you *still* need everything spelt out in words of one syllable.' Bianca shot her a look of pitying superiority. 'Alessio will keep Tara and ditch you. And why not? The way he sees it, you did the same thing to him!'

'Why do you still hate me so much?' Daisy whispered in a shaken undertone, appalled by the brunette's continuing malice. 'And what on earth are you doing here?'

'You loused up my brother's life once and now you're trying to do it again. Twins stick together,' Bianca told her succinctly. 'As to what I'm doing here at the villa...business, strictly business, although I do feel that I ought to apologise for inadvertently reuniting Alessio with Nina. You're such a passionately jealous little soul, and what hope have you got against a girl that age?'

Daisy turned bone-white. 'You bitch,' she mumbled strickenly.

'*Madre di Dio*, what the devil is going on here?' Alessio's whiplike intervention cut across the room like an icy wind on a hot summer day.

Sharply disconcerted, Daisy whirled round, cannoned into an occasional table and sent an exquisite vase of flowers smashing down onto the marble hearth of the fireplace. Glass flew everywhere. 'Oh, *hell*!' she gasped, and automatically dropped down, intending to gather up the shattered shards of crystal.

Bianca released her breath in a long-suffering hiss. 'I'm afraid that your wife is not prepared to let bygones be bygones, Alessio. I tried...now you can't say I didn't try...but you heard what she called me, didn't you?'

'Daisy, *leave* that glass alone!' Dark eyes blazing, the cast of his strong features implacable, Alessio followed up the scorching command by striding over and hauling

Daisy upright. 'Right now we can do without a blood-spattered bride playing a starring role here.'

'It must be a frightful embarrassment to be so clumsy,' Bianca commented drily.

As her teeth sank into the soft underside of her lower lip and absolutely brutalised the tender flesh, Daisy tasted the sharp, acrid tang of blood in her mouth. Bianca had heard Alessio's approach, she realised, and all Alessio had heard was Daisy insulting his sister.

'I'm sorry Daisy has been so rude,' Alessio drawled with gritty delivery, one powerful hand anchored to his wife's slight shoulder like an imprisoning chain, long brown fingers exerting meaningful pressure. 'But I'm sure that she wants to apologise for losing her temper.'

Daisy went rigid and remained mute, outraged to be dragged forward like a misbehaving child and ordered to eat humble pie. Frustration and fury lanced through her, for she was painfully aware that anything she said now in her own defence would not be convincing.

'Don't worry about it,' Bianca sighed with a forgiving smile.

Daisy surveyed the brunette with barely concealed loathing, every nerve in her body still jangling from what she had both witnessed and withstood in the space of ten nightmare minutes.

'Under the circumstances...' Alessio hesitated, and then shrugged a fatalistic shoulder. 'You *can* use the grounds for your fashion shoot. I appreciate that it would be difficult to find another venue at such short notice—'

'I knew Nina would change your mind!' Bianca carolled in a nauseating tone of girlish relief.

Daisy's teeth ground together.

'We only need a few hours and the crew are already here,' Bianca continued sweetly and apologetically. 'I know it's very inconvenient timing but I never dreamt that you and Daisy might be coming to this old place for your honeymoon!'

In a sudden movement that took Alessio by surprise, Daisy tore herself free of his restraining hand and stalked out of the room.

'*Dio...*' Bianca groaned in her wake. 'If I'd known it was likely to cause this much trouble for you, I'd never have asked!'

Daisy raced up the stairs like a woman jet-propelled. Not one more moment would she spend in this house, not *one* more moment...not for Tara, not for anybody! She was getting out right now! Her breath catching in sobs in her throat, she trailed her still unpacked suitcase across the dressing-room floor and struggled to close it, stuffing in sleeves and protruding hems of clothing disarranged in her haste to get dressed only minutes earlier.

'What the hell do you think you're playing at now?' Alessio enquired from the doorway.

Daisy jerked round on her knees, two spots of enraged colour burning over her cheekbones. 'Get out of my way, you swine! No, you're not a swine, you're lower than that! You're a snake—a sneaky, sly, double-dealing, *stupid* snake...because if you think I intend to stay here and put up with you, your girlfriend and your shrew of a sister you're living in fantasy land!'

Alessio folded his arms and stood his ground. 'You're not going anywhere, *piccola mia*,' he spelt out rawly.

'Do you think that treating me like a child means you can ground me like one?' Daisy launched back, angrier than she had ever been in her life, her eyes burning an incandescent violet challenge.

'I think that if I strip you naked, trash all your clothes and keep you locked in the bedroom you'll find it a little difficult to stray beyond these walls.'

'You wouldn't *dare*!' Daisy told him, flying furiously upright.

'Try me,' Alessio invited with soft menace, his shimmering eyes striking threatening sparks off her incredulous stare. 'When my daughter's happiness is at risk, I don't think there is anything that I wouldn't dare.'

'What's that supposed to mean?'

'It means that the day you walk out on this marriage I start fighting to keep Tara in Italy with me. I will not be shut out of her life again,' Alessio asserted with harsh emphasis.

Daisy went white with shock, a shiver of cold fear slithering down her rigid spine. That uncompromising threat electrified her. All of a sudden, Bianca's spiteful allegations no longer seemed quite so fanciful. Alessio was already letting her know that if their marriage failed he would fight to retain custody of their daughter. Was it at all possible that he might also be planning to use Daisy for as long as he needed her to get Tara settled in...before dispensing with her services as a wife and mother altogether? Or was that a paranoid suspicion?

'You are scaring me,' Daisy muttered in a surge of involuntary candour.

'Maybe you scare *me* when you haul out a suitcase barely twenty-four hours after you say "I do" for the second time!' Alessio was very pale beneath his golden skin but fierce determination harshly delineated his sculpted bone structure. 'Now, I don't expect you to become bosom pals with my sister but I do expect a mature acceptance that my family are also Tara's family and that when she arrives here at the end of the week she does not need to be dragged into the midst of some continuing, petty war that started before she was even born!'

'I did not restart the war.'

Alessio spread his lean, strong hands in a bold arc of impatience with a subject he clearly considered beneath his notice. 'I will not allow Tara to come home to us for the first time and find a hostile atmosphere—'

'And what are you intending to do to improve that atmosphere?' A laugh that was no laugh at all escaped Daisy as she recalled the humiliation of his earlier rejection. Fighting blindly to conserve her pride, torn with savage pain and confusion, she thrust up her chin in defiance. 'I hate you, Alessio. I *really* hate you for what you've done to me today!'

'Or maybe you hate me for what I didn't do!' Throwing her off balance, Alessio cast an explicit and suggestive glance back towards the disordered bed. Bold eyes flaming over her, he murmured thickly, 'I can hardly believe now that I walked away from temptation.'

Affected more than she could bear by that mercurial change of mood and direction, her breasts rising and falling with the accelerated pace of her breathing, Daisy said with hoarse emphasis, 'You'll get your face slapped if you try to walk back again!'

'When did that prospect ever inhibit me?' Alessio flashed her a look of sudden vibrant amusement. 'You ought to know by now that I relish a challenge.'

Without the smallest warning, Daisy's heart turned a somersault and her mouth went dry.

A wolfish smile curved Alessio's mobile mouth. 'But you can relax. You're safe for the moment. The staff are waiting to serve lunch.'

'Lunch?' Daisy echoed foolishly.

With difficulty, she tore her gaze from the intense lure of those entrapping golden eyes. All over again she was devastated by her inability to control or suppress her powerful sexual response to him.

'Our unwelcome guests will be busy in the grounds. We'll be alone,' Alessio pointed out soothingly.

'Unwelcome?' Daisy queried tautly, uncertainly.

'*Dio*...surely you don't imagine that I wanted this three-act circus descending on us?' Alessio's mouth twisted with expressive incredulity. 'But they'll be gone soon enough.'

'Why did Bianca need your permission to use the grounds?' Daisy prompted on the way downstairs, her outrage at the situation ebbing a little as she appreciated that Alessio was no more pleased by the invasion than she was.

'I own the villa now. When Vittorio decided to sell, I bought.'

'So what has your sister got to do with a fashion shoot?'

'Three months ago she became the owner of a photographic studio. She's trying very hard to make a mark on the fashion world. Nina's a top model,' Alessio explained. 'Bianca needs her star quality to sell this layout and as Nina is a friend of the family she agreed to help.'

Daisy reconsidered the view she had had of Nina and Alessio together, belatedly conceding that she had seen nothing that might not be described as an affectionate greeting. 'Nina...is a family friend?'

'Our parents move in the same social circles.'

'I saw you with her,' Daisy heard herself admit with shocking abruptness. 'She was all over you like chickenpox!'

Alessio shifted a broad shoulder beneath Daisy's piercing sideways scrutiny. 'Nina is very demonstrative. Showbiz-type personalities usually are. And, to be frank, *cara*, she's behaving generously. I *was* seeing her up until very recently.' He delivered the reminder with a hint of reproof.

Horrified to be riven with a white-hot streak of jealousy, Daisy found herself surveying her meal with little appetite. Just knowing that the beautiful, *generous* Nina was around made her feel deeply insecure. Only this morning she had been telling herself that she could handle a marriage of convenience, but already she was drowning in an emotional morass of pain and confusion. Why was it that no other man had ever had the power to tear at her heart with one teasing smile and stop it beating altogether by the simple act of donning a pair of jeans?

Having dismissed the staff, Alessio replenished her wine with his own hand. Daisy watched those long, lean, denim-clad legs advancing and momentarily shut her eyes in despair, because every treacherous pulse in her body was pounding insanely fast.

'You're not eating,' Alessio commented tautly.

'Maybe what I want isn't on the plate,' Daisy said wildly, loathing herself for her own bodily weakness. She was turning into a sex-starved animal but she would leave him, stark naked if necessary, before she allowed him to find that out!

'Just tell me what you want and I'll order it for you.'

Daisy gave an agonised little quiver, her imagination leaving her suspended between heaven and hell. 'I'm not hungry—'

'You haven't eaten since last night!' Alessio grated. 'Do you have a problem with food?'

'What is this *thing* you have about my eating habits?'

Alessio shot her a look of exasperation 'I knew a girl with anorexia nervosa at university. Sophia...Sophia Corsini, now, she—'

That particular name did grab Daisy's full attention. 'Your girlfriend was anorexic?' she cut in sharply.

'Sophia was in most of my classes but I never dated her,' Alessio countered with a faint frown of distaste and surprise at the suggestion. 'She was one very mixed-up kid. She dropped out in the middle of our second year.'

Her eyes lowering from his, Daisy mulled over that calm explanation. She believed him. Colour rose slowly in her cheeks. Bianca had made up a story and Daisy had foolishly swallowed it without demanding evidence or confronting Alessio. Clearly, there had been no other girl involved in the breakup of their first marriage. And yet hadn't she been ready to give credence to Bianca's spiteful allegations a *second* time? Should she tell Alessio what had really happened with his sister? Would he believe her? she wondered ruefully. Bianca was a very over-protective and possessive twin, but clever enough to hide it. Daisy was almost certain that she had been treated to a side of Bianca that Alessio had yet to experience.

'What are you thinking about?' Alessio probed, taking in her evasive gaze and guilty flush.

'You actually thought I might be anorexic too?' Lifting up her head, eager to move the subject in a safer direction, Daisy studied him, and an undeniable lurch of tenderness warmed her. He had been worried about her, concerned about her health. She picked up her knife and fork. 'Tense situations kill my appetite,' she told him. 'That's all.'

'But that wasn't what you were thinking about,' Alessio said perceptively, after watching her clear her plate in careful silence.

'Maybe I was thinking about just how well I know you...in fact, how well I *ever* knew you,' Daisy said unsteadily.

'I'm a very average guy,' Alessio asserted lazily, his lush black lashes partially screening eyes of vibrant gold which interfered with her ability to breathe.

'You think so?' Daisy responded a little unevenly, struggling to close out the flash-fire effect of those gorgeous eyes. 'You know...I need fresh air more than I need caffeine. It's very airless in here.'

But Alessio sprang up and caught her as she left the table, tugging her up against him with hard, insistent hands, every muscle in his big, powerful body tense as he stared down at her with unhidden frustration. 'We're married now. Don't shut me out...and don't run away from me.'

The hard masculine thrust of his virility against her taut stomach made her slender length hum and throb like a race car revving up. A bitter-sweet ache made her thighs clench, leaving her dizzy and disorientated. But even as her hips began to rise in a tiny, inviting circular motion as old as time, and the kind of fierce, unquenchable longing that burned engulfed her, Daisy fought her own frailty with frantic determination.

'We're making a home for Tara. That's all we're doing,' she told him unsteadily. 'Now...*please* let go of me!'

His smouldering gaze told her that he wasn't about to listen and then a door slammed, voices intruding from the hall, and Alessio released her with a raw expletive. On legs that felt as reliable as cotton-wool sticks, Daisy fled through the French windows. But she felt as though she had left half of herself behind in the broken circle of his arms. A stifled sob tore at her throat, her eyes smarting with stinging tears as she breathed in the hot, still air and saw right to the very heart of her turmoil.

Only loving had ever hurt this much. Alessio influenced her every emotion and response. And that was so achingly, terrifyingly familiar to Daisy. She could have coped so much better with being a sex-starved animal. The idea that she might still *love* Alessio petrified her. Loving him meant that the very last thing she could live with was a humiliating marriage of convenience cobbled together solely for their daughter's sake.

Indeed, much as she loved Tara, if Alessio told her once more that they were only married again for *her* benefit she would scream and push him out of a window, because every time he stressed the all-encompassing importance of Tara's needs it made Daisy feel as if she herself was of no account. And why was she so pathetically envious of his affection for her daughter? Because she wanted more for herself. In short, she was still hopelessly in love with the same male who had stolen her heart at seventeen. Why had it taken her this long to work that out?

In a daze of conflicting emotions, Daisy watched Alessio stride down the steps at the front of the villa, a devastatingly handsome male whose every lithe, graceful movement made her shockingly aware not only of him but also of her own extreme vulnerability. Hurriedly, she looked away again, only then giving some attention to the scene before her. Nina was posing in a gorgeous shoulderless sugar-pink evening dress against the dark yew topiary. Tara had once had a Barbie doll that looked remarkably similar. Impossibly perfect, dressed like a fairy-tale princess, complete with a cloud of golden hair.

Bianca drifted over. 'Stunning, isn't she?'

Daisy was watching Nina blowing a flirtatious kiss at Alessio between takes. 'I don't believe in the coincidence of you *and* Nina arriving today—'

'But Alessio does. Obviously I knew you were staying here,' Bianca confirmed drily.

Irritably brushing off the attentions of the fluttering make-up girl, Nina approached Alessio with the efficiency of a heat-seeking missile closing in on a target.

'You're a week too late,' Daisy told Bianca firmly. 'You should have tried this charade *before* the wedding!'

'I'm merely bringing a continuing relationship to your attention,' Bianca responded sweetly. 'Does Nina strike you as a woman who has recently lost her lover to a wife? She knows why Alessio married you and she knows it won't last long. She can afford to be understanding.'

Nina had engaged Alessio in animated conversation. Daisy tilted her chin and walked over. Nina ignored her. Alessio settled a casual, long-fingered hand on the base of her spine. Daisy leant against him in a sudden tiny but aggressive movement and dug her fingers into the back pocket of his jeans, her seemingly idle fingernails scoring the flexing muscles of his lean hip. The scent and the heat of him engulfed her. An infinitesimal quiver ran through her. A seductress well on the way to becoming a hopeless victim of her own ploy, Daisy sucked in oxygen in a despairing rush, feeling Alessio tense and shift, while she dazedly questioned the inconsistency of her provocative behaviour.

'Let's go for a walk,' Alessio breathed with telling abruptness.

Nina opened her green eyes wide. 'But I can't. I have to get into my next outfit in five minutes.' She frowned down at Daisy, too self-centred even to realise that the invitation had not been directed at her. 'Oh, yes, I almost forgot. Barry gave me a message for you.'

'Barry?' Daisy frowned, momentarily thrown by the reference.

'I went to view that house with him,' Nina said carelessly. 'I felt really sorry for him too. He's terribly broken up about losing you.'

Before Daisy could part her lips to challenge that astonishing assurance, Alessio intervened curtly, 'And the message?'

Nina looked coy. 'He said to remind Daisy of the proposition he made the night before your wedding.

'Barry wants you to give him the chance to manage the agency,' Daisy proffered beneath Alessio's chillingly unimpressed gaze while Nina walked back to the cameras wearing a feline smile of satisfaction. 'He's very ambitious. Why are you looking at me like that?'

Alessio shook free of her.

Daisy's lashes fluttered and she groaned, 'Oh, no, you're still a jealous toad!'

His eyes blazed with derision, his mouth twisting. 'You have to be out of your mind to think that,' he drawled with icy precision.

Yes, possibly she was... for wasn't she attributing emotions to him that he did not possess? There had to be some degree of caring for jealousy to exist. And Alessio did not care. Alessio's sole concern was Tara. Flushing a hot, mortified pink, Daisy spun away and headed off for the cover of the trees, feeling that she'd made an outsize ass of herself. Let Bianca and Nina play out their stupid farce, she decided ruefully. They would be gone soon enough.

How *could* she have hidden from what was in her own heart when she'd married Alessio again? Her emotions had threatened to tear her in two with their contrary promptings. Yet still she had refused to see them for what they were. She still loved Alessio. What price their marriage of convenience now? And in forcing her into that agreement hadn't Alessio really been giving her what she secretly wanted? She burned with shame at that acknowledgement.

Curled up in the shade of the giant oaks on the edge of the estate, she found herself inexorably reliving powerful and disturbing memories of the teenagers they had once been, so intensely and exclusively involved in each other that they had always wanted to be alone. Could she possibly settle for less now? Could she live with a man who only needed her to keep his daughter happy? In such an empty relationship, it would kill her by degrees to be a real wife to Alessio, she conceded painfully.

'Do you realise what time it is?'

Daisy paused halfway up the stairs and studiously consulted her watch. 'Half past nine.'

His lean features a set mask of self-restraint, Alessio nonetheless prowled like a sleek, dark, hungry predator across the hall and spread his hands expressively. 'Where the hell have you been until this hour?' he gritted from between clenched teeth.

'I went for a walk. I thought I'd give our visitors a chance to get on their bikes,' Daisy said tightly. 'Sorry I missed out on dinner but I made myself a sandwich in the kitchen. Now I'm off to bed. Goodnight.'

'Goodnight?' Alessio raked, the mask slipping slightly to allow her a view of the angry exasperation he was struggling to control.

Daisy hurried into the dressing room off their bedroom. Frustratingly, her case had been unpacked while she had been out. After locating a nightdress, Daisy removed herself again at speed and selected a small bedroom on the second floor. Only when she had got into bed and doused the light did she begin to relax a little. Alessio would get the message eventually. They could be... well, parenting partners. Anything more intimate was out of the question and as long as she kept her feelings to herself, as long as he had no suspicion of his power over her he couldn't hurt her again, could he?

Some time later, a distant dull thud broke the silence of the villa. Daisy frowned when within the space of a minute another thud followed... and then another. She lost count but realised in growing horror that the racket of slamming doors was getting louder and closer, not to mention more intimidating, by the second. The image of Alessio striding through the villa conducting something as uncool as a room-to-room search for his missing bride shook her rigid but Daisy stayed where she was, as stiff and tense as a sacrificial offering, until finally and with an almighty crash that matched her heartbeat the door flew wide.

'I ought to chain you to a wall in the cellar!' Alessio launched at her in a roar of raw derision as he strode over to the bed and stared fulminatingly down at her shrinking figure. 'At least then I'd know where to find you! You spend half the damned day hiding in the woods and then creep up here to the attics to spend the night. What sort of a marriage do you call this?'

'This is not a normal marriage—'

'But it's about to become one!' Alessio swore with conviction as he dragged back the bedding and hauled her up into his arms before she could even draw breath to evade him.

'Put me down!' Daisy screeched in shock, having been prepared for argument but not physical intervention.

'You're supposed to be in my bedroom. That's where you're going. And if you don't want to sleep in the bed with me you can sleep on the floor... but one thing I do know—you are sleeping in the same room. Why? Because you are my *wife!*' Alessio spelt out with wrathful emphasis.

'You blackmailed me into becoming your wife!'

'Come off it,' Alessio countered with blistering contempt, thundering down the stairs two at a time and striding along the corridor. 'On your terms the blackmail was manna from heaven!'

'I... beg... your... pardon?' Daisy gasped, devastated that he should already be harbouring such a suspicion.

'You want me every bit as much as I want you... and only this way could you have me without admitting that fact. Manna from heaven!' Alessio repeated with provocative bite as he dumped her down on the bed.

'That's an absolutely ridiculous accusation!' Daisy struggled to sound convincingly incredulous but she had turned scarlet.

'And since nothing will convince me that you don't want me... mutual lust being instantly recognisable... I can't understand why you're still running in the wrong direction!' Alessio delivered with savage candour. 'What more do you want from me? What does it take for me to get some co-operation? Do I need to tell you that there is a string of credit cards and a monthly allowance that would keep an oil sheikh happy waiting for you?'

Daisy paled and swallowed hard at the degrading suggestion that money might make her more amenable. Suddenly, playing the role of gold-digger who had gone out with a big unfeeling bang during their first marriage no longer felt like a source of secret amusement or a clever defence mechanism. Maybe it was time she told Alessio the truth about that financial settlement. She worried at her lower lip, feeling threatened by the prospect of even telling Alessio that much. But how could it hurt? At least he wouldn't be able to call her mercenary again!

'And the sound of your silence will not get us anywhere fast!' Alessio bit out.

Daisy cleared her throat awkwardly but Alessio had already vanished into the bathroom. In an abrupt movement, she yanked up two pillows and placed them carefully in a defensive line down the centre of the bed.

Alessio hit the mattress and the barrier simultaneously. He sat up again and vented an expletive in Italian. 'Sometimes you are so bloody childish...'

'It is not childish of me to believe that our relationship will work best if we sleep apart,' Daisy protested shakily. 'And, by the way, I am not greedy and grasping and I never was!'

An expectant hush fell.

'Is that the end of this astonishing rush of confidence?' Alessio probed drily.

Colouring with annoyance, Daisy breathed in deep and forced herself onward, telling herself that it would be very much to her advantage to embarrass him with the truth. She tilted her chin. 'Your father persuaded Janet to accept that settlement on my behalf. She put it in a

Swiss bank account and she didn't tell me it was there until last week.'

'*Madre di Dio...*' Alessio breathed in a shaken surge of comprehension, his deep voice fracturing. A split second later he attempted to breach the pillows but Daisy was ready for that eventuality.

She rolled out of bed and took up a defensive stance. 'So you can stop calling me greedy, and I don't need your credit cards or your lousy allowance because that settlement would keep Tara and me in comfort for the rest of our days!'

'You weren't lying when you said you didn't take a penny when you divorced me...' Spiky black lashes swept up to reveal shrewd, questioning eyes of gold as he surveyed her with intense interest and none of the embarrassment she had expected. 'So at what stage did you decide that you preferred me to think that you *were* greedy and grasping? What were you trying to cover up?'

Chagrined pink flooded Daisy's small face. The speed with which Alessio could assimilate new information and dissect it horrified her. 'I...I—'

'Then you genuinely did think that you were doing me a favour by divorcing me and keeping quiet about Tara,' Alessio reflected out loud. 'Daisy the martyr— now that does have a far more convincing ring of reality. You let my father bully you into the divorce, didn't you?' He drove a not quite steady hand through his luxuriant black hair and looked heavenwards, his strong jawline set fiercely hard.

The silence grew and lingered until her tension seemed to scream beneath its weight.

'Daisy...were you still in love with me when you divorced me?' Alessio enquired in a tone of the utmost casualness.

The silence was like the clash of cymbals in Daisy's ears. She was appalled. One little thing, just one little thing she had confessed, and within the space of a minute he was sprinting for the finishing line.

'Gosh, I'm so tired,' she mumbled round a fake yawn, desperate fingers splayed to conceal her hot, discomfited face.

'Come back to bed,' Alessio purred in husky invitation. 'I'll wake you up fast.'

Involuntarily, Daisy hovered, violet eyes wide, a vulnerable prey to the lure of him. She thought of his hands on her body and a shiver of raw excitement coursed through her. A hungry need that she could not withstand held her fast. Why not give him the chance to prove that *his* way could work? an insidious voice murmured in the back of her mind.

'I won't risk another pregnancy,' Alessio imparted with measured emphasis. 'Is that what is worrying you? I don't want another child.'

And instantly that voice in Daisy's mind was silenced. A curious pain stabbed through her in its wake. Surely more children should at least have been a possibility in the normal marriage which Alessio had said he wanted? Yet he'd cooly dismissed the idea of extending the family before it could even arise.

In an abrupt movement, her every suspicion as to his marital intentions reawakened, Daisy grabbed at the light quilt lying at the foot of the bed. Beneath Alessio's utterly incredulous gaze, she wrapped herself within its folds and curled up in a comfortable armchair.

CHAPTER NINE

IN DAISY'S dream, the most perfect baby in the world lay before her, unclaimed. She was in the very act of eagerly reaching out to take possession when a pair of cruel, unfeeling hands got there first. 'I said *no*.' Alessio's voice intervened in icy disapproval and the seductive vision of sweet-smelling, lovable baby vanished.

Daisy woke up with tears trapped in her throat. A maid was pulling back the curtains. She was in bed but she was alone. She had a hazy recollection of briefly, blissfully snuggling into masculine arms *and* of the moan of distress which had escaped her when she had been released all too quickly into the cool embrace of a sheet. Her cheeks reddened fiercely. How long would it be before Alessio appreciated that she ran in the wrong direction only because she couldn't trust herself too close? Or did he already appreciate that?

As for that stupid dream, she thought painfully, she hadn't realised just how much she would love another baby until Alessio had announced that there wasn't going to be one. She had experienced a deep sense of rejection. Her distrust and insecurity had taken over again. One unpleasant fact stared her in the face. If there *was* any truth in the suggestion that Alessio might be looking on their marriage as only a temporary expedient, a second child would definitely be on the forbidden list.

Even so, within twenty-four hours of remarriage, Alessio had still turned her every conviction inside out. Yesterday she had hidden behind her pride but last night she had made a first nervous step towards lowering her defences when she had told him about that Swiss bank account. She had to be honest with herself at least. She loved the rat. She desperately wanted to be convinced that their marriage *was* real and that it did have a future.

As her steps sounded on the stairs some twenty minutes later, Alessio strolled out of the drawing room. A shaft of sunlight glittered across his luxuriant black hair, burnished his eyes and threw into prominence his hard, classic cheekbones and beautiful mouth. Intense sexual awareness literally froze Daisy in her tracks. She couldn't take her eyes off him. She could barely breathe. Her heart pounded in her eardrums, the blades of unquenched desire scissoring cruelly through her taut length, filling her with embarrassing heat as every pulse raced.

Alessio threw back his head, hooded knowing eyes resting on her with a flicker of lazy amusement. 'I knew you would sleep late. You had an extremely restless night.'

Her face flamed.

'We're going out for lunch,' he drawled.

A Ferrari was parked on the gravel outside. There was something oddly, disturbingly familiar about the vehicle but Daisy wasn't capable of making a connection at that moment. She climbed in on shaking legs, scarcely conscious of what she was doing. A hunger that had no limit had possessed her, shattering her with its greedy intensity. She lifted a trembling hand to push back her hair, overtly conscious of the aching fullness of her breasts and the painful tautness of her nipples.

Soon after, in the thundering silence, Alessio brought the powerful car to a slow halt in a lay-by screened from the road by a thick line of trees. There was something even more awesomely familiar about that view beyond the windscreen. But still its significance escaped Daisy; it merely confused her more. With a seemingly casual hand Alessio reached out and released her seat belt. 'You deserve to be in agony,' he murmured softly. 'You're a stubborn little witch. You could try trusting me...'

'Trusting you?' Daisy was way beyond reasoning.

'If I can forgive you for Tara, you can forgive me for being too bloody proud to follow you over to London.'

Her breath caught in her throat, her eyes widening. In a handful of words Alessio had plunged right to the heart of the divisions between them, found them equal and dismissed them, almost...almost as if he had already worked out that her distrust stemmed from the tremendous pain she had endured when they had separated.

Alessio leant over her, smouldering eyes holding her entrapped. 'And this...this *now*—this is where we begin again. You, me, nothing else.'

Like a programmed doll, Daisy raised a jerky hand and slowly ran a helplessly caressing fingertip along the sensual curve of his firm mouth. 'I loved you so much,' she whispered, remembered distress fracturing her soft voice.

'That makes *such* a difference, *piccola mia*.' A vibrant smile slashing his dark features, Alessio parted his lips to capture that marauding finger and lave it with his tongue.

Daisy moaned low in her throat, a fierce ache stirring between her thighs and turning her boneless. Her eyelids lowered on passion-glazed eyes, her back arcing as she slid languorously lower in the seat. Her submissive response dragged a stifled groan from Alessio. He eased a hand beneath the hem of her dress, exploring the smooth skin of her inner thigh. Her legs slid softly apart. The mere stroke of a finger against the burning heat and moisture beneath her silky panties reduced her to whimpering, quivering subjection.

'This was supposed to be your punishment, not mine,' Alessio confessed thickly.

Daisy's gaze ran down the poised length of his powerful body to the throbbing hardness outlined by the tight fit of his jeans and she melted simultaneously. 'Go home?' she framed in a shaky, choky suggestion.

Alessio thrust a hungry hand into the fall of her hair and stabbed her lips apart in a raw, forceful kiss of sexual frustration. But then he pulled back from her and reinstated her seat belt, cursing under his breath when it proved recalcitrant. In complete bemusement, Daisy struggled to focus on him as he started up the Ferrari again.

'We're lunching with my parents,' Alessio proffered in taut explanation.

'Oh...' Daisy said simply, too much in the grip of other impressions and responses to react. Finally she was making that bewildering connection. 'This is the same car you used to take me out in and we used to stop here before you dropped me back at the Morgans'.'

'*Dio*, Daisy...have you only just worked that out?'

The *same* car, she though dazedly. He had kept the Ferrari all these years. Alessio wasn't sentimental. Yet he had also brought her back to the villa, to the same bedroom, the same bed... His own daughter had called him madly romantic and impetuous. Oh, dear heaven, Daisy reflected, seriously shaken by that novel idea. How blind could a woman be? Was it possible that Alessio was as obsessively set on recapturing what they had lost as she herself was?

'My parents are flying over to London in a couple of days, ostensibly to view houses...but really to lie in wait for their one and only grandchild from France. It would be a very nice gesture if you were to agree to them flying her back here,' Alessio murmured.

'No problem,' Daisy mumbled dizzily.

And astonishingly there wasn't. Daisy drifted into the imposing Roman mansion which had provided the backdrop for the most miserable, tension-filled weeks of her life and met not the Borgias in twentieth-century guise but two older people clearly under strain but as anxious to mend fences as she was.

'We didn't welcome you into the family as we should have done the first time you were married,' Vittorio admitted with rueful emphasis, his eyes meeting Daisy's levelly. 'We were still looking for someone to blame. And unfortunately watching the two of you together then was like watching two cars with blindfolded drivers racing towards a pile-up. Alessio seemed to suffer a personality change overnight. You weren't any happier. I engineered the divorce in the honest belief that I was doing what had to be done.'

Registering his sincerity, Daisy swallowed hard and nodded.

'But you still didn't tell me the truth about that settlement,' Alessio reminded his father grimly.

Vittorio Leopardi grimaced and sighed. 'At the time it seemed best to leave it buried.'

Alessio's mother cleared her throat and murmured with unhidden eagerness, 'I expect you'll want to have more children as soon as possible...'

Daisy tensed, her eyes flying to Alessio.

'I shouldn't think so,' he said, directing a quelling glance at his parent.

Daisy lowered her head. Stupid to feel rejected, she told herself. Even more stupid to feel suspicious of his motives. How could she blame him for feeling like that? Alessio could have only the most disastrous memories of her last pregnancy. But, whatever lay behind his reasoning, it still hurt, she acknowledged.

Alessio reached for her hand as they walked back out into the sunlight. 'You see... the monsters were in your imagination. My parents are well aware of how badly they behaved in the past.'

His understanding touched something deep inside Daisy. She met his golden gaze and her heart skipped a beat, her pulses pounding. Concentration became impossible. They didn't talk much on the drive back. Having narrowly missed a ticket for speeding, Alessio shot the Ferrari through the gates of the villa with a groan of relief.

'Do you remember what we did to recover from your very first meeting with my family?' he murmured thickly.

Daisy went hot all over and blushed. It had taken too many glasses of wine to carry her through that long-ago meal with the coldly disapproving Leopardis. Alessio had carried her up the stairs, laughingly asserting that he couldn't take her home until she had sobered up, and... she had tried to take his jeans off with her teeth.

'I'm still waiting for you to do that again.'

'You didn't wait then,' Daisy muttered, alarmingly short of breath.

'Practice makes perfect,' Alessio breathed in a husky, sensual growl.

They were crossing the hall in a direct line to the stairs when a maid appeared. 'There is a Signor Barry Stevens on the phone, *signora*,' she recited breathlessly.

'B-Barry?' Daisy stammered in surprise.

'How the hell did *he* get this number?' Alessio launched down at her accusingly.

'I don't know!'

His hard mouth twisted, his brilliant eyes suddenly icy cold. 'Obviously you've been in contact with him since we arrived.'

Daisy swept up the phone in the library. 'Who gave you this number?' she hissed down the line without any preliminaries.

'It was waiting for me when I got back to the office yesterday. I understand that you wanted me to call!'

'No,' Daisy groaned.

'So you don't have any news for me?' he pressed thinly. 'Then who left that flipping message telling me to contact you?'

'I'm afraid it must have been someone's idea of a joke. Barry... please don't call here again,' Daisy sighed wearily.

Alessio was still standing in the hall, his dark, strong face impassive and set like granite.

Daisy snatched in a deep breath. 'Alessio... either Bianca or Nina must be responsible for giving Barry this number because I have not been in touch with him—'

'Why the hell would either of them want to do something like that?'

'Both of them seem equally keen to cause trouble between us,' Daisy stated doggedly, her chin coming up in response to his blatant incredulity.

'I'm not into crazy conspiracy theories, Daisy. If your toy boy is missing you, find someone else to blame. But don't insult my intelligence by trying to drag my sister or Nina into the mess you've left in your wake!'

The acrid sting of tears struck Daisy's strained eyes. 'You said...you said that I could try trusting you...when are *you* going to try trusting *me*? she prompted painfully.

Alessio dealt her a look of bleak contempt and strode out of the house.

Daisy folded her arms in a jerky motion and then her patience snapped. What a moody, volatile swine Alessio could still be! No matter what he said, he was still as suspicious as hell of her every move.

Desperately keen to look as if she had barely noticed his absence, Daisy was floating on a Lilo in the swimming pool when Alessio put in a reappearance. Since it had taken so much effort to get onto the Lilo, she didn't twitch a muscle behind her sunglasses and maintained an attitude of sun-worshipping relaxation and cool.

'If you've got into that water without learning how to swim, I'll kill you!' Alessio spelt out in a raw opening salvo.

Daisy looked smug. 'I can swim...I can even life-save.'

'Since when?'

'Since I found an instructor who didn't think dropping me in the deep end and telling me I would float would miraculously do the trick.'

'Come out,' Alessio ordered.

'Why should I?' Daisy retorted, sitting up suddenly and without due care and attention. The Lilo lurched and she made a frantic attempt to correct her balance but still ended up being tipped into the water with a gigantic splash.

'Stop it...*let go!*' she spluttered when she found herself being towed back to the side, incredulous that Alessio had dived into the water in a quite ludicrous rescue bid fully clothed. 'I *told* you that I could swim!'

Alessio dragged her back up the steps regardless. 'I'd like to see some proof of your proficiency before I risk standing around while you drown.'

Infuriated by her inability to strike an impressive note of injured dignity around Alessio, Daisy snatched up a towel to dry her face, pushing her tangled hair out of her eyes with furious hands. 'You make me so mad sometimes, I could scream!'

'"O lady, speak again!"' Alessio quoted with deep irony.

It took a second or two for Daisy to absorb the shock of Alessio throwing lines of Shakespeare at her. *'Romeo and Juliet?'* she scorned with a curled lip. 'I don't think so. And I am not playing Desdemona to your Othello!'

'It would indeed be difficult.' Alessio elevated a winged brow sardonically. 'Desdemona didn't have a past that encompassed half the men in the UK.'

'How dare you?' Daisy gasped in outrage.

In thunderous silence, Alessio peeled off his sodden jeans and shirt, his rough, impatient movements lacking his usual grace and cool. Mesmerised against her will, Daisy watched him execute a perfect dive and plough in a fast, aggressive crawl through the water.

Walking to the edge, Daisy waited for him to hit the side and crouched down in readiness. 'You think I made love with every one of them, don't you?'

Stormy golden eyes struck hers like forked lightning. 'What do you think?' Alessio bit back with slashing derision, and launched into another deeply aggressive length of the pool.

The next time he touched base, Daisy murmured, 'Alessio...?'

'I don't want to know,' he grated, and, planting his hands on the tiled edge, he hauled himself up, water streaming from his lean, powerfully muscled body in rivulets that glistened on his bronzed skin. Watching him, Daisy found it extraordinarily hard to recall what she had been about to say. Inflating her lungs again was even more of a challenge. He strode past her stark naked and stood towel-drying his hair.

'Put your eyes back in your head and look the other way like a lady, Daisy,' Alessio advised silkily with his back turned to her.

A deep crimson flooded her cheeks. 'I—'

'I can *feel* you looking at me. I always could.'

'It's a little hard to ignore a naked man.'

'Is it? Do you recall that nudist beach I once took you to? You welded shut your eyes and hung onto your bikini like it was the only thing that stood between you and moral damnation!'

'That must have given you a laugh.'

'Actually... it shamed me into taking you home.'

'About those albums—'

'*Piccola mia*, you are not as a rule this persistent. I have no desire to talk about your rogues' gallery of photographic trophies.'

'I haven't had a single serious relationship since our divorce!' Daisy admitted grudgingly.

'Tell me something that might surprise me,' Alessio drawled in sardonic invitation.

Daisy paled. 'Oh, yes, I forgot... I'm such a shallow person, aren't I? I'd be wasting my breath telling you anything.'

As she attempted to brush past him, Alessio caught her arm in a powerful grip and yanked her back. 'No more running away,' he spelt out grimly.

'Let go of me!' Daisy blazed.

Instead he took her mouth in a hard, punishing kiss. Her world swung violently and dizzily on its axis, her legs buckling as his tongue stabbed between her lips in an expression of raw, hungry need. She struggled to resist and then surrendered as a river of fire ignited low in the pit of her stomach. With a moan of helpless response, burned by the ferocious heat of his desire, Daisy wrapped her arms round his throat.

'I'm still not speaking to you,' she mumbled shakily. 'I want you to know that.'

'I'm a jealous, possessive toad. We both know it. What is there to discuss?' Alessio demanded unevenly, divesting her of her bikini top and letting his hands rise to cup her bared breasts with a shameless groan of appreciation. '*Dio* . . . I would burn a thousand years in purgatory for this alone!'

Crushing her to him, he lifted her high in his arms and carried her into the villa. 'The staff. . .?' she began.

'I sent them home.'

They landed on the bed in a wild tangle of damp limbs. Alessio pulled her over him, golden eyes smouldering over the pouting swell of pale breasts adorned by succulent pink nipples. Her breath was trapped in her throat as he stroked the painfully taut buds, sending shivers of excitement coursing through her.

'You are the only woman I have ever loved,' Alessio murmured roughly. 'And I want to be inside you so badly, I ache.'

As he reached up and played with the excruciatingly sensitive peaks with his teeth and his tongue, Daisy cried out, shifting briefly to bury her mouth hungrily in the hollow of his strong brown throat. Her worshipping hands travelled up over his broad chest, loving the flex of his muscles and the rough curls of black hair that met her exploring fingertips. He tangled his hands in her hair and dragged her lips back to his in an explosive kiss that melted her bones to hot honey. The sun-warmed scent and the never forgotten feel of him engulfed her, leaving her utterly without defence.

'*Yes!*' she gasped as he forced her down to him again and the hard, smooth jut of his manhood pressed against her belly, extracting a whimper of urgent, breathless need from her.

She couldn't get enough of him. She couldn't get close enough to satisfy herself. He rolled over, an impatient hand skimming the clinging bikini pants from her slender hips. Her heartbeat thundered as he found the pale, damp curls at the junction of her thighs and moved onto discover the hot, silken flesh she opened to him. And then, as suddenly, she could hardly get breath into her lungs and what she could burned and rasped in her throat as sensation clawed at her with a bitter-sweet intensity that was more than she could bear.

As he explored the aching, wet emptiness at the very heart of her, a long, sobbing moan of tormented frustration was dragged from Daisy. Never in her life had she craved anything as much as she craved the hot, hard invasion of Alessio's body into hers. She clutched at him with wildly impatient, pleading hands, out of control, drawing her knees back in feverish invitation.

Alessio lifted her up to him, eyes ablaze with answering desire, and entered her with a single powerful thrust. A startled cry of pain escaped her as intimate muscles locked tight in instinctive rejection.

Alessio stilled in shock. Astonished golden eyes raked her hotly flushed face. '*Dio* ... you feel as tight as the first time we made love!'

Ungritting her teeth, Daisy looked up at him.

'Like a virgin,' Alessio breathed in hoarse, shaken addition. 'I hurt you.'

But the pain had already receded and her wildly sensitive flesh was now aware of his intrusion on a very different plane. Her eyes slid shut in voluptuous acceptance. She gave a sensuous little wriggle, excitement taking hold of her again. He felt so incredibly good inside her, filling her, stretching her.

'Just how long has it been since you made love?' Alessio demanded unevenly.

'Please...' she moaned, every fibre of her straining body maddened by the stillness of his.

'How long?' Alessio grated with all the persistence of a natural-born torturer.

'Thirteen years!' Daisy shot at him in a burst of anguished frustration.

'*Madre di Dio, piccola mia...*' Alessio growled in a daze of disbelief.

He studied her with stunned intensity, a dark surge of blood rising to highlight his cheekbones, his shimmering eyes clinging to hers. And then, with a driven groan, he sank into her, deepening his penetration with fiery dominance. He delved his tongue between her lips with a sense of erotic timing that made every nerve-ending scream. There was only him then, and the incredible intensity of what he was making her feel.

He drove into her hard and fast. She rode a storm of frantic, feverish excitement, her heart slamming wildly against her breastbone. Then, without warning, the excruciating ache inside her intensified sharply, making her sob out his name in torment. A split second later, the wildness inside her expanded in a blazing explosion of sensation, shooting a hot, sweet overload of pleasure into every quivering inch of her being.

Alessio shuddered in the clinging circle of her arms and with a shout of hoarse, agonised satisfaction he found his own release, collapsing down on top of her, heavy and damp with sweat and achingly familiar. A raw flood of tenderness filled Daisy to overflowing and made her eyes smart. But he had finally got the truth out of her—a truth she had never dreamt she might speak or he might suspect—and now she felt naked and horribly exposed.

'You were worth waiting for,' Daisy whispered tightly, painfully.

Alessio lifted his dark, tousled head. With a slightly unsteady hand he smoothed her silky hair from her brow, long, caressing fingers cradling her cheekbone in a gesture of almost awkward tenderness. Only then, disturbingly, his beautiful dark eyes slewed away from the anxious intensity of hers, his lush lashes screening his gaze, but not before she'd seen the daunting bleakness etched there.

'I feel bloody guilty,' he confessed, and immediately released her from his weight.

Daisy didn't know what she had expected from him but it hadn't been that admission.

'Why no one else in all this time?' Alessio prompted tautly.

Now, that question was predictable but not one which Daisy was prepared to answer honestly. Defensively she turned her head away, aching with love for him and suppressing a dangerous urge to close the physical gap he had opened up between them. 'When you have to look at a man and think, How would I feel if I got pregnant by him? it kind of chills your bones.'

Instead of laughing as she had hoped, Alessio sat up in a sudden movement and swore long and low in Italian. '*Porca miseria*,' he finally groaned. 'I didn't *use* anything!'

Daisy lay with all the life of a block of wood. His horror at that realisation had the same effect on her as several blows with a hatchet.

'Don't you understand?' Alessio gritted, as if he was expecting more of a reaction from her. 'I didn't take any precautions!'

'Relax,' Daisy urged in a choky little voice. 'I doubt if I'm as fertile as I was at seventeen.'

'*Dio* . . . what have I done?' he bit out, only half under his breath.

Daisy hunched herself under the cover of the sheet. Witnessing Alessio's appalled response to the risk that he might have fathered a child with her a second time was, she was convinced, the most humiliating and painful dose of hard reality that she had ever experienced. Hurt and bitter tears boiled up behind her lowered eyelids.

'I feel incredibly guilty,' Alessio said again.

'Go away,' Daisy mumbled thickly, not even caring what he might have to feel guilty about any more.

A surprisingly hesitant hand came down on her rigid shoulder. She shook it off and scooted over to the far side of the bed. 'Leave me alone!'

His weight left the bed. But ironically she didn't want what she had said she wanted and immediately started feeling bereft and deserted and resentful.

'Get some sleep,' Alessio urged heavily. 'I have to go out for a while.'

'Don't come back,' Daisy spat, and burst into floods of tears the minute the door closed. She crammed her fist against her mouth but she still sobbed herself hoarse.

Obviously Alessio had no feelings for her other than lust. And now he clearly wished he hadn't bothered with that either. So why had he dragged her off to bed?

No doubt it had been part and parcel of his desire to put on a show of marital harmony for Tara's home-coming. Their daughter would undoubtedly not be impressed by the fact that the parents she wanted to regard as reunited lovers were sleeping in separate bedrooms.

CHAPTER TEN

DAISY was still in bed when the phone rang. At first she ignored it but the persistence of the caller finally triumphed and she reached for the receiver in a sudden spasm of irritation, no longer able to bear that intrusive shrill.

The feminine burst of imperious Italian reproof that greeted her was instantly recognisable. 'Bianca?' Daisy flatly broke into the flood of complaint. 'This is Daisy, not one of the staff. Alessio's out. Shall I ask him to call you?'

'Actually it was you I wanted to speak to,' Bianca informed her, her annoyance suddenly replaced by saccharine sweetness. 'I'm well aware that Alessio isn't at home. Shall I tell you *how* I know? He's with Nina...'

Daisy tensed and then slowly expelled her pent-up breath in a hiss. 'Don't you ever give up, Bianca? Thirteen years on, you're still playing the same old silly tune!'

'Check it out for yourself if you don't believe me! Nina is staying in a holiday complex only a few minutes' drive from the villa.' Bianca reeled off the address with audible satisfaction. 'Alessio's Ferrari is parked at the door—'

'You're wasting your time,' Daisy told her angrily. 'I'm not a credulous teenager any more and I trust Alessio... do you hear me? I trust your brother!'

'But you put him in an impossible position. Alessio wanted his daughter. He *had* to marry you! You're the

171

intruder, not Nina!' Bianca condemned sharply. 'It's Nina he wants to be with and *is* with at this very moment! Why don't you get out of his life and leave him alone?'

Without hesitation, Daisy slammed the receiver back down on the cradle. She was shaking. Moisture beaded her short upper lip. In an abrupt movement, she sprang out of bed, knelt down, traced the phone wire to the wall and hurriedly disconnected it. It occurred to her that it would be nice if she could as easily disconnect the unsettling thoughts that kept assailing her no matter how hard she tried to block them out.

Why had Alessio behaved like a man suffering from a very uneasy conscience? Why had he twice said how guilty he felt? Daisy paced the carpet. As a rule, Alessio was outrageously stubborn and confident of his own judgement. Retreat was an unknown option to him and regret a rare emotion. But Alessio had been upset. That same scenario ran back and forth through her restive brain.

Alessio...appalled at the smallest risk that he might have made his wife pregnant. Why? Why *should* that be such a disaster? They were married. They were mature adults now. He adored Tara. He had admitted how very much he would have liked to share their daughter's early years. He did not dislike children. And surely the oddest thing of all was that he should have made no attempt to discover Daisy's feelings on the subject...

It was ridiculous even to *think* that he might be with Nina, Daisy scolded herself angrily. She had seen no evidence of questionable intimacy between Alessio and Nina the day before. Do you really think they would advertise if they planned to continue their affair in secret? a little voice asked drily. Indeed, hadn't the distinct lack of strain between them been in itself more suspicious?

Daisy pulled on a black cotton skirt and scoop-necked pink silk T-shirt. But she was not going out. No, definitely not. She would be waiting downstairs for Alessio when he came back. They had to talk, not least about Bianca. For heaven's sake, they had only been married a couple of days! On the other hand, wouldn't finding Alessio at that address be *her* proof that his sister had contacted her to tell her where he was? After all, how else would Daisy have been able to locate him?

Suddenly appreciating that she had a perfect excuse for checking out Bianca's story, Daisy did not hesitate. There was another car in the garage. It was bucketing down with rain but she didn't waste time running back indoors to get a coat. Driving out onto the road in the Mercedes, she told herself that it would be amusing to confront Alessio when he least expected her. And, whoever he was visiting in that complex, she was convinced it would not turn out to be Nina Franklin.

The Ferrari was sitting in a well-lit parking area. Daisy stopped on the other side of the road. As soon as she saw Alessio she would get out of the car. She didn't have long to wait. The door of a ground-floor apartment opened and a rectangle of light silhouetted Alessio's arrogant dark head and lean, powerful body. He was wearing his pearl-grey suit, the jacket open, his tie missing. Daisy slid out of the Mercedes.

And only then did she realise that Alessio wasn't alone. The door slammed noisily and Nina hurried down the path after him, calling out his name at the top of her voice. 'Alessio...!'

They walked together to the Ferrari, engaged in seemingly urgent conversation. Daisy stood and watched as they climbed into the car and drove off. Her legs felt as if they had turned to stone. She couldn't move. Rain

soaked her hair, dripped down her face and drenched
the silk T-shirt until it clung like a second skin to her
chilled flesh. She didn't feel cold or wet. Shock had tem-
porarily deprived her of sense and awareness.

And then a wave of sick dizziness ran over her and
she shivered violently. She hadn't believed, she *truly*
hadn't believed that he would be with Nina...that he
could have made passionate love to her and then gone
straight to another woman, a gorgeous, sophisticated
blonde in her early twenties. No wonder he had an uneasy
conscience...

The flood of pain which followed the disbelief hit
Daisy on the drive back to the villa. He had to be in
love with Nina. She could not believe that Alessio would
betray her for anything less than love. In her mind, it
all seemed so agonisingly clear. He *had* married her
purely to get hold of Tara. He hadn't once pretended
otherwise, had he? But evidently he had never expected
their marriage to last indefinitely.

The break would have come once Tara was settled in
Italy. Alessio would have waited until his daughter had
forged closer ties with his half of the family. He had
married her to *steal* their daughter, Daisy thought, in an
agony of grief and betrayal. Setting out to win her trust,
he had no doubt planned to ditch her as soon as she
became surplus to requirements. Meanwhile he could
continue to meet up with Nina whenever he liked.

'If it is the last thing I do in this lifetime, I will punish
you for this,' Alessio had sworn the very day he had
found out that he was a father. How could she have allowed herself to forget that threat?

Tears streaming down her face, Daisy stumbled back
into the villa, fighting to regain control of emotions
which felt uncontrollable. Dully she wondered why

Alessio had behaved as if he was jealous when surely he should not have cared less how she had lived in the years they had been apart. Maybe it had been a kind of crazy dog-in-the-manger possessiveness. Or maybe...just maybe he had seen the error of his ways and had raced off to see Nina tonight to break off that relationship. But then why would Nina have got into the Ferrari with him? she asked herself, ashamed of her eagerness to grasp at any explanation which might lessen the anguish of what she was feeling.

'Daisy?' a hatefully familiar voice murmured smoothly.

Daisy jerked and swivelled round. Strolling out of the drawing room with all the confidence of the mistress of the house, Bianca surveyed her and smiled with unconcealed satisfaction.

'You look like a drowned rat,' Bianca commented drily. 'I gather you hit pay dirt and, of course, you can't possibly want to be here when Alessio returns.'

With an immense effort, Daisy straightened her slight shoulders and walked past the sneering brunette into the drawing room. Her legs were trembling beneath her. But it demanded even greater discipline not to lay violent hands upon Bianca and throw her physically from the door of her brother's house. Bianca was here to gloat; she simply had been unable to resist the temptation to have a firsthand view of Daisy's devastation.

With an unsteady hand, Daisy reached for the brandy decanter and began pouring herself a drink, praying that alcohol would ward off the disorienting effect of shock and lessen the freezing coldness settling into her bones. 'I want you to leave,' she said without even sparing a glance at the other woman.

'Don't be childish,' Bianca urged impatiently.

'And before you leave I would like you to return your keys to this house. Now that your brother is married, I don't think it's appropriate for you to be walking in without warning whenever the fancy takes you,' Daisy completed before she braced herself and drank down the brandy all in one go, trembling as the heat raced down her aching throat and warmed the chilled pit of her uneasy stomach.

Bianca stared at Daisy, a faint hint of disconcertion drawing her brows together. 'I'm willing to drive you to the airport,' she announced, loftily ignoring the invitation to depart. 'You're obviously in no fit state to get yourself there!'

The airport. It would be so easy to take advantage of that invitation to run away. Indeed such a speedy retreat from a painful crisis would have all the ease and familiarity of habit, Daisy conceded painfully, drawing in a deep, shuddering breath to steady herself. However, she had Tara's feelings to consider. In addition, strange as it might seem, she wanted—no, she *needed* to confront Alessio this time. 'I don't require a lift to the airport, Bianca.'

'There's only one more flight to London tonight,' the brunette warned sharply. 'You haven't got much time.'

'I have all the time in the world,' Daisy countered tightly, frowning as a faint sound from somewhere beyond the room momentarily pierced her concentration. She focused briefly on the ajar door, listening for a split second before turning back to Bianca. 'I have all the time in the world,' she repeated with conviction, 'because I'm not going anywhere.'

Bianca studied her in contemptuous disbelief. 'You can't be serious! You can't want to be here when Alessio gets back. How could you want to humiliate yourself to that extent? If I caught my husband in the act of an adulterous tryst with another woman, believe me, I wouldn't be sitting humbly waiting for him to come home again!'

Daisy was rigid, her pallor pronounced. 'But then what I do... and indeed what Alessio does... is none of your business, Bianca. You're his sister, not his keeper.'

'Alessio and I are very close!' Bianca shot back at her in angry resentment. 'And I want you out of his life for good!'

Daisy uttered a strangled laugh. 'The same way you wanted rid of me the last time? You lied about Sophia Corsini and I swallowed your every lie whole,' she condemned, bitter resentment flooding through her. 'He never even went out with the wretched girl!'

Bianca flushed and then her jawline hardened, her mouth thinning as she made a recovery. 'Where on earth did you get the idea that I lied about Sophia? Alessio may be my brother but even I have never tried to pretend that he's the faithful type—'

'I'm sick of listening to your poison,' Daisy interrupted fiercely.

'You just haven't got the courage to face the truth. If you had any pride at all, you would be getting out before Alessio makes an even bigger fool of you! He doesn't want you; he *never* wanted you!' Bianca asserted in furious frustration. 'All he ever wanted was his daughter! How can you try to cling to him even after I've given you the proof that he's still involved with Nina!'

Without warning the door was thrust back noisily on its hinges.

Both Daisy and Bianca jumped, their heads spinning in unison. Alessio stood on the threshold, diamond-hard eyes blazing with outrage, his golden skin pale with anger.

'Nina is waiting for you at her apartment, Bianca,' Alessio breathed with chilling bite. 'She's most unhappy with the dramatic role you have assigned to her. She doesn't appreciate being used as a weapon—'

'I don't know what you're talking about!' Bianca broke in, a mottled flush overlying her tautened cheeks.

'Spurred on by you, Nina had no objection to causing a little minor mischief, but she draws the line at setting out to destroy my marriage. She's already ashamed of the lies you instructed her to tell yesterday. You misjudged your partner, Bianca.' Alessio's grim gaze rested on his sister in harsh condemnation, his nostrils flaring with distaste. 'She thinks your malicious games have got dangerously out of control . . . and, believe me, she's not the only one!'

Every scrap of colour had now drained from Bianca's complexion. She stared at her brother in mingled shock and embarrassment. 'Alessio, you don't understand,' she began shakily. 'I was only thinking of your happiness.'

Alessio crossed the floor, closed a determined hand round his twin's elbow and practically dragged her out of the room with him.

Daisy's knees wouldn't hold her up any longer. She sagged down like a broken doll onto the nearest seat. From the hall, staccato Italian broke from Alessio, scorching anger powering every syllable, Bianca's responses running from defensive to pleading to—finally—tearful. Throughout, Daisy's temples pounded with tension. She couldn't yet think straight but she could not miss hearing the resounding slam of the front door as Alessio saw his sister off the premises.

'You're soaking wet, *piccola mia* . . .' Alessio gritted, crouching down until he was on a level with her, his vibrantly handsome features still dark and taut with fury, although there was a curious tenderness that bewildered her in the golden eyes that rested on her strained face. 'You need to get out of those clothes before you catch pneumonia.'

Stiff as a little clockwork soldier, Daisy cloaked her gaze in self-defence. Springing upright, Alessio swooped down on her again and swept her up into his arms without another word. A startled gasp burst from Daisy. She was not in the mood to be soothed like a distressed child.

'Nina wants to apologise to you but I told her that this wasn't the right time.'

'Apologise . . . she wants to *apologise*?' Daisy pressed in disbelief. 'Alessio, if you don't put me down I'll scream!'

In response to her challenge, Alessio merely tightened his arms round her as he started up the stairs. 'Daisy . . . my relationship with Nina was never anything but casual. A prudent male thinks twice before he becomes intimately involved with the daughter of family friends.' Thrusting back their bedroom door, he murmured grimly, 'Nina's ego was hurt when I married you and Bianca found her an easy target. But Nina, spoilt and self-centred as she is, has a conscience—'

'I didn't notice it yesterday when she was blowing kisses at you and spouting all that nonsense about Barry!' Daisy retorted, tearing herself violently free of his hold as soon as he began to lower her to the bathroom carpet. 'And I don't know what kind of a story you've invented as a cover-up but it won't wash because I wasn't born yesterday! You were *with* Nina tonight!'

'Bianca is staying with her. That's why I went over there. I phoned before I left but when I arrived Bianca had gone,' Alessio explained with an impatient frown, his brilliant eyes assessing Daisy's now flushed and furious face. 'When I confronted Nina, she was very upset—'

'And only yesterday you told me that she was behaving *so* generously!'

At that tart reminder, faint colour accentuated the taut slant of Alessio's hard cheekbones. 'I was feeling uncomfortable because I dropped Nina the minute you came back into my life. Yesterday, I genuinely couldn't see the wood for the trees, but I was furious with her tonight—'

'Is that why you tucked her into your Ferrari with you?' Daisy prompted in a tone of fierce accusation.

'So that's why you're wet.' Alessio surveyed her with dawning comprehension. 'You *followed* me?'

Her cheeks burning but her chin angled high, Daisy told him about his sister's phone call.

Alessio vented a sharp imprecation. 'I was determined to find Bianca, and Nina thought she knew where she was. When we drew a blank, I dropped Nina straight back home again. If you saw us together, surely you noticed that she was crying?'

'Sorry, I forgot my binoculars. Now go away. I want a bath,' Daisy announced brittly.

Alessio studied her, his golden eyes incredulous. '*Dio* . . . in the midst of all this?'

Daisy planted a determined hand on his chest, pressed him back and slammed the door in his face. But the instant she was alone she slumped, the anger she had forced to the fore in self-defence draining away. She had

gone on the attack sooner than let Alessio see how pitifully fragile her self-control was.

So, Alessio had finally become suspicious and, setting
out to confront his sister, had ended up dealing with
Nina first. Intense relief washed over Daisy as she tasted
the truth. Bianca had been telling a pack of lies and now
that Alessio was aware of his twin's venomous loathing
for his wife Bianca would never be in a position to cause
trouble again.

Shivering now with cold, she ripped off her sodden
clothing and stepped into a shallow bath. But her sense
of relief was short-lived. Misery invaded her afresh.
Nothing had really changed between them, she thought
wretchedly. Alessio might not be in love with Nina but
he didn't love her either. And he had reacted to the
possibility of another baby in the same way that he might
have reacted to a death threat. She couldn't even cherish
the hope that extending the family might help to bring
them closer.

The door opened.

Daisy tensed, feeling hunted. *'What?'* she demanded.

'You have a count of three to vacate that bath,' Alessio
murmured dangerously softly. *'One—'*

'I'm staying put!'

'Two—'

'You're turning into a domineering tyrant!' Daisy
screeched, nearly falling out of the bath in her haste to
snatch up a towel.

She emerged from the bathroom with pronounced reluctance. Alessio was lounging back against the foot-
board of the bed. He rested diamond-bright eyes on her
hotly flushed and mutinous face. 'When you were with
Bianca, you made a reference to a girl called Sophia . . .'

Daisy paled and chewed her lower lip. 'Thirteen years ago, Bianca told me that Sophia had been your girl-friend and that you were seeing her again—'

'*Madre di Dio* . . . no longer do I need to wonder why you agreed to the divorce!' Alessio bit out rawly.

'At the time it seemed to make sense,' Daisy muttered ruefully.

'*Porca miseria* . . . the damage Bianca has caused! I never dreamt that she could be such a bitch!'

'But then she doesn't behave like that with you,' Daisy sighed.

'She made that call to Barry Stevens...' A bitter tension had hardened Alessio's strong features and roughened his deep voice. 'I'm sorry that you have had to endure her malicious attacks, even sorrier that I refused to listen when you tried to tell me what was happening!'

He was still appalled and mortified by his sister's be-haviour. Daisy was struggling to overcome a powerfully embarrassing urge to wrap consoling arms around him. Any move to offer comfort would be uniquely revealing to a male as shrewd as Alessio. And Daisy was not pre-pared to tell him that in spite of everything she loved him even more than she had loved him as a teenager. Only this time she wouldn't run away—she would stay and fight, if need be, to give their marriage a future.

'I'm not blaming you for what Bianca did. It's over and done with. Forget about it,' she urged in a rush.

'That's very forgiving of you,' Alessio murmured tautly.

A thunderous silence stretched.

Alessio strode restively over to the window. Then he swung fluidly back to face her, expelling his breath in a hiss. 'I've been acting like an insanely jealous and ir-rational teenager ever since I saw those photo albums of yours,' he admitted in a driven undertone. 'When I found out today that...well, that there had never been anyone else I was really ashamed of my behaviour. I had no right whatsoever to question your past.'

Daisy rubbed abstractedly at the deep-pile carpet with a set of bare pink toes. 'I've always been pretty possessive about you too,' she muttered.

Alessio threw back his darkly handsome head, his brilliant eyes bleak. 'I wouldn't have acted like that if I hadn't been so afraid of losing you again,' he gritted.

'I thought it was Tara you were afraid of losing,' Daisy whispered slowly.

'Much as I love our daughter, *piccola mia*, I have to confess that I used her as an excuse to make you marry me again. I was a man with a mission last week,' Alessio grated unevenly. 'And my mission was to win, by any means within my power, a second chance with the girl I loved and lost as a teenager. If I had only wanted Tara I would never have forced you into marriage.'

Daisy's violet eyes were wide. With immense difficulty she relocated her voice. 'But you kept on *telling* me that it was all for Tara's sake!'

'That was pride talking. *Madre di Dio*...' Alessio groaned. 'You fell apart in horror when I first mentioned marriage! So I cornered you and blackmailed you into it—'

'You bought the agency because you wanted me back,' Daisy mumbled dizzily, struggling to conceal her delight.

'I thought if I pushed hard enough I could somehow make you feel what I was feeling,' Alessio confessed roughly. 'That first day I saw you again, it was like coming alive for the first time in thirteen years! *Dio*...I had your phone number within an hour of you leaving me again!' Crossing the room with a look of fierce decisiveness stamped on his taut features, he reached for her with determined hands. Dark golden eyes blazed down at her. 'This marriage *can* work. I love you enough for both of us!'

Daisy braced shaking hands on his broad shoulders, her throat closing over. 'Alessio,' she said thickly, 'I love you too.'

He stared down at her fixedly.

Daisy swallowed convulsively. 'I never stopped loving you but I thought you only wanted Tara and I was so scared of getting hurt again.'

With a stifled groan, Alessio crushed her to him, snatching her up off her feet to plunder her readily parted lips with an aching, desperate hunger every bit as strong as her own as he brought her down to the bed. Intense happiness and excitement swept Daisy to a breathless height of emotion that drove every other thought from her mind.

Leaning over her, Alessio curved a possessive palm round one delicate cheekbone, his fingers lacing gently into her hair as he studied her with wondering, mesmeric intensity.

Then, disturbingly, his strong face shadowed. 'I still feel so damned guilty about this afternoon,' he confided heavily. '*Dio* ... I was crazy with the need to make love to you but there is no excuse for that kind of carelessness. If I've made you pregnant again, you're going to hate me!'

Daisy focused on him in bewilderment. 'Hate you?'

'You were so miserable when you were carrying Tara,' Alessio said tensely. 'I know that having another baby is completely out of the question and I'd never ask you to go through all that again for my benefit, but—'

'You said you didn't want another child because you assumed that that was what *I* wanted to hear...' A breathtaking smile slowly blossomed on Daisy's face as she made that leap in understanding. 'But there were a whole host of things wrong between us then... Now that everything's right...actually...I'd love another baby.'

Alessio looked stunned. For a count of ten seconds he simply stared at her. Daisy grinned, enjoying the knowledge that for once he had not been one step ahead of her. 'I mean *this* time I could really enjoy the experience,' she pointed out chattily...

Sheathed in a diaphanous negligé set, Daisy strolled in from the balcony and watched Alessio pulling on a pair of jeans. Next door to watching him take them off, it was one of her favourite pursuits. Every fluid movement of those long, bronzed, hair-roughened limbs utterly entranced her. Had it been a year, had it really been a whole year since they'd remarried?

She surveyed the elegant bedroom of their town house in Rome. After lunch, they would be driving down to the villa for the weekend. Last night they had attended a surprise party thrown by Alessio's parents to celebrate their first wedding anniversary. The Leopardis had flown her aunt over for the festivities and Janet was staying with them for several days. Indeed even Bianca had put in a brief appearance and Daisy had ended up feeling a little sorry for her sister-in-law.

When Alessio had exposed Bianca's malicious lies, his sister had gone home to her parents for sympathy, only to find herself the target of yet another bout of outraged recriminations. Unhappily for her, it had not occurred to her that her parents were *genuinely* eager to see Alessio's marriage succeed or that they were overjoyed at the prospect of getting to know their grandchild. Finding herself and her opinions very much out in the cold, Bianca had cut herself off from her family for months.

However, last night Bianca had approached them with a small present and stilted congratulations, her discomfiture painfully apparent.

'We made it in spite of you,' Alessio had growled ungraciously, only accepting the present after Daisy had given him a speaking glance, but then adding, 'And do I need to remind you what people say about Greeks bearing gifts?'

Certainly it would be a long time before Alessio trusted his sister again.

'You look ravishing, *piccola mia...*'

Snatched from her reverie by that innately sexy voice, Daisy collided with Alessio's intensely appreciative gaze and blushed like a teenager. They had made love until dawn had broken the skies but her heart still skipped an impressionable beat.

'It's such a beautiful morning.' She had been out on the balcony reliving the sheer romance of the previous night when Alessio had presented her with a magnificent diamond eternity ring and informed her that this had been without doubt the very happiest year of his entire life.

Alessio closed possessive arms round her and pressed a whisper of a kiss to the sensitive skin at the nape of her neck. 'It's still early. How do you feel about breakfast in bed?' he murmured wickedly.

Taut with delicious tension, Daisy leant back against his hard length, and then a trio of knocks, loud enough to wake the dead, sounded on the door. Tara peered round the barrier with exaggerated care.

'Honestly, you two are the limit . . . it's only ten in the morning!' Emerging fully into view, Tara brandished a rather startlingly clad infant for their inspection. 'Nanny's doing the packing, so I got Jen dressed.'

Sinking down on the bed with a smile, Daisy opened her arms to receive her two-month-old daughter, Jenny. Soulful dark brown eyes looked up at her mother from below a virulent lime-green baseball cap.

'What's she wearing?' Alessio demanded, apparently transfixed by the garish lime, purple and orange miniature dungarees.

'Dad, if I have a sister fourteen years younger, it helps if she's got street cred. Take it from me, this is what the cool baby is wearing this season . . . not those disgusting embroidered dresses with those weird frilly socks which Mum loves. I took pity on Jen when I was out shopping with my friends yesterday.'

'That was very thoughtful of you.' Daisy tried not to laugh as Alessio came down beside her, deftly stole Jenny from her lap and gently lifted the baseball cap in the hope of finding his youngest daughter's tiny face.

Alessio's gaze briefly met Daisy's in a shared instant of vibrant amusement as they watched Tara prowl round the room, eye-catching as a bird of paradise in colours that were a remarkable match for her baby sister's. Their daughter was chattering at length about her plans for the family's amusement over the weekend. And they *were* a family, Daisy reflected, a soft sigh of unvarnished contentment escaping her.

Alessio had spent the past year showing her in a thousand different ways just how much he loved her and valued their marriage. Her pregnancy had been a time of real happiness for all of them. Alessio and Tara had both been thrilled to bits and Daisy had been as cosseted as a precious piece of highly breakable china. Jenny had been born a week early and with the bare minimum of fuss. With the assistance of a sensible English nanny, Daisy was thoroughly enjoying motherhood the second time around.

Tara had settled into school, made plenty of new friends and now spoke Italian with enviable fluency. Her outgoing, confident personality had eased her passage everywhere. Her grandparents adored her, and though in the early months of her move to Italy their indulgence had led to Alessio and his daughter having several tussles for supremacy Tara now had a healthy respect for her father and his rules.

'Right,' Tara said bossily as she bent down and scooped her baby sister away from the combined attentions of her besotted parents. 'Jen needs her nap now. We don't want her being all cross and cranky on the drive down, do we? You two don't need to hurry downstairs—'

'We *don't*?' Daisy echoed in surprise.

'Of course not. Lunch is hours away and even Janet's still in bed,' Tara acknowledged carelessly as she made for the door again. 'You know, three is a nice round number...'

'I beg your pardon?' Daisy frowned.

Tara popped her head back round the door, an impish smile on her mobile features. 'That means you can return to what you were doing when I came in. I'm putting in an order for a little brother. As babies go, Jen's really cute, but she needs company in her own age group.'

'Jenny's only ten weeks old!' Daisy gasped as the door shut.

A vibrant smile curving his sensual mouth, Alessio lowered his dark head to hers again, wolfish amusement glittering in his intent gaze. He closed two gentle hands round Daisy's slight shoulders and slowly pressed her back on the pillows. 'As an excuse to spend a great deal of time in bed, the idea has incredible appeal,' he confessed with husky satisfaction.

'I'll consider it... in about six months,' Daisy muttered breathlessly, drowning in his dark golden gaze.

'*Dio, piccola mia*, I love you so much; how did I ever survive thirteen years without you?'

Daisy ran a possessive set of fingers along a long, lean male thigh temptingly and invitingly clad in taut denim. 'I love you too,' she sighed. 'You put your jeans on just so that I could take them off again...'

Leigh Michaels has always loved happy endings. Even when she was a child, if a book's conclusion didn't please her, she'd make up her own. And, though she always wanted to write fiction, she very sensibly planned to earn her living as a newspaper reporter. That career didn't work out, however, and she found herself writing for Mills & Boon® instead— in the kind of happy ending only a romance novelist could dream up!

Leigh likes to hear from readers; you can write to her at PO Box 935, Ottumwa, Iowa, 52501-0935, USA.

Look out for:
HIS TROPHY WIFE by Leigh Michaels
in Tender Romance™, July 2001

FAMILY SECRETS
by
LEIGH MICHAELS

CHAPTER ONE

THE WAITRESS must have seen her coming across the lobby, for a steaming cup of coffee was waiting on her favorite table when Amanda Bailey pushed open the glass door of the little restaurant. "Thanks, Kathy," she called to the gray-haired woman in the pink uniform who was refilling cups for customers at the long counter.

"You look as if you need it," the waitress called back cheerfully.

Amanda nodded. "The whole place is a madhouse to-day."

"So what's new?" Kathy's tone was dry. "This has been building for two weeks. If I'd known movie-making was so exciting, I'd have taken the whole month off and gone to Minnesota where it's quiet."

Amanda knew better. Kathy wouldn't have missed this for the world. It wasn't every day that a movie was filmed in a small town like Springhill, and even though this wasn't a big production, just a made-for-television film, the whole town was at fever pitch.

Since most of the townspeople weren't directly involved, they would get to have all the fun of watching the film, with none of the work that went with it. But Kathy was right about one thing. After the past few weeks, with advance people and crew arriving and getting ready for shooting to start, Amanda should be used to the ceaseless bustle around the inn.

Of course it was wonderful to be so busy. The inn's guest rooms were booked solid for the next thirty days—or until the cameras stopped rolling, the final set was dismantled and the last crew member had left town.

And if we all survive the confusion, Amanda thought, then we can celebrate.

She stirred sugar into her coffee and surveyed the inn's lobby through the glass wall of the coffee shop. She'd never seen so much commotion in the place before. A clump of people were waiting impatiently for the elevator, and nearby, another small group was arguing—she couldn't hear what the problem was, but the body language was obvious. The walnut-paneled room, usually quaint and quiet and cozy, looked like a kaleidoscope today, full of shifting colors and patterns as people hurried through. Hollywood types, the doorman had called them, with their exotic clothes and fashionable haircuts. Amanda said he made the label sound a bit derogatory, and would he please not use it.

A slender young woman with auburn hair came through the front door and paused by the registration desk to look around the lobby. She saw Amanda and waved, but continued to survey the room for another couple of minutes. Finally, however, she came into the coffee shop and dropped with careless grace into the chair across from Amanda's. "I'm supposed to be meeting the locations manager," she said. "He's still short one house and we're going to look at a rental I've got listed."

"He's still looking for sets? Steph, they start filming tomorrow."

Stephanie Kendall rolled her eyes heavenward. "I know. It's one of the great joys of being in real estate. If the rental doesn't work, we'll look until we find what he wants—or drop from exhaustion. Fortunately this particular location isn't in the shooting schedule for a couple of weeks.''

"I heard they're using your house for one of the sets.''

"Yes. And you won't believe what they're doing to it. Thanks, Kathy.'' She took a long drink of the iced tea the waitress had set in front of her.

Amanda frowned. "You wouldn't let them hurt that gorgeous house, would you?''

"Oh, no. They agreed not to touch the structure, and as for the wallpaper—'' she shrugged ''—I was going to have to replace it all, anyway, after Zack got loose with the black crayon.''

Amanda winced. Stephanie's son, Zack, was a darling three-year-old, but even his fans had to admit he had more energy than two average toddlers.

"The best thing about the whole deal,'' Stephanie went on, "is that the garden has never been in such beautiful shape. I hate to think what it cost the production company to manicure it like that. If only I had a full-time landscaper.''

"What are you going to do while they're shooting?''

"Go up to the lake house, of course. I've locked up all the crayons I could find, but with Zack it doesn't pay to take chances. It'll only take a week to finish the scenes in the house, so I'll drive in every day.''

"If you need someone to watch the kids, Steph…''

"In the middle of all this, you'd take on Zack and Katie? You need your head examined, my friend—you've got your hands full running the inn. Is Chase here yet?''

Amanda checked her wristwatch. "Any minute now. The limo left for the airport an hour ago, so if the plane was on time…''

Stephanie shook her head. "How can you stay calm

when every other woman in town is so excited she can't sit still?''

''Oh, I'm excited. It's a terrific boost for the local economy to have an entire production company here for a month, and the inn's profit-and-loss statement ought to look a whole lot better after—''

''Come on, Mandy, I'm not talking about money and you know it. Chase Worthington is the sexiest man on American TV, and you're going to spend the next month under the same roof with him! Now that's *got* to make an impression on you.''

Amanda bit her lip and then said reasonably, ''You might remember that the roof in question is a pretty big one. It's hardly the same as getting stranded with him on a deserted island.''

''Oh? That sounded rather glib, Mandy. Don't tell me you've been thinking about it, after all.''

''Of course I haven't. Anyway, I never have quite understood how someone can have a crush on a person she's never met.''

Stephanie looked puzzled for an instant. ''Oh, that's right, you were still in college when he was here filming *Winter of the Heart* a few years ago. Those of us who did meet him feel terribly possessive, since he's the only genuine celebrity we have any personal connection with. Not that he'll remember, of course—most of us just lined up for autographs. By the way, Jordan's got a new sales manager working for him.'' Stephanie's careless tone didn't fool Amanda for a moment. ''He seems very nice. I thought we'd go out for dinner, the four of us, sometime soon.''

''After the movie's finished, perhaps. Till then I'm really too busy.''

Stephanie's eyebrows rose. ''And after the cast leaves town, what will the excuse be?''

Kathy called from the cash register, "Amanda, I'm running out of change." She waved a ten-dollar bill. "Could you get me a roll of quarters from the front desk?"

Relieved at the interruption, Amanda carried her empty coffee cup to the counter and took the bill.

Stephanie followed her into the lobby. "I wonder what happened to my appointment," she muttered.

A bustle outside the main entrance drew Amanda's attention. The doorman, in his neat dark gray coat, held the door of the inn's limousine, which had pulled up under the canopy. The chauffeur and a bellboy were lifting bags from the back.

Springhill certainly didn't get a lot of celebrities, but over the years a sprinkling of the rich and famous had come to town. Chase Worthington was simply one more on the list, Amanda reminded herself, and took a deep breath.

He got out of the car, tall and lean, dressed in jeans and sunglasses and a loose-knit cotton sweater with the sleeves pushed up to reveal strong forearms. As he stepped onto the sidewalk, the sunlight caught his hair, momentarily making the soft brown strands look like pure spun gold. He turned toward the hotel entrance, then paused.

The sexiest man on American TV, Stephanie had called him, and Amanda had no difficulty seeing why. There was something about the man that exuded power and virility and sheer raw animal magnetism.

And yet there was nothing theatrical about him. He was not posing; Amanda was sure of that. He looked almost as if he'd seen something he hadn't expected.

Amanda felt a vise close on her chest. It was an effort to breathe, as if every molecule of oxygen had to make right-angle turns to get to her lungs.

Don't be silly, she told herself. He was merely pausing to get his bearings, or waiting for his costar to get out of

the car, or thinking about how much his life had changed
since the last time he'd come to Springhill to make a movie.
There was certainly nothing physical for him to look at;
compared to the brilliance outdoors, the lobby was dark.
With the sunglasses he wore, he couldn't possibly see anything but shadows inside.

"Good heavens," Stephanie muttered. "He's even bet-
ter-looking than I remember."

Amanda started to shake her head and caught herself just
in time. She'd almost said that Chase Worthington's at-
tractiveness didn't lie in his handsome face—or at least not
entirely. It was more than looks; she'd been prepared for
them, for she'd seen his face often enough on his weekly
television drama and on magazine covers. What she hadn't
expected was the personal impact of the man. She'd been
almost rocked off her feet.

He had the kind of aura that seemed to give off warmth,
but not the comforting kind of heat a bonfire might produce.
His was the concentrated, controlled flame of a furnace,
which might at any moment explode out of control and
consume everything in its path. No wonder Springhill's
feminine residents had been streaming steadily through the
inn's lobby all afternoon hoping to get a glimpse.

A woman, her face shaded by a gigantic wide-brimmed
hat, stepped out of the car. Jessamyn Arden, the female
lead, clutched Chase's arm as if she was about to lose her
balance; she put her other hand up as if to shield her eyes
from camera flashes. Since there were no photographers,
Amanda decided the gesture must be a reflex action.

Stephanie gave a genteel little sniff. "Jessamyn must
think she's already on camera," she murmured.

Amanda smiled, but her mouth felt stiff. She stepped
forward and was waiting by the door when the pair came
in.

Chase pulled off his sunglasses. His gaze raked the lobby and paused for a second on Stephanie.

That wasn't startling. The redhead was genuinely gorgeous, and Chase was known as a connoisseur of women. Despite what Stephanie had said, he might remember her face.

Amanda was equally unsurprised when he didn't seem to notice her at all. Her flaxen hair and green eyes and ivory skin were attractive in a quiet way, but beside Stephanie's dramatic coloring, she faded into the walls.

She took another step toward the pair. "Welcome to Springhill, Miss Arden." Her voice was lower than usual, with a hint of huskiness. "And Mr. Worthington. I'm the manager of the inn, and if you need anything, I hope you'll…"

She didn't finish, because from the corner of her eye, she saw that another woman had emerged from the limousine. A younger woman, it appeared, though Amanda was certain Jessamyn Arden wouldn't care for that particular comparison. The woman was no competition for Jessamyn in looks, however; her makeup was too heavy and inexpertly applied, and her clothes looked badly creased. She was carrying a leather tote bag.

A personal assistant, perhaps? She probably should have anticipated that Chase or Jessamyn would have something of the sort. Where on earth was she going to find another room?

Of course, Chase Worthington had requested a suite with at least two bedrooms. Did that mean this young woman was something more?

The woman started toward the entrance, and a moment later a child clambered out of the car and followed her. Amanda's eyes widened as she watched the little boy cross the sidewalk. He had curly dark brown hair and was dressed in rumpled white shorts and a soft blue shirt. He would have been a handsome child, she thought, if he hadn't been crying. But his face was blotchy and tear-streaked, and looked a little dirty.

"So that's the famous Nicky," Stephanie said under her breath. To Chase she said, "He must be what—four years old now?"

The actor nodded. "Just last June." He frowned. "I know I ought to remember you, but…"

Stephanie smiled and introduced herself. Amanda wasn't listening; she was still watching the child. He stumbled as he followed the young woman into the lobby, and stopped to rub his eyes. His breathy sobs—the sound of a frustrated and exhausted child—filled the room.

Amanda's heart gave a slow and painful twist. She hated to see the child so unhappy—but of course she knew nothing about the circumstances. Still, it took an effort to drag her gaze away from him and back to the adults. "As I was saying, if there is anything I can do to make your stay more comfortable…"

The child sidled up to Chase Worthington and buried his face in the ribbed bottom of the man's soft cotton sweater. Chase's hand came to rest on the boy's hair, stroking the disordered curls. "There is, as a matter of fact," he said, and smiled at Amanda. The deep brown of his eyes seemed to light with a golden glow. "Is there a gift shop? Something that might have a teddy bear? Nicky seems to have left his favorite in the Los Angeles airport, and we've been hearing about it all the way."

Jessamyn Arden gave a sniff, as if annoyed that she wasn't the center of attention. "And how," she muttered.

Chase glanced at her, one eyebrow raised.

Jessamyn fluttered her eyelashes apologetically at him

and turned to the young woman. "If you'd been watching him properly, Sally, as a nanny ought—"

"He must have hidden the stupid thing on purpose," the younger woman said. "And what you know about being a nanny would fit in a teaspoon, so—"

Reminded of his loss, the child started to wail again, and in seconds his face was screwed up into a red mask. Amanda noticed, however, that he didn't close his eyes completely. His face was no longer buried in his father's sweater, and he seemed to be assessing his impact on the audience.

"That's enough, Nicholas," Chase Worthington said unemotionally.

The shrieks died into whimpers once more.

Quite a professional performance, Amanda thought. "The gift shop is around that corner," she said, pointing.

Chase lifted the child into his arms. "Thank you, Miss…"

"Bailey," she said almost unwillingly. "Amanda Bailey."

He repeated her name softly and smiled at her again. "Come along now, Nicky. We'll see if we can find a replacement."

"No wonder he doesn't take care of his things," the nanny said under her breath. "When there's always another one…"

She might well be right, Amanda thought. As his nanny, the woman was obviously in a better position to judge the situation than she was. On the other hand, the child was only four….

She realized that the desk clerk was practically paralyzed with awe, so she reached for the guest book and spun it around for Jessamyn Arden to sign. "Take Miss Arden up to suite sixty-three,'' she told the bellman, and the clerk jumped for the key and handed it over.

Jessamyn signed her name with a flourish. "A dinky place like this has sixty-three suites?" she said.

"Or rooms," Amanda said pleasantly. One problem down, she thought as Jessamyn followed the bellman across the lobby. But what was she to do with Chase Worthington's son and his nanny? She couldn't simply assume he intended them to share his suite, but since he hadn't made other arrangements...

She wasn't aware she was still holding the coffee shop's ten-dollar bill until Stephanie took it out of her hand and passed it to the desk clerk. "I'll take care of getting Kathy's change," she said briskly. "Obviously you're overwhelmed by work, Mandy. Or something like that."

Amanda bit her tongue, hard.

Chase came back to the lobby. Behind him trailed Nicky, dragging a brand-new, lop-eared stuffed rabbit. It obviously wouldn't look brand-new for long. The child's face still held a trace of sullen stubbornness, as if he'd accepted the animal only grudgingly. But Chase seemed contented; he was dusting his hands together with satisfaction as he approached the desk.

"Mr. Worthington will be in suite sixty-seven," Amanda told the desk clerk, then turned to Chase. "I didn't realize you were bringing an entourage, so I'm afraid..."

Two small wrinkles appeared in his brow. "I asked for a large suite."

"That's the largest we have, two bedrooms and a sitting room. But—"

"That will do just fine. Sally and Nicky will share a room."

Amanda beckoned to the bellman, who had returned to

the lobby and was wheeling a luggage cart toward the freight elevator in the service wing.

He looked confused. "But Miss Bailey, the lady was awfully anxious to get her bags, and I promised I'd bring them right up."

The cart was piled high with suitcases, at least a dozen of them, all sleek dark green leather. "Those are all Miss Arden's?" Amanda said faintly.

He nodded.

She sighed. "All right, John. Go ahead." She took a pair of big brass keys from the desk clerk. "I'll show you up myself, Mr. Worthington."

Though the old-fashioned elevator had been converted to self-service, there had been no way to make it larger or faster. The close quarters had never disturbed Amanda before, but today she felt almost stifled, and the ride to the sixth floor seemed never to have taken so long.

She stared at the grillwork in the elevator door and tried to ignore the sensual aura that radiated from the corner where Chase Worthington stood. She'd never experienced anything of the sort before; the man generated a sort of personal force field that was even more intense in a confined space.

She sneaked a sidelong glance at him. He was leaning against the wood-paneled wall with his eyes closed.

It's your imagination, she told herself firmly. He's not trying to create a sensation. But of course that was the problem; he didn't have to try.

A soft, slightly sticky hand gently stroked her arm, and Amanda felt a twinge deep inside as she looked down into Nicky's big hazel eyes. Poor little guy, she thought. He was obviously worn out, so perhaps he wasn't really as spoiled as he'd first appeared.

Despite his dirty face, he really was a handsome child,

with the longest dark eyelashes she'd ever seen on a small boy. His skin was fair, with a soft flush across his high cheekbones, and there were a few freckles sprinkled on the bridge of his nose. His eyebrows were as dark as his hair, and their aristocratic arch would have told her he could be stubborn even if his conduct hadn't already given him away. His mouth was soft and finely shaped—

"Don't bother the lady, Nicky," the nanny said sharply.

Amanda started to speak, then thought better of it.

Chase opened his eyes. "Come here, Nicky." He swung the child up into his arms. "You're tired out, aren't you, buddy?"

Nicky shook his head defiantly, but a moment later he snuggled his face into his father's neck, and by the time they reached the door of the suite, his eyelashes lay heavily against his flushed cheeks.

Amanda unlocked the door and led the way immediately to the larger of the two bedrooms. "If you need protective rails for his bed, we've got some in the storage room," she said.

Chase glanced around the room and carefully laid the child on the double bed farthest from the door. "He'll be fine."

Amanda tugged a blanket from the bottom drawer of a big chest and draped it gently across Nicky. He whimpered a little.

"I'll just have to get him up for his bath and his dinner," the nanny said.

Chase frowned. "It seems to me you'll have an easier time with both if you let him sleep a while first."

The nanny's eyes snapped, but she said, "Yes, sir."

Amanda handed her one of the keys to the suite. "The restaurant is open from six in the morning to midnight. We also have room service—not quite around the clock, I'm afraid, but I think you'll find it adequate." She led Chase back to the cozy sitting room and pointed at a door. "The other bedroom is through there. It's smaller, but it has a king-size bed. I thought—"

"Thank you, Miss Bailey." His voice was almost a drawl. "I appreciate your consideration."

Amanda felt herself turning red. All she'd meant to say was that Nicky and his nanny would be more comfortable in the double room. She hadn't expressed it very well, true, but it wasn't necessary for Chase Worthington to turn a simple statement into a suggestive one! She said stiffly, "The kitchenette is stocked with fruit and cheese, and if there's anything else you'd like—" She stopped abruptly, wondering what he'd make of that opening.

But Chase said only, "I can't think of a thing at the moment."

Amanda gave him the other key and moved toward the door. She'd made sure everything was in place a couple of hours ago when she'd brought the fruit basket up, and she was grateful that there was no need to check the rooms now. She couldn't quite imagine strolling through Chase Worthington's bedroom, with him right behind her, to make sure the proper number of towels were hanging in his bath! "I hope you'll enjoy your stay."

He shrugged. "Well, that depends on how the work goes. I don't mean to sound ungracious, but Springhill wasn't my choice. If this movie wasn't a sequel to the one we shot here a few years ago, I doubt I'd have ever set foot in the place again."

Amanda nodded. "The natives like it, but Springhill isn't exactly an exhilarating experience for visitors. It will be far livelier than usual with the production company around. I wasn't here the year you did *Winter of the Heart,* so I'm looking forward to all the excitement I missed then."

"I hope we don't disappoint you." His tone was dry.

"I'm sure you won't." He was obviously very tired and probably anxious to be alone. But as she paused with one hand on the doorknob, an impulse beyond her control made her say, "I'm sorry about Mrs. Worthington."

He nodded curtly, but said nothing.

Amanda quietly let herself out of the suite. That was dumb, she thought. What had made her say that? As if it would matter to Chase Worthington, two full years after his wife's death, that a complete stranger felt sorry about his loss!

Stephanie was still in the lobby, sitting on the arm of a wing chair and patiently waiting for the locations manager to show up. The limousine driver was standing beside her. "I thought I was going to go deaf," he was saying as Amanda crossed the lobby. "The kid carried on like that all the way from the airport. I got the impression he'd done it all the way from Los Angeles."

"Considering how impossible my own offspring can be," Stephanie murmured, "I should bite my tongue. But that is a thoroughly disagreeable child."

"You're right," Amanda said.

Stephanie's eyes went wide. "You agree with me?"

"Oh, yes—I think you *should* bite your tongue." And I ought to shut up, as well. But she went on, anyway. "Nicky Worthington is four years old and he's in a strange new place and he's lost his favorite teddy. Maybe you should at least wait till tomorrow to decide he's impossible."

"Ouch." Stephanie made a face and followed her to the registration desk. "You win. I apologize. But I still suspect I'm right, and if you're thinking of trying to rescue that child, Mandy, give it up."

Amanda straightened a stack of papers. "Rescue him from what?" she asked, the question directed more to herself than to Stephanie. "And even if I thought he needed rescuing, what business would it be of mine?"

"None," Stephanie said crisply. "And it's going to be a very long four weeks if you don't remember that."

The desk clerk put the telephone down and inserted a message slip into a mailbox. "I didn't even know Chase Worthington had a kid."

"You didn't? Oh, you're new in town, aren't you, Tricia? So of course you don't know all the background." Stephanie propped her elbows on the marble slab that formed the front of the registration counter. "Well, let me fill you in."

"Are you indulging in gossip, Stephanie?" Amanda asked.

"Of course not. I'm giving necessary information to an important member of your staff so she doesn't slip and put her foot in her mouth." She turned back to the clerk. "When Chase Worthington and Desiree Hunt came to Springhill a few years ago to film *Winter of the Heart,* they—"

"Desiree Hunt?" Tricia said. "Isn't she the one who—"

"Don't get ahead of me," Stephanie warned. "You'll mix me up. When they came to make the movie that spring, Desiree Hunt was also Mrs. Chase Worthington. A couple of months after the film was done, their baby boy was born, and two years later—"

"I've seen that movie," Tricia objected. "She doesn't look pregnant."

"No, she doesn't," Stephanie agreed. "She was delighted with herself for keeping it hidden. She did such a good job of concealment, in fact, that there were rumors at the time that the baby wasn't hers at all."

Tricia looked confused.

Amanda thought it time to step in. "All the tabloids

made it sound as if something fishy was going on," she explained. "You know the sort of thing they pass off as news."

Stephanie looked at her in surprise. "You amaze me, Mandy. Don't tell me you're a closet fan, after all!"

"I admit I read magazine covers while I'm waiting in line at the supermarket. Doesn't everybody? But that doesn't make me any kind of fan—it's just impossible to avoid the man's name."

"And here I thought you didn't even watch his show."

"Of course I do, sometimes." Amanda smiled. "When there's nothing else worth watching."

Stephanie looked at her thoughtfully for a moment and then turned back to Tricia. "At any rate, the tabloids hinted that the baby was Chase's love child, and suggested Desiree had adopted him."

The usual scurrilous trash, in other words, Amanda thought. She reached for the pile of afternoon mail and started to sort it.

"It made a great story," Stephanie went on, "though personally I think there was nothing to it. Desiree was playing a sixteen-year-old, and of course the producer would have had a fit if he'd discovered halfway through the filming that she was pregnant. At any rate, just about two years ago she was flying to Hawaii to do another movie when the plane crashed— Oh, here's the locations manager, finally. I've got to go." She met him halfway across the lobby and with a casual wave vanished out the front door.

"I remember that crash," Tricia said. "There were several actors on the plane, weren't there?"

"Hmm?" Amanda considered the stack of bills and sighed. "Yes, there were."

"But why is Chase here now?"

"Because this movie's a sequel to *Winter of the Heart*."

"I know that. I mean, why would he do it? Won't it bring back all kinds of bad memories?"

Amanda looked up from the last envelope and thought about what Chase had said upstairs, about not wanting to come back. Still, he could have turned down the job. The fact that he hadn't engendered all sorts of intriguing possibilities. "Maybe he hopes it will bring back good ones, instead."

"Oh." Tricia sighed. "I hadn't thought of that. Coming back to the place they were so happy and bringing his little boy... That's awfully romantic."

Yes, it was. Amanda wondered if that was why Chase had reacted as he had, with that curt nod, when she'd brought up the subject of Desiree. "Go ahead on your dinner break if you like. I can take care of the desk and these bills at the same time."

But she didn't get much work done. Jessamyn Arden called to complain that her room was too warm, and Amanda sent the bellman up to check the air conditioner. A couple of crew members who were bunking together reported a lack of towels, and the hotel handyman came down from the last available guest room to report that the leak in the hot-water pipes was beyond his ability to fix. Amanda took one look at his water-soaked uniform and decided the matter was critical. She was on the telephone trying to reach a plumber when Chase approached the registration desk.

She cupped her hand over the phone. "I'll be with you in a minute."

"I'm in no hurry." His voice was lazy. He reached across the desk for the daily newspaper that lay beside the telephone, and his hand brushed her arm.

Amanda felt the contact like a jolt of electricity. It took all the poise she possessed not to jump or pull away. Instead, she handed him the other sections of the paper, trying to look calm. She was grateful that the plumber came to the phone just then so she didn't have to say anything more.

Chase leaned against the desk with his back to her, ankles crossed, apparently absorbed in the front page and completely unaware of her. But she couldn't keep from looking at him. His hair seemed so soft that her fingertips itched to touch it, and the strong line of his profile begged to be traced.

She swallowed hard. This was embarrassing. She hadn't felt like this about a man since…

I've *never* felt this way about a man, she admitted.

It wasn't that there had never been any males in her life, either, whatever Stephanie seemed to think. But none of them, no matter how attractive, had ever caused her to react the way Chase made her react. And all he'd had to do was appear in the same room and breathe the same air.

And why should she be surprised about that? If Stephanie was right, half the women in Springhill had already gone nuts over Chase Worthington; it'd be no wonder if he conquered the other half by the time he left town. There was something very unusual about the man, as if he produced some magic chemical that attracted females as surely as nectar drew bees.

Keep your distance, Amanda, she warned herself. It's none of your affair how attractive Chase Worthington is, any more than it's your business how he brings up his son. As long as she remembered to follow her own rules, she'd have no trouble.

She noticed how wide and strong his shoulders were under the cotton sweater and how his hair swirled sleekly away from the crown of his head.

And she knew that despite her determination, Stephanie was right. With this man under the same roof, it was going to be a very long four weeks.

CHAPTER TWO

CHASE LOWERED the newspaper and looked at Amanda over the edge of it. "This *is* a small town, isn't it?"

The remark was so far from anything she'd expected that it took her off guard. "What?" Oh, great. She sounded almost panicky. "I'm sorry, I don't quite know what you mean."

Chase folded the paper and handed it back to her. "Getting a plumber to come at this hour of the day is a miracle."

Amanda shrugged. "I called his house and caught him at dinner."

"That's what I mean. The plumbers I've encountered all have unlisted home phone numbers."

"Well, the inn is a fair-sized account for Springhill."

Chase propped one elbow on the marble counter. "Tell me about the other advantages of small towns."

When he smiled, the impact of his personal appeal was even stronger. The skin at the corners of his eyes crinkled invitingly, and his face seemed to glow. She'd never noticed before, despite all the photographs she'd seen, that one of his canine teeth was slightly crooked. The tiny imperfection lent him a rakish charm that no perfect smile could possess.

Amanda felt a little dizzy. It was a good thing they hadn't figured out a way to broadcast that personal radiance, or the feminine half of the nation would come to a screeching halt on Thursday nights during his show.

The soft chime of the telephone drew her attention to the switchboard. By the time she transferred the call to the requested room, she still hadn't regained her balance—but she could at least pretend that the way he looked at her wasn't turning her insides to jelly.

Chase had propped both elbows on the marble counter and put his chin in his hands. It was the kind of pose someone Nicky's age might assume when studying a fascinating object, and Amanda wondered if he realized it. "Do you do everything here?" he asked.

"I can. I started as a chambermaid."

"And worked your way up to manager?" He sounded a bit doubtful that the position was much of an improvement.

Amanda lifted her chin. "Did you come down to chat about jobs, Mr. Worthington?"

"Not exactly. I'm looking for a bookstore. The gift shop's closed, and I just realized I have a whole evening ahead of me and nothing to read."

"Not even a script to memorize?"

He shook his head. "That would be a waste of time. It's been through four revisions already, and no doubt they'll still be changing lines as we're shooting. Tonight I just want something relaxing, and Nicky's copy of *Green Eggs and Ham* isn't going to do it."

Amanda smiled. "Well, there's good news and bad news."

"Somehow I was afraid of that."

"We've got a lovely bookstore just a few blocks away. But it's already closed for the day."

The liquid brown eyes were full of hope. "And you know the owner's home phone number?"

"Yes," Amanda admitted. "I also know that he plays softball every Monday evening, so—"

"Damn."

The switchboard chimed again, with an internal call this time. As Amanda picked up the phone, Jessamyn Arden's suite number appeared on the computer screen. Please, not the air-conditioning again. It was August, and though Springhill was overdue for a heat wave, the weather had been pleasant and not at all humid. To tell the truth, Jessamyn would probably be more comfortable if she shut the air-conditioning off and opened the windows.

"I want a new television delivered," Jessamyn demanded.

There were two in her suite; surely they hadn't both gone on the blink. "Which set are you having a problem with, Miss Arden?"

"Both of them. They're too small. I can hardly see the screen."

For one mad instant, Amanda considered suggesting Jessamyn have her eyes checked. Instead, she said calmly, "Those are the largest we have in the hotel, but I'll see if I can get a different set for you first thing tomorrow."

Jessamyn Arden didn't even respond; she simply hung up.

Chase said thoughtfully, "You aren't going to dig into your bag of home phone numbers for Jessie? I'm sure you know someone who sells televisions."

Amanda eyed him warily. He sounded calm enough, but if she said the wrong thing now and he mentioned it to Jessamyn Arden or the producer, there could be all kinds of backlash. "If I didn't reserve panic calls for emergencies, I wouldn't have any friends left," she admitted. "And since the televisions she's got are both working, I thought—"

"I hope you consider books an emergency," he said earnestly.

"Look, Mr. Worthington, I can't call the softball field

because there isn't a telephone.'' She saw the twinkle in his eyes and started to laugh. ''All right, you can cut out the manipulation. I've got a library of my own. I'll bring up some books for you later.''

''Later?''

''After the desk clerk gets back from her dinner break. I can't just go off and leave the inn to run itself.''

''That's very sweet of you to take the trouble to go home and bring books back for me.'' His smile was very different than the one she'd seen before. This one was soft and intimate, as if they shared some special secret.

Amanda swallowed hard. Don't look at him, she ordered herself. Then she couldn't possibly get in trouble—could she?

''It's no great effort,'' she said. She hoped he wouldn't notice the breathless edge to her voice. ''I have an apartment on the second floor.''

''You live right here in the hotel?''

She nodded. ''It's part of my job to be available most of the time. What sort of books do you like?''

He leaned against the desk and parried, ''What have you got?''

''It's a pretty wide assortment. Do you like mysteries? Bestsellers? Nonfiction?''

He nodded. ''All of them,'' he said simply. ''May I be rude and ask to browse?''

Amanda hesitated. But what real reason did she have to refuse? She could hardly tell Chase Worthington she was afraid to be alone in a room with him—he'd no doubt find that revelation plenty amusing. And though she had long been convinced that the contents of a person's bookshelves revealed character in a way nothing else, short of psychoanalysis, could, she wasn't about to tell him that, either. It would only pique his interest, and that was the last thing she wanted to do. The kooky way she reacted to him was bad enough, but surely it would pass in a day or two; there wasn't any point in making things worse by rousing Chase's curiosity.

No. Now that she'd admitted the existence of her library, she'd better be graceful about letting him use it. He wasn't interested in anything more than a suspenseful novel to while away a dull evening, anyway.

"Oh, why not?" she said almost to herself. "I'll call you when I'm free."

"I'll just wait. I haven't anything better to do."

"You might enjoy a walk around town. It's completely safe, even after dark."

He shook a finger at her. "Careful. Someone might think you're trying to get rid of me."

Amanda gave up. The desk clerk would be back in a few minutes, anyway.

Only when Tricia returned did Amanda realize that taking Chase up to her apartment would make a wonderful tidbit for the inn's grapevine, and by then it was a little late to fret about it. Rather than wait for the elevator, she took him up the service stairs behind the registration desk.

"Not the most elegant corner of the building, is it?" Chase observed.

The staircase could use a fresh coat of paint, she realized. Funny how easy it was to miss that sort of thing when one saw it every day. On the landing, she pulled open the fire door.

Chase looked down the long paneled hallway. "How old is this place, anyway?"

"It was built around the turn of the century."

"Well, overall it's in much better shape than it was four years ago."

"Yes, we've done a great deal of work in the past couple

of years. The suites are all new, and most of the rooms are larger.''

''Are you a partner?''

''No, just the manager. But I've been allowed almost a free hand by the owners, and I'm very proud of what we've accomplished. An inn in a town this size isn't often a profitable venture, but we've done some innovative things.''

''For instance?''

He really sounded interested, Amanda marveled. ''Well, since we had more space than the hotel business demands, we've added a number of apartments for permanent residents—like this one.'' She unlocked the door and led the way into a cozy sitting room with a gas-log fireplace and a kitchenette tucked in the far end.

Chase paused on the threshold. ''It looks just like my suite. The floor plan, I mean.''

Amanda nodded. ''It's on the same corner of the building. Up on the top floor, however, you can look out over the town and the river and the surrounding countryside. Down here, I have a view of the air-conditioning plant and the parking lot.'' She smiled. ''That's why the apartment is rent-free to the resident manager. I'm not complaining, you understand—the walls are so thick even midnight garbage pickups don't disturb me.''

In a large wire cage in a corner of the sitting room right next to the kitchenette, a bright-eyed blue parakeet leapt onto a swinging perch and let out a wolf whistle. When Amanda didn't answer, he tipped his head to one side and said tentatively, ''Play ball?''

''Later, Floyd,'' she said as she opened a door at the side of the sitting room and flicked on a light.

The smaller of the two bedrooms had been converted to a den. Two walls were lined with adjustable bookshelves, and a small desk gave her a place to retreat when the office downstairs was too busy for concentration. A rocking chair occupied a corner, and a convertible couch provided an extra bed for guests. At the moment, however, there was no space for it to be pulled out, because taking up the entire center of the room was a standard-size crib.

Chase looked from it to the rocking chair to the low shelves full of children's books. "You have a baby?"

She thought she heard the barest hint of incredulity in his voice. And was it her imagination, or was he really looking at her ringless left hand, which was hovering at eye level as she reached for a book from the nearest set of shelves?

"I kept a friend's toddler over the weekend," she said. "The bellman was supposed to take the crib back to the storage room today, but apparently he didn't have time."

"Jessamyn kept him too busy stowing her bags, no doubt." Chase didn't sound interested anymore, and his gaze slid over the books. "Good heavens, that's the earliest *Dr. Seuss* I've ever seen. Is it a first edition?"

"Probably."

"What do you mean *probably?* Do you know what it's worth if it is?"

Amanda shrugged. "I don't really care. I like the book."

"Well, that's an enlightened view of collecting." He moved on to a higher shelf. "I haven't seen a copy of this in years, either."

"There is some order to the way things are arranged," she began.

He didn't look up. "No, don't tell me. I'm having too much fun just exploring."

Amanda leaned against the door and watched as he moved around the room. She had expected him to head straight for the bright-colored paperbacks—the thrillers and bestsellers and mysteries, the kind of thing he'd have found at the bookstore. But he seemed more interested in the older volumes—not classics necessarily, but the kind of books Amanda had held on to because she might want to reread them someday.

He settled for an old whodunit and a collection of short stories, but looked longingly at a shelf that held an astounding array of recent political books. Amanda pulled a volume down and handed it to him.

He looked at the cover and smiled. ''Thanks. How'd you know I'm fascinated by the Kennedys? You're a lifesaver, Amanda.''

She hesitated, wondering if he had noticed what he had called her. Names didn't matter, she told herself. And neither did this tiny favor. He might read a few of her books, but it didn't make them friends, and she'd be wise to remember that. She snapped off the light and pulled the door shut.

The parakeet glared at them and grumped, ''Dirty bird.''

Chase paused and looked at the cage. ''What did you say his name is? Floyd?''

Amanda nodded. ''Odd name for a bird, isn't it? He's actually Pretty Boy Floyd.''

''He's named for a criminal?''

''I suppose so. Don't look at me, I'm not the one who chose it. He belonged to one of our long-term residents who died last winter.''

''And you inherited the bird?''

''Well, someone had to take care of him. I'd known Mrs. Henderson for years, ever since I started cleaning her apartment when I was in high school. So I knew all her birds, too, and—''

''I thought you'd only come to town recently.''

She was puzzled for a moment. ''No. I grew up in Springhill.''

"But if you weren't here four years ago when we did *Winter of the Heart*…"

She had said that, but she hadn't expected him to remember. Apparently Chase Worthington was a better listener than she'd given him credit for. She kept her voice level. "I was away at college. By the time I came home for the summer, the production was finished and all the excitement was over."

Floyd shrieked and demanded, "Play ball!"

"Sorry, Floyd. No games on television tonight." Amanda saw a smile tug at the corner of Chase's mouth. "It sounds pretty strange to reason with a bird, doesn't it? Baseball is one of his favorite things. Mrs. Henderson was a big fan, and Floyd not only imitates the umpires, but he whistles the first seven notes of *The Star-Spangled Banner*."

"I'll bite. Why exactly seven?"

"I suppose it's all his attention span could absorb. It's enough to drive you absolutely nuts, since seven notes isn't a whole phrase and it ends on a ghastly high note that leads nowhere. Think about it." She crossed the sitting room and opened the door to the hallway. "Enjoy the books, Mr. Worthington."

He stopped in the doorway. "Don't you think you should stop calling me that?"

Amanda could feel the flutter of a pulse in her throat. "Any special reason?"

"Because it makes me sound like a stranger, and I'm sure you don't usually loan your books to people you don't know and like. Good night, Amanda." He strolled off down the hall, softly whistling *The Star-Spangled Banner*. He paused after the seventh note and started over once more.

That was no surprise, she thought. Floyd had struck again.

Amanda closed the door and stood there for a full minute, leaning against it. Then, even though she wasn't hungry, she made herself a sandwich and carried it into the small sitting room. Floyd peered through the wires of his cage at her plate, and automatically Amanda broke off a bit of bread crust and a sliver of lettuce and put it in his food dish.

She kicked off her shoes and sank down on the deep couch. Two bites later she set the plate on the flat-topped antique trunk that served as a coffee table and put her feet up beside it.

She'd thought she'd been prepared.

It would be easy, she'd told herself. Chase Worthington would be just another guest. She would treat him as she had treated all the inn's guests during her years as manager. She would address him with respect, do her best to fill any special needs and leave him alone.

She had never anticipated that he might not leave her alone.

"Oh, be reasonable, Amanda!" she told herself crossly. "He wanted something, and he charmed you into providing it!" Only a fool would jump to the conclusion that he found her so personally attractive that he'd be sitting on her doorstep for the next four weeks. Even if he was vaguely interested, the man had a job to do. She'd gotten a glimpse of the shooting schedule. It was obvious to anyone that starting tomorrow Chase Worthington would be too busy working to have time for much else—even his son.

She was surprised, in fact, that he'd brought Nicky with him. It didn't seem a reasonable trade at all, to drag the child halfway across the country to a completely new place, away from his familiar routine, for the sake of a few minutes a day of his father's time. The unhappiness in

Nicky's face today seemed to say he agreed; he would rather have stayed at home.

But then Nicky Worthington's life had never been exactly normal, Amanda reflected. His picture had been on the cover of *Today's Woman* magazine before he was a month old. He'd gone on location with Desiree Hunt a few weeks after that. And he'd been barely two when her plane crashed....

Amanda moved her plate, opened the trunk and took out the antique quilt she kept there. Underneath was a pile of fat scrapbooks. She opened one and slowly began to turn the pages.

She hadn't paid any attention to Chase Worthington before *Winter of the Heart*. He'd been just another of the handsome men on the daytime soap operas, and they all looked alike to Amanda. But when the movie project was announced, and Springhill was named as the site...

Even though she hadn't been in Springhill during the filming, Amanda had felt a personal interest in the project because it was her hometown. She had faithfully read the articles from the local newspaper, waited impatiently for *Winter of the Heart* to be shown and cried along with the rest of the nation at the tragic ending. She knew what Stephanie had meant about feeling possessive about Chase; Amanda, too, had begun to feel a personal interest in the stars, as if they somehow belonged to Springhill. She had read with interest about Nicky, and she had watched with fascination in the following years as the Worthingtons' careers had soared. She'd even started to clip and save the articles about Chase's television series, Desiree's increasingly prominent parts in feature films—and the crash.

The earliest articles she'd clipped were beginning to turn yellow already. Amanda hadn't known back then how to properly protect newsprint; she'd glued the stories into a cheap scrapbook, and the acid-filled paper had done its damage before she learned there were better ways.

She'd even clipped a few of the scandalous stories Stephanie had mentioned. ''Chase Dupes Desiree!'' one of them shrieked. Another trumpeted, ''He's Not Desiree's Baby!'' She turned past those without reading them and stopped to look at the cover of *Today's Woman*—Desiree Hunt, gorgeous in a figure-hugging exercise suit, cradling three-week-old Nicky.

When she saw that photograph, Amanda had to smile, for Nicky looked puzzled and a little cross-eyed, his thatch of dark hair standing on end and his aristocratic eyebrows arched as if he was wondering what the heck those bright lights were for, anyway.

There was the story and photographs of the wreckage of Desiree Hunt's plane, and the tabloid stories about the other women in Chase Worthington's life since his wife's death. Of course if those reports were all true, Amanda thought, the man wouldn't have time left over to shave in the mornings, much less do any work!

And then there were the recent articles—the renewal of Chase's television show for another year and all the hoopla in the Springhill newspaper about the sequel to *Winter of the Heart*. They were calling it *Diamonds in the Dew,* and by the time the shooting was over, the newspaper said, millions of dollars would have been dropped into Springhill's economy. The production company would buy food and lodging and materials; it would rent houses and apartments for sets; it would hire extras by the dozens. The effects would ripple through the local economy for months to come.

And when it was all over and that ripple had settled once more into smooth water, there would be little left to remind them that it had ever happened. The extras would have memories of the day they had shared sets with the stars; Stephanie Kendall would have new wallpaper; Amanda Bailey would have a fatter scrapbook. That was all.

"And don't forget it," she told herself fiercely. "You never thought you'd meet him. And even though you have, it doesn't change anything at all."

SHE DIDN'T FIND IT difficult to keep her distance from Chase Worthington. In the next two days she saw him exactly three times—once in the early morning as he boarded the minivan the production company had rented to transport the cast to the shooting site, once sharing an ice-cream soda with Nicky in the coffee shop, and once in the late evening when he returned her books to the registration desk.

He'd looked tired that night, and when she'd asked if he wanted to borrow anything else, he's simply shaken his head and rubbed the bridge of his nose as if his head hurt. "No time," he'd said. "I've got that damned script to read these days."

It was no more than she'd expected, of course. And it was just as well, too, not to have her fantasies fed by any closer contact. It was completely insane of her to want to draw him close and rub his back and soothe him till he wasn't tired anymore.

Still, she couldn't help a sense of sadness. Even apart from the crazy breathless way he made her feel, she had enjoyed that brief hour in her library.

She saw Nicky more frequently, however, going in and out of the hotel with his nanny. And she heard him, too, shrieking defiance in the halls and throwing toys down the stairwell and, once, laughing uproariously.

She had stopped her work entirely the afternoon she heard that. Nicky's laugh was a wonderful sound, half chuckle and half gurgle and altogether infectious.

But that was the only time she heard him laugh, and by Wednesday she was beginning to think she'd mistaken some other child's glee for his. Either Nicky Worthington was the most spoiled child in the western hemisphere, she had concluded, or he was miserable. And there didn't seem to be any way to find out which.

She left the half-finished payroll on her desk and took a coffee break. The waitress was talking to a male customer at the counter, and she didn't see Amanda come in. "They want me in the movie," Kathy was saying to him. "Can you believe it?"

"What kind of a part?" the customer asked.

"Oh, just an extra. I told them they'd better think real careful about it, because I can't be in two places at the same time, and they sure all like this restaurant."

"Well, it's obvious why they like it."

Kathy giggled.

Amanda went behind the counter to get her own coffee, and her ears perked up as the man said, "What do you think of Chase Worthington?"

She filled her cup and slowly turned around to survey him. She hadn't seen him before; she knew she'd have remembered those sharp eyes and the way his ears stood slightly away from his head. She carried her cup around the counter and took the stool two down from his. "You're new in town," she said.

He turned to look her over. "Yeah. But the more I see around here, the more I think I'll stay awhile."

The oily jerk assumes we're all hicks eager for a little masculine attention, she thought. "You're with the production company?"

"On the fringes," he admitted modestly.

"What's your job?"

"Public relations. You know, getting press releases out and that sort of thing."

Amanda sipped her coffee. "That's interesting."

"What's yours?"

"I'm the hotel manager."

"Ah. I don't suppose you'd have an extra room tucked away, now would you?" His voice was almost wheedling. "I didn't know I was coming till the last minute, and so I didn't make a reservation in time."

"We're booked full, I'm afraid. You might try the next town."

Kathy had put both hands on her hips. "How about the Chamber of Commerce, Amanda? They were putting together that list—"

Amanda cut her off. "It's only thirty miles, and there's a little motel there that…well, I'm sure it's clean."

The customer shifted uneasily. "But you see—" his voice dropped to a confidential murmur "—I'm not just putting out the good news, you understand. My job is keeping certain things under wraps, if you know what I mean."

"I'm not sure I do, Mr.…" Amanda looked at him inquisitively.

"Smith. Joe Smith. You know how it is when a bunch of city folks, especially film people, hit a little town like this. They sometimes get just a bit out of control, and we wouldn't want that news to get around, would we? Now say, for instance, that Chase Worthington was to have too much to drink in the hotel bar one night and embarrass himself, well, we wouldn't want a story like that to get out, would we? It wouldn't look good for a clean-cut hero like Chase."

Amanda shook her head. "No, I can see that it wouldn't."

The customer seemed to mull the situation over. "You

know, you could help me with that," he said finally. "I
mean, as the hotel manager, you'll be in a position to know
everything that's going on."

"Embarrassing things," Amanda said musingly. "And I
could help you keep them quiet."

"Exactly. You let me know in time to do something
about those things, and I'd be prepared to pay something
for your help."

"I imagine a story like that would be worth quite a lot
to the right people."

"Well, yes, it would. That's why it's important that we
get there first, ahead of the other—" He stopped abruptly.

"The other tabloids?" Amanda asked sweetly. "Is that
what you were going to say, Mr. Smith? Which one of
those sleazy rags do you work for, by the way?"

"I beg your pardon! I didn't say—"

"Oh, come on. You're not doing public relations for this
movie, because there isn't such a department. In a town the
size of Springhill, if the production company wanted a pub-
lic-relations office, the publisher of the local newspaper
would volunteer his time—and his whole staff. Honestly,
you'd better work up another cover story if you expect to
dig up any dirt around here." She picked up her coffee cup
and started for the door.

"You can call it dirt if you like, but people like to read
it," he said to her back. "And it's still worth money, so
any time you change your mind, Miss Hotel Manager…"

Kathy's mouth had dropped open. She snapped it shut
and reached for a broom. "Time to get rid of the filth,"
she said coldly, and started toward him.

Joe Smith didn't wait to see if she meant it. Amanda
held the restaurant door open for him. "Don't worry about
your coffee," she said kindly. "I'll pay for it myself, so
don't feel you have to stick around any longer."

As Mr. Smith vanished out the door, Kathy sat down on the end stool and groaned. "I can't believe I let him take me in like that. I thought he was buttering me up because he liked the pie so much."

"He had pie, too? Oh, well, put it on my bill. It was worth it to see him routed like that." But Amanda soon stopped laughing. Mr. Smith—or whatever his name actually was—probably wouldn't stay down for long. And though the majority of the people in Springhill were delighted by the production, there were no doubt a few who would tell stories—or even make them up—if the money involved was substantial enough.

The elevator reached the lobby and the Worthingtons' nanny stepped out. Nicky followed her just as the door started to close again. He got clear, but the rabbit he was dragging by one ear wasn't quite as lucky; its fuzzy tail, too small for the door sensors to recognize, was caught. Nicky tugged, and the tail popped loose, sending him tumbling onto the carpet. He bumped his head against an ashtray stand and began to wail, a low cry that escalated like a tornado siren.

The nanny turned around and put her hands on her hips. "Nicky, that's enough. Now get up and come along, or I'm going to leave you right here."

Amanda dropped to her knees beside the child. "It's all right, darling, don't cry." Her fingers sought the back of his head to check for a bump; she didn't think he'd hit hard enough to hurt himself, but it was possible. "Is your bunny injured?"

Distracted, Nicky stopped wailing and checked the rabbit's tail. "I don't think so." He licked his lips and looked up at her. "But my head hurts."

The back of his neck felt hot, and his eyes were bright—

fever-bright, Amanda thought. Those things hadn't been caused by a bump on the head.

"Nicholas," the nanny called. "I'm waiting."

Amanda stroked Nicky's curls back from his forehead and looked thoughtfully at a watery little protrusion, rather like a blister, on his temple. "This child is sick."

The nanny sniffed. "That is one of his favorite tricks when there's something he doesn't want to do."

Amanda bit her lip and counted to ten. "Developing a fever on command is a trick most schoolchildren would kill to learn," she said evenly. "Somehow I doubt Nicky's managed to figure it out. Why don't you take him back upstairs and put him to bed? If you don't have a thermometer, I'll be happy to bring one up."

The nanny said, "I'll thank you not to tell me how to do my job. Come along, Nicky."

Amanda stooped and lifted the child into her arms. His compact little body was heavier than she'd expected, perhaps because he was so limp in her grasp. His face just fit in the curve of her neck; the sensation of heat against her skin frightened her.

The nanny's voice was sharp. "What do you think you're doing?"

"I'm going to take care of Nicky. Why don't you just go about whatever it was you'd planned?"

"This is...this is kidnapping!" the nanny shrieked. "Wait till I tell Mr. Worthington what you're doing!"

Amanda gritted her teeth. "Please do," she said. "And tell him I'll be waiting for him, too."

CHAPTER THREE

AT THE REGISTRATION desk, Tricia was almost leaning over the marble counter in her effort to take in the whole scene. Amanda punched the elevator call button. "When Mr. Worthington comes in, Tricia, send him up to my apartment. He knows the way."

The elevator door closed long before Tricia's mouth did. Not that Amanda particularly cared what Tricia thought. And as for that so-called nanny...!

She stripped the quilted coverlet off her bed and put Nicky down on the cool sheets. He stirred and said, "Is Nanny coming?"

"I don't know, dear. But your daddy will be here before long."

Nicky seemed to think that over, but all he said was, "Can I have a drink of water?"

"Just as soon as I take your temperature." She was shaking down the thermometer as she spoke. Nicky looked unhappy about it, but before he could decide to make a fuss, she slipped the cool glass rod under his tongue and gathered him close, stroking his hair while she waited. He resisted for only an instant before he relaxed in her arms.

He was too docile, she thought. The child she had seen throw tantrums at the drop of a toy would not have submitted so casually to being snatched away from his nanny by a virtual stranger. Was he even sicker than she thought?

But his fever wasn't as high as she had feared, and she

found three more tiny blisterlike spots on his face, where his curls had covered them. A minute later he spilled his glass of water, and when Amanda took his wet shirt off she saw a dozen more spots on his chest and stomach, surrounded by angry red marks where he'd been rubbing. It was almost a relief; at least now she knew what she was dealing with.

"Do you itch, Nicky?"

He nodded miserably. "All over."

"Well, we can do something about that in a minute." She draped his shirt over the foot rail of the brass bed and started to untie his sneakers.

"What's your name?" Nicky asked.

"Why don't you call me Mandy?"

"Mandy." He seemed to be trying it out. "I'm sorry I spilled the water."

She blinked in surprise. So the child did have a few manners, after all. "Accidents happen," she said casually. "It's all right."

It took Chase Worthington longer to get back to the inn than she'd expected. Nicky had his lukewarm bath and was back in her bed, his spots coated with calamine lotion and his eyelids heavy, before she heard the furious hammering on her apartment door that could only mean his father had arrived.

Nicky sat bolt upright.

"Don't be scared, darling. It's only your daddy coming to see you're all right." She handed him a glass of orange juice with a straw. "I'll be back in a minute."

She stopped halfway across the sitting room and called, "It's not locked. Come in."

A moment later, she decided it had been a very good decision to keep her distance. Chase flung the door open so hard it almost bounced off the wall. Behind him, peering over his shoulder as if she were looking into a witch's chamber, was the nanny.

"Where is he?" Chase demanded. "What in the hell do you think you're doing, anyway, snatching a child away from his caretaker in a public lobby?"

Amanda stepped aside and pointed toward the bedroom door. "Nicky's in there. His head still hurts, so you might try not to bellow."

"I could have you arrested for kidnapping!"

Amanda shrugged. "Don't you at least want to see him first? I promise I won't disappear in the meantime."

Chase scowled at her. His hands formed into fists, then relaxed a bit as he turned toward the bedroom.

"By the way," Amanda called, "there's a very good children's medical guide on the table next to the bed. You might want to read the section on chicken pox." She sat down on the deep couch and waved a hand at a chair. "Make yourself comfortable," she said to the nanny. "It may be a while—it's a rather long section."

The nanny sat down. "Isn't that just dandy?" she muttered. "I take a job that's supposed to get me all sorts of connections in Hollywood, and where do I end up? Stuck in a little town next to nowhere with a brat who has chicken pox!"

Amanda had to bite her tongue to keep silent. What kind of nanny was she?

The apartment walls were thick, and Amanda could hear nothing from the bedroom but the murmur of Chase's deep voice. At least Nicky wasn't creating a fuss over what had happened, and that was a relief. Chase hadn't been exaggerating; technically she *had* kidnapped the child.

When he reappeared in the bedroom doorway the nanny jumped to her feet. "I'll just bundle Nicky up and take him back to the suite," she began.

"How could you have missed this?" Chase's voice was level and cold.

"I—Mr. Worthington, he always says he doesn't feel well when—"

"The child is burning up!"

"He was fine this morning." She pointed a finger at Amanda. "You said yourself she kidnapped him. Who knows what she did to make him look sick?"

"Oh, for heaven's sake," Amanda said. "If you'd shown any interest in finding out what was wrong, I would never—"

Chase interrupted her. "I've been having my doubts about you as it is, Sally, but this is the end. You're fired. Pack your bags. You've got time to catch the afternoon flight."

The nanny pursed her mouth in distaste and said with mock respect, "Yes, sir. I hope you enjoy playing nursemaid." She slammed the door behind her.

"Oh, Lord," said Chase. "What am I going to do? Nicky can't come to the set when he's so sick, and I can't just stop the shoot to be with him for...how long?"

"Four or five days, I'd guess."

Chase swore under his breath.

Amanda didn't have a lot of sympathy. "I'm sure you can always get another nanny. Considering the qualifications the last one had, they must be a dime a dozen. In the meantime, don't let me keep you away from your work. I'll look after Nicky till you make some arrangements."

"I can't ask you to do that."

They were still staring at each other, neither willing to give an inch, when Nicky appeared at the bedroom door. His makeshift pajamas, one of Amanda's favorite T-shirts, trailed almost to his toes. "Mandy!"

"Yes, darling?"

He looked accusingly at her. "You said you'd come back."

"And I'm right here. You shouldn't be out of bed, you know." She scooped him up and tucked him under the blankets again. "What would you like, Nicky? More juice? Some ice chips?"

"Juice," he decided. "But come back soon this time."

By the time she returned with the fresh glass, however, Nicky was asleep. His absurdly long lashes lay heavily against his flushed cheeks, and one small hand was curved around his stuffed rabbit. Her eyes softened as she looked down at him.

Chase rose from the rocking chair at the side of the bed and came quickly toward her.

"You're not going to wake him now, are you?" Her voice was low.

"Of course not. Do you think I'm heartless enough to disturb him? Besides, he seems to have taken to you."

Amanda shrugged. "Kids are funny that way. Don't worry about it, Chase. I'll look after him."

"I don't know how to thank you."

"You don't have to. I'd have done the same for any child."

"I know you would. If you're sure you don't mind, I should go back to work. I just walked out in the middle of a scene."

For the first time she noticed the careful touches of makeup on his face, and the silk shirt that was unlike anything she'd seen him wear around the inn, and deep inside her something started to tremble. It wasn't fair. Why did he have to be so damned good-looking? And why was he even more attractive like this—when his face was filled with worry and fatigue, instead of careless ease?

She locked her fingers together to keep from reaching

out to smooth the tired lines from his forehead. "Go ahead," she said softly. "I'll leave the door unlocked so you can stop in to see him later."

As the evening wore on, she began to think Chase didn't intend to come back at all. In fact, it was almost midnight when she heard his steps crossing the little sitting room.

Amanda had bathed Nicky again and coated every spot she could find—there were a whole lot more of them now—with lotion to stop the itching, and he had curled up against her while she read him a story. The only light was the small pool cast by the bedside lamp.

Chase stopped in the bedroom doorway and leaned there, his jacket slung over one shoulder, watching, until the story was done. Amanda's low soft voice had worked its magic; Nicky was almost asleep by the time she finished, and so Chase only kissed his son's forehead and went out again.

Amanda waited a few minutes longer, till she was certain Nicky was sound asleep, and then she quietly slipped away. She was rubbing her eyes; it had been a long day already, and she'd be amazed if the child slept through the rest of the night. But she was too keyed up to rest. Maybe a cup of hot chocolate would help.

She stopped dead in the center of the room when, despite the dimness, she saw Chase sitting on the couch. "I didn't feel like going upstairs," he said lamely. "If you don't mind, I thought I'd sit for a while."

In case Nicky wanted him, Amanda reminded herself. "Of course I don't mind. But how are you going to work tomorrow if you don't have any sleep?"

"I could ask you the same question."

"But it's not the same thing, is it? The inn can function even if I look haggard. You, on the other hand, can't fool a camera. Would you like a hot drink? Cocoa, maybe, or tea?"

"Either." He followed her into the kitchenette.

Amanda turned on the light. Inside the wire cage, the parakeet raised his head from the tucked position and glared at her balefully. "Damn," she said, and doused the light again. "I forgot to put Floyd to bed, and if he starts whistling, Nicky will be up like a shot." She picked up the thick quilted cage cover. "Say your prayers, Floyd."

The parakeet gave a grunt. "Bless me," he croaked.

"Good boy." She tugged the cover over the cage. "There, I think it's safe now."

Chase perched on a tall stool next to the breakfast bar that separated the tiny kitchen from the sitting room. He had traded the silk shirt he'd been wearing earlier for a lightweight sweater, and now there was no trace of makeup on his face. His hair was rumpled and his eyelids drooped—as if, like Nicky, he needed a bit of comforting and a good night's sleep.

But the man still radiated that incredible aura. It was muted now, no doubt because of his exhaustion, but in the close quarters of the kitchenette it was no less effective.

Amanda stirred the milk and added cocoa and sugar. "How did the shooting go today?"

"Much better before the grand interruption than after. The director was not particularly understanding." He rubbed his temples. "I'm sorry, Amanda. I intended to take Nicky off your hands this evening and look after him myself tomorrow. But—"

"The director hit the ceiling at the very idea?"

"You might say."

"Don't worry about it. I told you I'd take care of Nicky till you made other arrangements."

"But you have a job. You can't just—"

"Fortunately I can do most of it from here. If I have to

go downstairs, I'll get one of the maids to sit with Nicky. We'll manage.''

Chase nodded. "Of course I expect to pay—" Amanda glared at him, and he stopped almost in midword. "Thank you very much," he said meekly.

"That's better." She gave a final stir to the hot chocolate, poured it into mugs and shook cinnamon over the top. "Cheers."

She turned on the lamps beside the couch and sat down, propping her feet on the flat-topped trunk. Chase settled at the end of the couch and turned almost sideways so he was facing her. He was studying her very intently; she could feel his gaze, and it made her nervous.

"You have wonderful bones, you know," he said finally, reaching over and tracing the high stark line of her cheekbone with his fingertip.

Amanda smiled a little. As pickup lines went, she'd heard better. He must be even more exhausted than she'd thought. "They hold me up just fine. I guess that's all I ever expected of them."

Chase didn't laugh. "Did you give your picture to the casting director? We need a lot of extras."

"No. Even if I had the time, I haven't the inclination."

"Really? You seem to take quite a interest in film and theater. There's a shelf of books on the subject in your library."

Be careful, Amanda, she told herself. There was no sense in letting him suspect that much of what she knew about acting she had learned while reading about him. "Oh, I had a couple of bit parts in college plays. Not that I ever had any talent, but at least I got rid of the silly urge every teenager has to be a famous actor." She sipped her hot chocolate. "Sorry. That came out all wrong. I really didn't mean to say I think your choice of profession is juvenile."

He smiled. "Sometimes, usually about the twelfth take, I'd agree with you. Besides, after midnight no one should be held fully responsible for what they say."

"That's a nice thought."

"And I couldn't take offense, anyway. I was the exception, you see—I didn't want to be a famous actor. In fact, it never even occurred to me to try acting."

Amanda stared at him. "Then how, pray tell, did you end up as the sexiest man on American TV?" She saw the glint of enjoyment in his eyes and added hastily, "That's Stephanie's description, mind you."

For a moment he only looked at her, and Amanda could feel heat rising in her cheeks.

"Remind me to ask Stephanie if she wants a job promoting my image," Chase said lazily. "My career choice was purely accidental. I was a journeyman carpenter, working with a cabinet-maker and learning the trade, and we were building display cases in a guy's family room when he asked if I'd ever considered acting. I thought he was kidding, till I found out the display cases were to hold his awards for television advertising. He had hundreds of them."

"And he cast you?"

Chase nodded. "It sounded like a good way to pick up a little extra cash, so I started in ads and moved to the soaps, and before I knew it there was a made-for-TV movie and then the series."

She shook her head in amazement.

"Disgusting, isn't it?" Chase said softly. "I haven't even starved for the sake of my art."

She couldn't help laughing at the hint of self-mockery in his voice. "Do you like movies better, or the television series?"

He answered without hesitation. "Movies, because every one is so different."

"That's interesting. I would have thought—"

"And television, because I can go home every night and I like the role."

"So you're really saying you're not going to give up either."

Chase nodded. "I'm just a man who can't make up his mind."

"But surely you don't have to choose."

"I don't know. Sometimes I think Nicky suffers for it."

"Do you always take him on location with you?"

"Usually."

She finished her hot chocolate and said thoughtfully, "I'm a bit worried about Nicky."

Chase tensed a little; she could feel his muscles tighten even though he wasn't actually touching her. "Oh?"

"Not about the chicken pox. That's a nuisance but not complicated. He'll be fine."

"I'll no doubt be lynched for bringing the damned disease to Springhill. Any kid who's walked through the lobby lately has probably been exposed."

"We've had it here before," Amanda said dryly. "It's not like the bubonic plague. But that wasn't what I meant. It's hard to explain and it's none of my business, but…"

He leaned toward her again and cupped her chin in his palm, turning her face till she had to look at him. "You're scaring me now. Out with it."

"Chase, he's perfectly all right with me. But what if someone else had picked him up? He didn't even protest. Yes, he was sick, but to have a stranger sweep him up and take him away from a familiar person… He should have been screaming bloody murder with every step."

"He wasn't all that attached to Sally."

"I can understand why he wouldn't have been, but—"

"She'd only been with us for a few weeks."

"At least that helps explain why you hadn't fired her before this."

Chase sighed. "She looked so good when the agency first sent her, and I thought maybe I was just being too demanding. I was hoping that with a little time... I knew Nicky hasn't been his usual self the last few days, of course. Believe it or not, he normally has a sunny personality."

"When he gets his own way?" She smiled to take a little of the sting out of the remark.

"Well, I'm sure that happens more often than is good for him. But I thought his bad attitude was mostly the change of scene, not the nanny." He rubbed the back of his neck as if the muscles were tight and sore. "And now I have to start all over again."

Amanda took pity on him. "You don't have to do anything tonight. Look, why don't you get some sleep, Chase? Nicky's not all that sick, you know, but if you want to be close, you can sack out in the den. If he wakes up I'll come and get you."

She almost didn't disturb him, though. It was four in the morning when Nicky awoke, and Chase was so sound asleep she hated to rouse him. He was sprawled on the couch, one forearm substituting for a pillow. She stood for a moment and watched him in the dim light that spilled into the den from the sitting room, and thought that in his own way Chase looked as much like a sleeping angel as Nicky did.

And that was another delusion. Even sound asleep the man had a certain magnetism—she could have stood there and watched him for hours—which had nothing to do with harps and halos.

But she had promised, and so she leaned over him and put a hand on his shoulder. "Chase?"

He roused instantly, but the deep brown eyes looked cloudy, as if he wasn't quite sure where he was, or why. Then he focused on her, and he raised his fingertips to touch her face.

The contact almost scorched her skin. *Definitely* he was not an angel. "Nicky wants you," she said softly.

"Did he have a nightmare?" His voice was husky.

"No. He just wants some comfort."

Nicky gave a gurgling little chuckle at the sight of his father with the textured pattern of his sweater sleeve still deeply impressed on his cheek. Amanda had to bite her lip to keep from smiling at that herself. The characters he played were always so elegant, even in the midst of mayhem, that it was hard to believe Chase Worthington wasn't just as perfect in real life. Except that he was even more attractive, somehow, like this.

"Tell the truth, Amanda," Chase said. "This heartless little tyrant doesn't want comfort. He thinks that just because he's up, the rest of the world should be, too." But his tone was tender, and the way he hugged Nicky left no doubt about his feelings.

She left them there together and went back to her makeshift bed in the sitting room. She didn't know how long Chase stayed with his son because, knowing she didn't have to listen quite so closely for a little while, she fell deeply asleep herself.

The apartment was quiet when she awoke, and sunshine was streaming in. Amanda felt warm and cozy and relaxed, until she stretched and realized just how bad a substitute the couch was for her own bed.

But it was no wonder she felt so cozy, for an extra blanket from the bedroom was draped over her and carefully tucked in. She hadn't gotten it out herself because she'd been afraid to be too comfortable; she needed to stay on the edge of wakefulness, in case Nicky called out.

But it had been dear of Chase to be concerned about her comfort. Not only had he covered her, but he'd probably tiptoed out at the crack of dawn to avoid disturbing her—and Nicky, too, of course.

Nicky's fever was down, and he said his head felt better.

"That's good," Amanda said. "Let's pop you in the tub to soak while I fix your breakfast."

Nicky made a face. "Another bath?"

"It'll help stop the itch."

He considered and finally agreed. He was splashing merrily when the bellman knocked on the door. He had brought an enormous suitcase on a luggage cart. "Mr. Worthington said you'd need these things."

"Nicky's clothes, I suppose? Not for a few days."

"It's mostly toys, I think."

"I don't need those, either, even if I had room for them." Amanda opened the suitcase to be sure. The array of toys that filled the case would have been enough to stock a small store. She shook her head in amazement as she picked out a couple of games and a few small toys, then snapped the lid shut. "Take the rest back upstairs. What I really need, John, is a single bed set up in the den. Can you do that for me this morning?"

"Mandy!" Nicky called from the bathroom.

"I'll be there in a minute, darling."

"Mandy, I'm hungry!"

The bellman gave her a sympathetic look as he lifted the suitcase back onto the cart. "Sure, I'll get the bed. I don't envy you your job, Miss Bailey. I wouldn't baby-sit with that little terror on a bet."

"Don't be too sure. Before it's over we may all be taking turns."

As she shut the door, Nicky appeared, dripping and dragging a towel. "I said I'm—"

"I heard you, Nicky. What a nice loud voice you have." She wrapped the towel around him. "But we have to get you completely dry first so you don't catch a cold."

"I don't want to be dry!" His voice rose to a steady wail. "I want a chocolate doughnut and I want it now!"

Amanda sat back on her heels and began to applaud.

Nicky stopped in midshriek and stared at her.

"That's a dandy tantrum," she said. "I'm impressed. But I've got things to do this morning, so I'm afraid you'll have to put off the rest of the screaming for a while. As soon as you're dry, you may have oatmeal with fruit, or toast and peanut butter, or an egg for breakfast—"

"I want a chocolate doughnut." His lower lip was thrust out, but he spoke quietly.

"If that's the only thing that will satisfy you, you're not so awfully hungry, I guess." Amanda reached for her blow-dryer.

By the time he was covered with lotion again and dressed in another of Amanda's T-shirts, he'd decided that toast and peanut butter was acceptable. He sat at the breakfast bar, with his chin hardly above the edge, and picked the crust off his toast.

Amanda watched from the corner of her eye as she loaded dirty glasses into the dishwasher. "Did your nanny honestly let you eat chocolate doughnuts for breakfast?"

He nodded. "With cocoa, too. I like cocoa." His voice was hopeful.

No wonder the child was impossible sometimes, she thought. With all that chocolate, and the sugar and caffeine it contained, he couldn't help but be hyperactive.

"Did you know my mommy died?" he asked soberly.

"Yes, Nicky."

"That's why I have nannies. Are you my new nanny?"

"No, dear."

"Oh. That's too bad. I like you."

Her heart gave an odd little twist. "I like you, too, Nicky."

Before she had a chance to feel sentimental, Nicky had bounced on. "Why do you have a bird in your house?"

"Because he's a pet bird."

"Why's he in a cage?"

"So he doesn't get loose in the hotel and get hurt. If you're all finished with that toast, shall we feed a bit to Floyd?"

Nicky looked doubtful. "Will he bite?"

"Not if you hold very still and don't frighten him."

He didn't hold still, of course; he squealed and dropped the scrap of toast before Floyd came within six inches of it. The bird tipped his head and remarked, "Strike one."

Nicky's eyes went wide. "He talked to me!"

Amanda, who was still astounded sometimes at how very appropriate Floyd's random remarks could be, tore off another bit of crust. "Do you want to try again?"

"Make him say Nicky!" the child commanded.

"I can't."

"Why not?"

"Because he has to think about each word and practice. Can you say antidisestablishmentarianism?"

Nicky giggled. "'Course not. It's too big!"

"All at once, yes. But I bet you could say it if you took a little bit of the word at a time and practiced long enough. If you keep saying your name to Floyd, he might learn it. But you'll have to be awfully patient and talk to him every time you go by his cage. It might take days."

It took three more tries before Nicky could hold the bit of toast long enough for Floyd to snap it up, and another few minutes of coaxing before he learned to stroke the bird's pale blue breast feathers with the very tip of his finger. "He's soft," Nicky whispered almost in awe.

By evening, the bird and the boy were buddies. When Chase appeared a little after eight o'clock, Nicky was standing on a stool by the cage, feeding Floyd bits of lettuce and repeating, "Say Nicky!" at intervals.

Chase raised his eyebrows at Amanda. "Poor Floyd looks a little frazzled."

"He's had a busy day. But it's helped keep Nicky's mind off his spots." She picked up the cage cover. "I think that's enough for now, Nicky. Say your prayers, Floyd."

Floyd had to think it over before he obliged, and his head was tucked under his wing before the cover was completely in place.

"And it's Nicky's bedtime, too," Amanda said gently. "We were just waiting to see if you'd be home soon."

Nicky stuck out his lower lip and eyed her, obviously wondering if having his father as a witness would make a tantrum any more profitable. Before he'd made up his mind, Chase picked him up, and he flung his arms around his father's neck.

"You look a little frazzled, too, Amanda," Chase said. "Do you want me to take him off your hands for the night?"

She shook her head. "I'm a pro at this. All my friends have kids, and I keep them for a week at a time."

"If you're sure…"

"I've moved him into the den, though. I'm in no condition for another night on the couch."

He laughed at that as he carried Nicky off to bed. It was almost an hour before he appeared again, and Amanda was half-asleep, lulled by the music of a soft string quartet that was playing on the stereo.

"I didn't mean to be so long," Chase said. "Between drinks of water and good-night kisses and just one more story, it takes a while. Do you have any idea how many picture books you own?"

"It isn't the stories he wants, it's you." She patted back a yawn.

"I suppose I should go," Chase said. "You need your rest, too."

Amanda thought he sounded halfhearted about it, and for just a moment she indulged herself by imagining why he might not want to leave. It was silly, of course. He could hardly be unaware of the effect he had on women—but it certainly didn't mean he felt anything overwhelming himself.

"Why don't you stay for a while?" she said. "Just in case Nicky doesn't settle down right away, of course."

"Of course," he said calmly. The string quartet faded into silence, and he moved over to the stereo and glanced at the row of compact discs. "May I?"

"Feel free. Have you eaten?"

"We had a dinner break on the set." He chose a piano concerto.

"A glass of wine, perhaps?"

"That sounds good, but sit still. Just tell me where."

"In the refrigerator. Glasses are in the cabinet above the sink."

He rattled around her kitchen for a couple of minutes, then came out and handed her a long-stemmed wineglass, one of the few bits of good crystal she owned. He sat down beside her.

"You said something about nightmares last night," Amanda said finally. "Does Nicky have them a lot?"

"Now and then. Not as much as he used to."

"I always like to be prepared for things like that."

"I can't believe how lucky I am that you were there at the moment Nicky needed you—and that you'd agree to take him on." He raised his glass in a silent toast.

Amanda shrugged. "I like kids and I enjoy having them around."

"I don't doubt it, but…" He set his glass down and put his index finger under her chin to turn her face up to his. "Thank you, Amanda."

His eyes were almost gold, she thought in surprise. It must be the reflection of the lamps.…

His kiss was no more than a soft, warm, fleeting brush of the lips. It was over before Amanda could gather her thoughts, much less do anything to stop him.

Not that she wanted to stop him. The kiss had only been a brief thank-you, more a salute than anything else. It was nothing to take offense at, and nothing to get particularly excited about, either, even if he was the sexiest man on American TV. She should just smile at him. A calm, ordinary smile.

She tried. But something seemed to be wrong with her lower lip, because it trembled just a little. She ran the tip of her tongue across her lip, trying to steady it.

Chase's eyes narrowed. Very deliberately, he took Amanda's wineglass out of her hand and set it on the trunk, and slipped one arm around her.

The second kiss was just as gentle, but that was where all resemblance stopped. If the first had been a sweet salute, this was rather like biting into a hot chili pepper. It took Amanda's breath away and robbed her of the power of speech.

And she knew that, exactly like a chili pepper, once the first stunning impact of that kiss had passed, she would be left with the desire to try another.

CHAPTER FOUR

"DADDY," said a plaintive little voice from the doorway, "what are you doing?"

Chase turned his head. "I'm kissing Amanda," he said. His voice sounded as if he was having trouble getting his breath.

Amanda gave a little squeak of protest and tried to pull away. Chase's arms tightened around her.

"Oh," Nicky said. "Why?"

"Because I like her and it seemed to be a good idea. What are *you* doing, Nicky?"

The child shifted his weight from one bare foot to the other. "I need a drink of water."

"You need a spanking," Chase said under his breath. He released Amanda without hurry and went to tend to his son.

She was changing the compact disc on the stereo, even though it still had a while to play, when he came quietly up behind her and put his hands on her shoulders. "Amanda—"

She jumped. "I didn't hear you."

"Sorry," he said, and let her go. "I didn't mean to startle you. Another glass of wine?"

"Maybe just a little."

By the time he came back to the living room with the wine, Amanda had curled up in a chair. She thought she saw his eyebrows lift, but he didn't comment.

"You didn't spank him, did you?" she asked.

"Of course not. Why would I— Oh, I did say that, didn't I?"

"Yes, you did."

"He wasn't being bad, just nosy. Four-year-olds have a sixth sense, you know. They can always pick out the precise moments when they're really not wanted."

She smiled despite herself. "Well, at least your answer seemed to satisfy him."

"It had the advantage of being the truth, too." He sounded quite calm about it.

Amanda bit her lip and looked down at her wine. All Chase had said was that he liked her. He no doubt liked lots of women, and he'd probably kissed a good many of them, too. Nicky certainly hadn't seemed shocked at the sight of his father with a woman in his arms.

Don't let your imagination get out of hand, Amanda, she warned herself. The fact that she practically went up in smoke whenever Chase touched her didn't mean he felt anything on the same scale.

He chose the end of the couch farthest from her chair and sat at an angle that let him face her. He tried to stretch out his legs, but the trunk was in the way, and he shifted uncomfortably.

"Go ahead and put your feet on top of it," Amanda said.

"It's an antique."

"Not really. And it's sturdy, or else it wouldn't be there."

Chase nodded. "Because of all the kids you have around, of course." With his feet on the trunk, ankles crossed, he looked as relaxed as if he was lying in a backyard hammock. "Do you select all your furniture with them in mind?"

"Not always. I had a wicker rocking chair in this room

for a while. One of my young friends bounced in it once too often, and I scolded her. She looked up at me with a hurt face and said, 'But, Mandy, if the chair isn't to sit in, why do you have it?' And you know, she was right.''

"You actually got rid of it?''

"Oh, no. But I put it in my bedroom, where the kids don't usually go. You were sitting in it last night.''

He feigned terror. "I hope I didn't bounce too much.''

Amanda laughed, and the mock fright vanished from his face.

"I'm fascinated,'' he said softly. "Since you get such a charge out of your friends' kids, why don't you have any of your own?''

Amanda shrugged. "My life just hasn't worked out that way, I guess.''

"You sound as if it's all over,'' he objected. "How old are you, anyway—twenty-five?''

She smiled a little. "You're close. Do you guess weights and tell fortunes, too?''

"You're a mere baby yourself, with lots of time to have a family. Oh, to be so young again, with all the world to choose from.''

"At thirty-four, you're not exactly antique yourself, Chase.''

"You've been reading my publicity handouts.''

Amanda felt a gentle wave of color rise in her cheeks.

"You have? Honestly?'' He sounded delighted.

"Well, there hasn't been anything but movie news in the local paper recently.'' It was a foolish protest, and obviously Chase knew it, for he grinned at her and didn't say a word. She put her chin up a fraction. "No one could live in Springhill for long and not know all about Chase Worthington. You've been a favorite topic of conversation for years.''

"It's not fair," Chase mused. "I can't go to the local library and read up on you. So tell me what your publicity handouts would say, Amanda. Besides the fact that you love kids and you kiss like an angel, that is."

"Chase…"

He looked at her innocently over the rim of his wine-glass. "Does that mean you want me to change the subject? Because I'm not going to."

Amanda gave up. "There isn't anything interesting about me. I was born here, I grew up here—"

"Tell me about your family."

She hesitated, then shrugged. "Nothing much to tell. I was a late child, and an only one. My father was an appliance repairman, and my mother did good deeds."

"Past tense?"

"Mother died when I was in college, and my father a couple of years ago. That's why I came back here. He was ill, and I took this job so I could be close to him."

"That's sweet."

There was nothing sweet about it, but Amanda wasn't going to tell Chase that. She had sworn more than once that she would never come back to Springhill, and at the time her father's illness had seemed like the intervention of a sullen vengeful fate, dragging her back against her will. But it hadn't been so bad, after all. They had even made a sort of peace between them, eventually….

"When he died a year later," she said, "the owners of the inn were just starting to renovate the place, and it looked like a challenge, so I stayed. Sounds pretty dull, doesn't it?"

"Quiet," Chase amended.

"There's nothing wrong with a quiet life. That doesn't mean it's boring." She tried to pat back a yawn.

Chase set his glass down. "It looks as if I should carry

you in to bed, too.'' The lazy note in his voice left his
words open for interpretation.

Amanda's eyes widened in momentary shock. Then she
forced herself to laugh; he had been teasing—hadn't he?
''Just like Nicky, I suppose? With drinks of water and bedtime stories?''

''And especially good-night kisses. Just so there's no
misunderstanding, Amanda Bailey—I'd love to spend the
night with you.'' His tone was slow and sultry.

Amanda made a conscious desperate effort to keep
breathing, for she seemed to have forgotten how. ''I didn't
invite you to stay, Chase,'' she said finally.

''I know you didn't.'' He stood up. ''That's why I'm
leaving right now before my self-control runs out. See you
tomorrow.'' His lips brushed her cheek.

She closed the door behind him and leaned against it,
her hand cupped over the place his lips had touched. Until
she had met Chase Worthington, she would never have
imagined that a simple peck on the cheek could make her
whole body feel like a violin string stretched taut.

She'd bet that Chase Worthington could tell some fantastic bedtime stories, too. She had no doubt that making
love with him would seem just like a fairy tale....

THE NEXT MORNING, while Nicky napped, Amanda bribed
the chambermaid to keep an eye on him while she cleaned
the rooms at that end of the second floor. Amanda, meanwhile, slipped down to the registration desk in a feeble
effort to catch up on her work. It was really amazing how
much she had accomplished on the telephone in half an
hour while Nicky was overseeing Floyd's bath. Still, there
were a great many things that required personal attention.

She didn't realize until she reached the lobby that she
had gotten a bit claustrophobic after a couple of days in a

sickroom. Her little apartment was cozy and comfortable, but she'd rarely spent more than a few waking hours in it at a time. There were too many other things to do—regular inspection tours of the inn, checking to be sure the work she had ordered had been done, training new employees, greeting guests and making certain they were comfortable. When she wasn't working, she strolled in the peaceful little park nearby, or shopped in the stores downtown, or visited her friends. Springhill might be small, but there was always something going on if one looked for it.

Her desk was clear, but only because the bellman had been bringing her mail and messages upstairs. But in two days, a lot of minor problems had arisen around the inn, and Amanda sat down at the registration desk to run through the list with Tricia.

Thank heaven for a good staff, Amanda thought. If they had called her about every one of these minor episodes, she'd have worn out the stairs, as well as her patience. Not that she could have done any more than her employees had in most cases. Even if they had let her know every time Jessamyn Arden complained about the temperature in her suite, what could Amanda have done but send the bellman up again to check and adjust the controls? Somehow she doubted any air-conditioning technician could fix the problem to Jessamyn's satisfaction.

And as for the tabloid reporter reappearing, with a roll of cash in hand...

"I thought, under the circumstances," Tricia said, "that it might be just as well to leave you out of that one, Amanda. If he'd gotten a hint of why you weren't around..."

Amanda shrugged. "If they have nothing better than Nicky's chicken pox to put on the front page of next week's edition, the whole publication is in trouble. Still, I'm glad you took care of it without me."

"It wasn't difficult, though it must be the first time the law against loitering has been put to use in Springhill."

"I always wondered why the town council bothered with that one. Oh, when you have a chance, will you check the bathroom in 412 and make sure the leak in the hot-water pipe is fixed? The plumber's bill was in this morning's mail."

"I already have. It's fine." Tricia stood up as footsteps approached the desk. "Good morning, Miss Arden. May I help you?"

"I'm just picking up my messages." Jessamyn Arden's voice seemed to float across the lobby. Her slightly affected accent made it sound as if she intended to burst into song at any moment.

The clerk retrieved a stack of pink slips from the row of small mailboxes behind the desk.

Jessamyn paged through them, then crumpled the stack into a loose ball and dropped it over the counter. Messages fluttered like autumn leaves over the floor.

"You can throw them away," Jessamyn said. She moved to one side in order to use one of the mirrors set into the woodwork behind the desk to readjust her wide-brimmed hat, and caught sight of Amanda. "Oh, does this mean Nicky's better?" she cooed. "Perhaps I'll come and visit him after work."

"I think he'd like a visitor," Amanda said, and hoped it was the truth. Despite what Jessamyn had said about Nicky, perhaps he hadn't taken an active dislike to her on the trip from Los Angeles. How well did he know her, anyway? "A guest would break the monotony and make it easier for him to stay in for another couple of days."

Jessamyn paused. "A couple of days? You don't mean he's still contagious?"

"Probably, until the last of his spots dry up a bit more. But surely you've had chicken pox?"

Jessamyn shivered. "I haven't the vaguest idea, but I simply couldn't take the chance. With the whole production depending on me..."

Amanda didn't think it would be prudent to point out that Jessamyn had no doubt been exposed on the trip from Los Angeles. "In that case," she said calmly, "I'll give Nicky your best wishes."

"Please do. The precious little darling, I feel so badly for him." Jessamyn went out. The heels of her delicate shoes were so tall that she had to take tiny mincing steps, which made her whole body sway enticingly.

"The precious little darling," Tricia repeated under her breath. She stooped to pick up the messages Jessamyn had scattered. "I'll bet she's already forgotten him! How is the poor kid, anyway?"

"Having a rough time today. His patience is entirely worn out with this itching and he's afraid he'll never get better." Amanda nodded at the wad of pink paper the clerk held. "Did all those messages come in this morning since she went to work?"

"Oh, no, she's just headed for the set now. She's given orders that her telephone isn't to ring from midnight to nine in the morning—no matter what. So we've disconnected it."

"At that rate we'll need an extra clerk on the night shift just to handle telephones."

"Not a bad idea."

"And what do you plan to do if the director wants to call her with a change in shooting schedule?"

Tricia smiled. "I intend to thank heaven that I work days—so it isn't my problem."

Stephanie Kendall breezed in, cool and professional in a white linen suit, and picked up the house telephone before she saw Amanda. She put it down and leaned across the desk. "I thought you were still in quarantine with the terror."

"He's not a terror."

Tricia answered the telephone and turned to Amanda. "It's the maid. He's awake."

Amanda could hear Nicky wailing in the background, even though she was four feet from the telephone. "Tell her I'll be right there."

"That," Stephanie said, "does not sound like Prince Charming."

"Oh, come on, Steph. How delightful would Zack be under the same circumstances? Away from everything he knows, miserably sick and locked up with a stranger."

Stephanie drew herself up straight. "My perfect Zack would never…" Then she gave up the pose and burst into delighted laughter as she imagined what the unstoppable Zack might actually do under those conditions. "Oh, all right. You've made your point, Mandy." She followed her friend up the service stairs.

Amanda was relentless. "Maybe I should bundle Nicky up and take him out to the lake house to play with Zack, and in a couple of weeks we'll see how Zack handles chicken pox!"

"Not this summer. Please. I don't have time for it this summer."

"Well, I didn't, either, and see what happened."

"At least you're getting a chance to know Chase better," Stephanie murmured. "What was it you said about the hotel being so big you'd hardly see him at all? Of course, the circumstances aren't exactly romantic, but..."

Try as she might, Amanda couldn't quite keep warm color from creeping into her cheeks. But it wasn't entirely last night's kiss she was thinking of, she realized; it was also the way Chase had looked the night before that, sound asleep and sprawled on the couch in her den with the pattern of his sweater sleeve mashed into his face. No, it wasn't especially romantic, she thought. Stephanie was right about that. But it had been warm and real and incredibly exciting to be close to him....

Stephanie was looking at her oddly, her head tipped to one side.

"Are you coming in?" Amanda asked.

Stephanie shrugged. "Wouldn't miss it for the world."

The moment Amanda appeared, Nicky flung himself against her and clung like an octopus. But as she patted his back and murmured to him, his howls died to the occasional sob, and within a minute he was sneaking peeks over her shoulder at Stephanie.

I was right, Amanda thought. A visitor to break the routine would do wonders for Nicky. Any new face would do—except, apparently, the chambermaid's. Amanda wondered why he'd reacted so strongly. She'd told him, before he went to sleep, that she might go downstairs for a while, so it couldn't be that he was afraid when he awoke to find a stranger nearby.

"That is the biggest case of chicken pox I've ever seen," Stephanie said.

Nicky sniffed one last time and sat up. "The biggest?" he said doubtfully.

"Yes, and I've seen some championship cases. I think Mandy should have a picture to remember it by, as a matter of fact.'' She winked at Amanda. ''Shall we draw one for her, or let her get the camera?''

''Draw,'' Nicky decided.

Amanda got paper and a bucket of crayons, and Nicky settled down on the rug. Stephanie sat beside him, heedless of her white suit. ''If there's something you need to do, Mandy, Nicky and I will keep each other company for half an hour.''

Nicky stopped drawing and looked wary, but he didn't make a fuss.

Amanda shook her head in confusion. ''Let me get this straight. Your kids are in daycare, and you're here taking care of Nicky so I can go to work?''

Stephanie shrugged. ''I'm between appointments. Besides, you've helped me out more times than I can count. It's rather pleasant to have a chance to pay you back.''

Amanda went to make her regular inspection tour. The half hour was nearly up when she came back to the apartment to be greeted by the murmur of voices and Nicky's infectious laugh.

Stephanie got up and dusted herself off. ''I'd love to stick around and play and be late for my appointment,'' she said, and shook a teasing finger at Nicky. ''You are just too funny, my fine friend.''

Amanda followed her into the hall. ''My fine friend?'' she repeated. ''Whatever happened to the little terror?''

''All things considered, he's actually pretty sweet. A bit spoiled, of course. Watch out, Amanda.''

Stephanie so seldom used her full name that Amanda was surprised. ''What do you mean?''

''Be careful not to get too attached to him.''

Amanda studied the pattern in the carpet. ''I know,'' she said quietly.

"And even more important, don't let him get too attached to you."

"Oh, that's all right. Nicky knows I'm not his new nanny, and this is only for a few days, till he's feeling better."

Stephanie murmured something that might have been disapproval or frustration. "Well, when he's over the worst, bring him out to the lake to play with Zack."

"It'll be a few days before he's up to anything like that."

"Good. The way he looks now, Zack would probably think Nicky was a connect-the-dots drawing!"

Stephanie was laughing, but her earlier concern hadn't left Amanda entirely unmoved. Surely Stephanie had been wrong about Nicky's attachment to Amanda, though. He'd befriended Stephanie easily enough.

But just in case, as she helped him into his pajamas that evening, Amanda told him once more that when he was better and could go out again, he'd have a new nanny, as well.

Nicky looked at her for an endless moment, his hazel eyes big and bright, and Amanda braced herself for questions she didn't want to answer. But he said nothing, just popped his head through the neck of another of her T-shirts, picked up his stuffed rabbit and climbed onto her lap as she sat in the rocking chair in the den. It was the first time she'd ever seen him suck his thumb, and it made her feel sad somehow.

Five minutes later he'd had enough cuddling, and he slid out of her arms and went out to say good-night to Floyd.

The bird sidled back and forth on his perch, his head bent inquisitively to one side, as Nicky coached him to repeat his name. But Floyd was silent, and finally Nicky climbed down and heaved a big sigh. "He'll never say it, I bet."

"It was only yesterday that you started. It takes patience, Nicky." She picked up the cage cover. "Say your prayers, Floyd."

"Bless me," the parakeet croaked. Then he whistled his abbreviated version of the national anthem, like a television station going off the air, and tucked his head under his wing.

Nicky stuck out his lower lip. "But he says things for you!"

"It's not really for me, I'm afraid. He talks so much because the lady who used to own him worked with him every single day for years. Now, how about *your* prayers, Nicholas? I think your daddy's working very late tonight."

The boy climbed into bed obediently enough, but he sat up with his arms wrapped around his knees and said, "I'll wait for him." There was a note of determination in his voice that couldn't be ignored.

"Go to sleep, and I promise to wake you up when he comes."

Nicky thought about that. "Cross your heart?"

She did, and hoped that Chase wouldn't think it was too late to disturb her. No matter what hour it was, surely he'd want to look in on his son. "Now it's time for prayers."

Nicky grinned and in a fair imitation of the parakeet's voice croaked, "Bless me."

"Well, you're certainly a faster learner than Floyd is. How about 'Bless Daddy...'"

He nodded. "And bless Mandy."

"That's very thoughtful, dear." She guided him through a simple prayer. "Now, how about saying thank-you for some of the good things today?"

"Not the itches."

"No, of course not. But you had a visitor..."

"And I got to watch *Peter Pan* and eat watermelon..."

His list was a lengthy and enthusiastic one, and even though Amanda suspected it was inflated for the purpose of keeping her at his side, she didn't mind.

When he finally ran down, she offered a bedtime story. Nicky negotiated for two, then chose three picture books from the shelf and sat looking from them to Amanda with such woebegone eyes she had to laugh.

He was a natural little actor, she thought. Just like his father.

She read all three stories, kissed his heavy eyelids and tiptoed out.

Don't let yourself get too attached to him, Stephanie had said this morning, and Amanda knew what sensible advice it was. In a few days, Nicky would be well. In a few weeks, he would be gone, and she would never see him again. The prudent thing to do was to keep her heart under lock and key.

The trouble was, the warning had come a couple of days too late.

THE KNOCK ON HER DOOR was scarcely worth the name; it was more like a timid scratch. When she opened it, Chase seemed to study her as if she'd been a fashion model on the runway—though she couldn't have looked less like one, with her bare feet, jeans, casual top and hair loose around her shoulders.

"I was afraid you'd given up on me by now." He smiled and touched a fingertip to the corner of her mouth.

Every nerve in Amanda's body shuddered with pleasure. "I almost did. Are you shooting lots of scenes or just having trouble getting through them?"

"A little of both. We're using up a lot of film, that's sure."

She led the way into the kitchen and pulled a bottle of wine out of the refrigerator.

Chase shook his head. "What would really taste good," he confided, "is a cup of coffee."

"At this hour?" But she reached for the pot, anyway. "If you insist...and speaking of insisting, you're to wake Nicky to say good-night."

"Your orders?"

"Of course not. I wouldn't dream of telling you what to do."

"Oh, really? Then why did Nicky's suitcase full of toys find its way back to my suite?"

"Because he didn't need them."

"I see," Chase said thoughtfully. By the time he came out of the den a few minutes later, Amanda was pouring the coffee. He sniffed the aroma of the dark brew and gave a sigh of satisfaction. "Nicky didn't want to wake up. In fact, I'm not sure he'll remember anything at all in the morning."

"I'll tell him you tried. Want to sit on the balcony?"

"You have one?"

"Well, it's more of a fire escape, actually." She pulled the curtains back from the full-length glass in the corner of the sitting room and opened the door to a tiny terrace, just large enough for two chairs and a couple of big clay pots. One held a gigantic tomato plant, heavy green fruit weighing down the branches. The other was filled with an assortment of flowers.

"It's beautiful tonight." Chase stretched and yawned. "Cool and peaceful and a bit of a breeze. Not at all like it was while we were shooting the garden scenes today."

"At Stephanie's house? I'd love to see what it looks like. She was telling me about all the work they've done."

"Come over anytime. Everyone else in Springhill has, I think."

"See? I told you you're the most interesting thing in town."

He reached out to tug gently at a lock of her hair. "Am I, Amanda?"

That was careless, she told herself. What she'd said was truer than she wanted to admit, and she'd let it slip out without thinking. "Of course, that's not saying much—this is generally a pretty dull town. Isn't the crowd interfering with your work?"

He smiled just a little. "No. The garden's roped off so spectators can't get in the way, but I'll get you in closer. You know, I still think you should be an extra. We're going to need some tomorrow."

"I can hardly bring Nicky."

"Oh. Of course. How's he doing?"

"He's much better. He doesn't think so, because he's tired of being shut in, but other than taking a couple of extra naps, I think he was pretty much his normal self today. In another day or two, he can probably be out of isolation."

"Then I'd better get a phone call in to the nanny registry."

"Yes," Amanda said. She felt as if she were cutting off her arm, but it was the only sensible solution. "How many nannies has he had since his mother died?"

Chase frowned. "Three, I guess."

"In two years?" Amanda was horrified.

"It's an ongoing problem."

"No wonder he—" She bit her tongue.

"What?"

She hesitated and finally said stiffly, "I'm sorry. I'm

poking my nose into something that's none of my business.''

"Look, if there's a better solution I wish somebody would find it," Chase said impatiently. "You can't sign a nanny to a lifetime contract. Heaven knows I tried, but the first one went home to nurse her rich aunt, and the second one got married and moved to New Jersey, and the third one—''

"You fired.''

"No, she got a job she liked better. It was the *fourth* one I fired. Sally lasted such a short time I hadn't even counted her. And what was I to do about it? There are some things money can't buy. I was already paying them the earth, and when they took the job they each agreed to stay a year at least. But even if I could have enforced the contract, what kind of care would Nicky have gotten after that?''

"I see your point.''

"Well, if you think I run through nannies, you should have seen what it was like when Desiree was hiring them.''

"Nicky had nannies then, too?''

"Don't sound so shocked. Desiree worked as many hours a week as I did. And when she was home…'' He stopped and sipped his coffee, and after a moment he said, "And daycare is no answer, either, for someone with a job like mine. So what do you suggest, Amanda?''

"I'm sorry. I had no idea.'' Her tone was chastened. Stephanie and the others in her circle of friends traded kids almost as casually as they swapped paperback books, with no one keeping track of who had baby-sat the most. It was such a natural thing that it had never occurred to Amanda that someone else might not be part of such a supportive network. But Southern California was not Springhill, and Chase's friends were not like Amanda's.

Chase leaned closer, and his fingertips skimmed a lock

of flaxen hair that had tumbled over her shoulder. "I'm sorry, too. I shouldn't take out my frustration on you."

She managed to smile. "It's all right."

His fingertips lingered on the curve of her arm. "Amanda, if I took a bit too much for granted last night…"

She was startled. Chase, taking too much for granted? All he'd done was kiss her. Or—horrors—did he suspect how deeply that simple caress had shaken her? "I'm not sure what you mean."

Chase said dryly, "Just because I haven't seen a man over the age of four hanging around you doesn't mean there isn't one."

"Oh. That."

"And if I was out of line in saying what I did about wanting to go to bed with you, I'm sorry. Not that it wasn't true, because it was. But if there is a man in your life…"

She shook her head and saw his eyes light with self-confidence and desire and just enough humor to make her feel wary. What was the man thinking, anyway? That she was crazy enough about him to ignore common sense?

And why shouldn't he think that? She very nearly was.

"That's good," he said softly.

She added hastily, "There's no man at the moment, at any rate. But who knows about tomorrow?"

"That's right," Chase said blandly. His voice sounded as if it had been rubbed with sandpaper, and his breath was warm against her temple. He kissed her cheek and slowly let his lips slide across the sensitive skin to her mouth. "Anything might happen tomorrow."

CHAPTER FIVE

OVER BREAKFAST the next morning, as Nicky was stirring his cereal into complete sogginess, he said, "It's not fair. Floyd can whistle and I can't. And he can take a bath in a cup. I have to get wet all over."

He was feeling better, Amanda concluded. He hadn't made a fuss about baths in a couple of days, since he'd realized that soaking in warm water really did stop the itching for a while.

She leaned across the breakfast bar and studied him. His aristocratic dark eyebrows were drawn together in a furrow this morning, and the chicken pox on his face had begun to fade. No new ones had appeared in at least twenty-four hours, and the existing ones were drying up, so he wouldn't need to be kept away from other people for much longer. The thought made her feel sad. She was going to miss this little guy.

"You could make a contest of it," she suggested. "See whether you can learn to whistle before Floyd says your name."

He pursed his lips and blew, unsuccessfully, and looked so disgusted that Amanda had to turn briskly back to her recipe book to hide her amusement. "It does take practice, Nicky. Are you finished with that cereal?"

He nodded and carried the bowl carefully to the sink so she could dump the remainder down the disposal. "What are we going to do this morning?"

"I thought we'd bake cookies. Remember the story we read about the gingerbread man last night?"

Nicky nodded. Then he dragged a chair up beside her, climbed onto it and got a spoon—which Amanda interpreted as wholehearted approval of her plan.

While the cookies were baking, he stood beside Floyd's cage and repeated, "Say Nicky!" until Amanda was about to go mad. Finally he gave up and came back to sniff the pan of spicy gingerbread that had just come out of the oven. "Those cookies tickle my nose," he announced. "Birds are silly, anyway. I have a dog at home."

"Oh, do you?"

"A big dog." He eyed Amanda as if wondering how much she'd believe and threw out his arms. "Bigger than the whole world!"

I'll bet, Amanda thought. Imaginary dogs came in all sizes.

"He's got spots and stripes and lots of fuzzy hair."

"Where is he staying now, when you're not at home?"

That, plainly, was a problem Nicky hadn't considered. He sighed. "Well, I'd like to have a big dog."

"It would be lots of fun, wouldn't it? But there would be difficulties, too. Who would take care of him when you can't?"

Nicky ducked his head and looked up at her through the long fringe of eyelashes. It was one of his best tricks, almost as if he was summing up his victim before striking. "You would," he said confidently.

He could be right, Amanda thought, if circumstances were only different....

Don't even *start* to think like that, she warned herself. Nothing was going to be different.

She wrapped him in an apron, gave him a dull knife and set out several small bowls of colored icing. "We'll use raisins for eyes and red-hot candies for buttons and coconut for hair,'' she said, and started to frost the gingerbread men.

"I'll make one that looks like me,'' Nicky said. He industriously plastered icing on a cookie. It broke in two, and he put it down with a sidelong look at Amanda. "He can't be broken. The Nicky cookie has to be special.''

She handed him another gingerbread man. "Absolutely.''

"Do you think I'm special?''

"Of course you are, Nicky.''

"Daddy says I'm *really* special. I'm a chosen child.'' He smiled triumphantly.

Every muscle in Amanda's body tightened. She forced herself to speak casually. "You're adopted, you mean?''

Nicky nodded. "That's it. My mommy didn't carry me in her tummy. The mommy who died, I mean.''

"Yes, I see, dear.''

What a story, she thought. The man from the tabloid would pay dearly to get hold of that tale straight from Nicky's own lips! It would be all the confirmation he needed of the old rumor that had Chase foisting his love child off on his wife....

The thought reminded her that she hadn't mentioned the reporter to Chase, or to anyone in the production company. He might still be hanging around, looking for someone willing to talk. There wasn't any way to stop him from asking questions, she supposed; it was a free country. But at least they could be on guard.

"There,'' Nicky said finally. "He's done. Now I'll make one who looks like Daddy.''

He also made three Mandy lookalikes before he was quite satisfied, and a nanny—a skinny and slightly over-baked cookie that he adorned with a scowl drawn in frosting. "Because that's all they do,'' he confided. "They frown and say, 'Nicky, don't get dirty,' all the time.'' He rubbed his eyebrow and left a streak of icing on his forehead.

Amanda laughed and kissed it away. "I hope the next one will be a whole lot nicer."

Nicky didn't bother to answer that, but the sigh he heaved made him sound much older, and tired.

After dinner that evening, he climbed onto her lap on the couch as they watched a television special about baby animals. He perked up when he saw the kangaroos and asked if that was how all mommies carried their babies.

Amanda was still trying to find an answer to that when he added pensively, "The mommy who did carry me in her tummy—why did she give me away?"

Amanda swallowed hard. Dear Lord, how on earth was she to answer that question? And where was Chase when she needed him? How she would love to hand this child to him and listen to his answer! She cuddled Nicky closer and played for a little time to think. "What does your daddy say about that?"

"He says she loved me, but she couldn't take care of me."

"I'm sure he's right, dear. I'm sure that she loved you very much."

Nicky didn't seem content with the answer, but he didn't press. It was almost as if he'd been over this ground many times before. "When will Daddy come?"

"I don't—"

There was a knock at the door. Nicky sat up and called, "It's open!"

Chase put his head around the edge of the door. Nicky bounced out of her lap and ran to his father, who swung him up to sit on his shoulders.

"Do you leave your door unlocked all the time?" Chase asked.

"This is Springhill." She smiled up at him. He looked even taller from this angle, with Nicky clutching his hair. "Besides, I expected I'd be too lazy to get up to answer when you came."

"Or too busy with the hooligan here."

"That, too."

Nicky was clamoring to get down. "I saved a Mandy for you to see, Daddy," he said.

"A what?" Chase put him down and Nicky dashed for the kitchenette.

"A gingerbread cookie he fondly believes resembles me."

"Oh, I see. He means a pretty one."

Amanda's face turned a delicate pink. She was being silly, of course. That was the kind of casual compliment that Chase didn't even think twice about, and though she didn't question that he meant it, such a simple thing shouldn't affect her this way.

Chase smiled and sat down beside her. "If that's all it takes to make you blush..."

"It's not fair," Amanda muttered.

"Perhaps not, but it's fun. And if you're going to complain about your complexion, don't expect me to listen." His fingertip flicked gently against her cheek. "Your skin is like porcelain, except it's soft and warm and glowing."

That really sent color flooding into her cheeks.

Nicky came back with two cookies. "This one's Mandy," he said. "But you can't have her, Daddy. I'm keeping her forever. So I brought a cookie Mandy frosted for you to eat." He painstakingly arranged the cookies on the top of the trunk, then wriggled up between Chase and Amanda on the couch and started to watch his show again.

Chase munched the cookie. "This is pretty good, Amanda. I bet you get a lot of practice, what with all your little guests."

"I've baked a few thousand gingerbread men in my time, yes. It's the thing I'm famous for. One of my friends is a cartoonist and teaches all the kids to draw. Another has a pool and has given them all swimming lessons. I let them decorate cookies. You should see the place at Christmas-time...."

You're babbling, Amanda, she told herself. Cut it out. He can't possibly be interested!

He was watching her with a slight smile and a ginger-bread crumb clinging to the corner of his mouth. Amanda had to restrain herself from brushing it away. Or perhaps she could just kiss it away.... Her pulse sped up a little at the very thought.

"You're home early tonight," she said, and belatedly realized how awfully domestic that sounded. No matter what she said, she was only getting herself in deeper. "I mean—"

But Chase seemed oblivious to her gaffe. "I finished shooting a bit early and skipped dinner so I could at least say good-night to Nicky." He tousled the child's hair, but Nicky's attention was focused on the tiny creatures on the television screen. "Not that he appears to care."

"You haven't eaten?"

"I thought after he was in bed, I'd try to entice you down to the restaurant with me."

The prospect was tempting. She'd already eaten with Nicky, of course, but the main attraction of Chase's invitation was hardly the food. She shook her head reluctantly. "We're short-staffed at night, so I don't know who I'd get to look after him. But there's always room service." She added diffidently, "Or I could fix you something. We had a pot roast tonight, and there's some left."

"That sounds just fine." He followed her to the kitchen and watched as she started to unload the refrigerator. "You actually got Nicky to eat pot roast?"

She bristled a little. "It's very good."

"I don't doubt it," Chase said hastily. "I just meant that he seems to have an aversion to anything that's nutritious."

"Well, if he's allowed to have chocolate doughnuts, of course he's going to prefer them."

Chase winced. "I get the message."

The kitchenette hadn't been built for two people, and the third time she had to ask him to move out of her way Chase finally sat down at the breakfast bar and propped his chin in his hands.

Amanda started to tear up lettuce for a salad. "You look tired," she said.

"This shooting schedule is a killer. But after this project is finished, I'll have a month or so free before the television season gets into swing."

"Is it as busy as this?"

Chase shook his head. "We work long days when we're shooting, but that's only three days a week. And a lot of the preparation and paperwork I can do at home."

"Where's home?" She knew, because there'd been a picture of his house in a magazine recently. In fact, she was asking more to keep him talking than out of curiosity; his voice had a husky edge to it tonight, and she loved to listen to it.

"It's just a little house, really. I built it last year."

She was startled. "You personally?"

Chase's eyebrows rose. "You mean, did I put up the rafters myself? No."

"Oh, of course. But you did say you'd been a carpenter."

"Different sort, I'm afraid. But I drew the basic design. It's a contemporary—lots of glass and wood—and not too far from the beach."

"Sounds lovely." She set a salad in front of him.

"It's very private."

That reminded her of the tabloid reporter. Chase listened to her story about Kathy chasing Joe Smith out of the restaurant with a broom and laughed. "She'll probably make next week's issue—the tabloids will be speculating about what she's covering up," he said.

"It doesn't bother you?"

Chase sobered suddenly. "I didn't say that. But after a while, you learn not to worry about it anymore. There are always a few who are going to believe that kind of trash, but most people know better."

She thought about the early stories of Nicky's adoption and nodded, but she wasn't quite convinced.

"The production is actually running ahead of schedule," he went on. "Joe Smith might like to know that—he could probably create a whole issue about the slave-driving habits of the director. Maybe we should call him up and tell him. They pay rather well for tidbits like that."

"I'll keep it in mind next time I'm short of cash," Amanda said dryly.

Chase laughed. "And wonder of wonders, none of the scenes on tomorrow's list involve me at all, so I have a day off. Do you think Nicky will be able to go out in public?"

Amanda tried to smother the disappointment that washed over her. She hadn't expected to be relieved of duty quite so soon. "He's past the contagious stage, so I don't see why not. Better take it easy, though, and don't let him get too much sun."

"Well, I thought we'd start his reentry into society rather quietly. The inn has a Sunday brunch, right?"

Amanda nodded. "A very good one, too."

"We'll check it out. Then a short trip to the nearest park, probably followed by a nap." He grinned. "Big excitement, you can see."

"After four days in isolation, it will certainly be exhilarating for Nicky. I'm sure you'll enjoy yourselves." She set a plate in front of him with a flourish. "Your pot roast, sir."

Chase didn't even look at it. "Actually, I was hoping you'd come along, Amanda. The least I can do to thank you for everything you've done is buy you brunch. And as for the park—" his voice dropped to a sultry, almost tremulous confession "—I admit I have ulterior motives in asking you."

Amanda's eyebrows rose slightly.

"You must know where all the best playgrounds are."

She laughed. "That's a very effective little scene. You might have been late getting into the field, but I'd bet you were born an actor, Chase Worthington."

He smiled. "Actors are just people, too, you know." He cut a bite of pot roast and ate it thoughtfully. "You're right. This is very good. Nicky has better taste than I gave him credit for."

Amanda started to rinse the dishes and stack them in the dishwasher. "What would you do if it all fell apart, Chase?"

"Acting, you mean?" He shrugged. "I'd probably go back and finish learning to be a cabinet-maker."

She considered that for a minute. She liked the calm matter-of-fact way he'd spoken, as if he wouldn't miss stardom and all the hoopla that surrounded it, even if it vanished tomorrow. Or was he simply so self-confident that he considered the possibility of losing his position and fame too remote even to consider?

She asked curiously, "Do you ever do carpentry anymore?"

"Now and then. I built a few shelves in the new house—I'd have done more of the finishing work if I'd had the time. But as it is, between the series and the occasional special and this project…"

"That's all TV," she mused. "Don't you ever want to do feature films? I'm sorry, maybe I'm being nosy."

He dismissed her concern with a wave. "I might, if the right projects come along. The work is more intensive, but I'd have longer periods in between to spend with Nicky."

"The older he gets, the more important that's going to be."

As if he'd heard his name, Nicky appeared and climbed onto a tall stool next to Chase. "I'm hungry, Mandy."

Amanda, who had been keeping one eye on the television screen, said, "I'll bet that's because you just watched the baby birds get their dinner."

Nicky grinned. "Cheep!" he said, and opened his mouth very wide.

Amanda took a bowl of mixed fruit from the refrigerator and spooned a bite at a time into Nicky's mouth.

"Nicholas, that's disgusting," his father said.

"That's what makes it so much fun," Amanda told him. "But if you don't like it…" She put a few bits of fruit into a small dish and set it in front of Nicky. "No more baby bird, pal."

"When he's finished," Chase said, "I'll take him upstairs to his own bed so you can have a decent night's sleep for a change."

Nicky stuck out his lower lip and stirred his fruit.

Amanda's heart gave a little jolt of pain. "I don't mind,"

she said quietly. "But of course you'll want all day tomorrow with him, so…"

"Which reminds me, you haven't really given me an answer. Will you come to brunch?" Chase reached across the breakfast bar and stroked the back of her hand with a gentle finger. "Come play with us tomorrow, Amanda?"

Nicky looked up at her hopefully, and for a moment she saw a tremendous resemblance between the two of them. Or was it just the pleading expression in their eyes? One pair was dark brown, the other hazel, but they were equally earnest.

Don't, she thought. She had done her Good-Samaritan deed, and it was over. The more time she spent with the Worthingtons—either of them, or in combination—the more difficult it would be for her when they left Springhill.

Her hand tingled under the soft stroke of Chase's fingertips. Who was she trying to fool? Nothing she did in the next few weeks could possibly make her miss Nicky more than she already would. And as for Chase…

Her heart beat just a little faster as she looked into his eyes. If this was foolishness, then she was going to enjoy it while it lasted. She'd worry about the aftereffects when they happened.

"All right," she said. "I'll meet you in the grand ballroom at noon."

THEY CAME to her door, instead. Chase said it was because he was illustrating proper conduct to Nicky and showing him that a gentleman never left a lady unescorted. Besides, he said with a gravity belied by the twinkle in his eyes, Nicky had been up since six, and he wasn't certain he could have survived another half hour of the child's asking exactly why they couldn't go and get Mandy yet.

Nicky, on the other hand, insisted that only he could

properly supervise Floyd's bath, and before Amanda could talk him out of it, he'd put a cup of water in the parakeet's cage. They were late to brunch because of it, for Floyd spattered Nicky's new white shorts and they had to go back to the suite to change his wet clothes.

"As long as we're at it, does Nicky have anything practical?" Amanda sorted through a suitcase full of color-coordinated pastel play clothes. "No wonder the nannies are so frustrated with trying to keep him clean. They'd be better off to put him in jeans and let him play."

She settled for a pair of green shorts that were almost the color of grass, so Nicky could run and slide at the park without getting too stained, and the coordinating top, which was at least dark enough not to show every speck of dirt. "There," she said when he was dressed again. "You're all ready to go to the park. You're lucky, you know. I wish I could go to brunch in my play clothes."

Chase looked her over, from the top of her shining hair to her khaki trousers and low-heeled shoes. "That looks like a pretty sensible outfit."

"Well, you've never been to the park with me, have you?"

"Something tells me I'm in for an experience." He tugged at his necktie in mock distress, but there was a note of laughter in his voice. Amanda shivered a little in anticipation.

The inn's ballroom was grand by Springhill standards, though Amanda supposed it wasn't much compared to some of the places Chase must have been. It was nicely proportioned, however, with high ceilings and beautifully grained oak paneling. There were also some elegant crystal chandeliers that Amanda was convinced had survived the building's decades of deterioration only because they'd been so seriously out of fashion. Now, of course, they were back in style, and she insisted that every crystal drop be kept sparkling.

"I don't think this room was open a few years ago," Chase said. "It's very pleasant."

"I've always thought so. And even though it's not exactly worthy of its name, a party held in a place called the Grand Ballroom has an extra dash nonetheless."

The brunch definitely had that little something extra. Not only was the food varied, extensive and colorful, but the setting—small stations scattered throughout the room, each topped with a lush floral centerpiece or a giant ice carving—invited the hungry diner to browse before making his selections.

The staff seemed unsurprised to see them together. A hotel grapevine was an amazing means of communication, Amanda had always believed. Some of the regular patrons, however, were almost openmouthed when they spotted the trio. Amanda tried to ignore the looks as she led Nicky up to the buffet line. Let them wonder why he was skipping along beside her, holding her hand and chattering, while Chase followed.

They started with miniature Belgian waffles with blueberries and whipped cream. Nicky dug into his with enthusiasm, and was soon wearing a multicolored mustache. When he asked for a second waffle, Amanda was startled. "I'll pass that on to the chef," she murmured. "It's probably the biggest compliment he'll get all year—even bigger than being asked to cater the director's party next Sunday."

Chase snapped his fingers. "The party! That's what I wanted to ask you about."

Amanda wiped Nicky's face with his napkin. "I'm not directly involved in catering, so I'm free if you want me to watch Nicky that night."

Chase didn't answer, and eventually she looked across the table at him, her eyebrows raised.

"I wasn't asking you to baby-sit, Amanda. I want you to go to the party with me."

"But the invitation list is limited to cast and crew, isn't it?"

"It's not exactly exclusive. Besides, the director said we're welcome to bring guests, so if you're worried about having the gate barred in your face..."

"Not if I'm with you."

"Good. That's settled. Are you determined to have that second waffle, Nicky, or shall we see what else is available?"

Nothing was settled, Amanda thought. She hadn't agreed to go; she'd merely observed that the star could probably get whatever he wanted. But before she could say anything, Chase and Nicky were on their feet, politely waiting for her.

Suddenly, she decided she *would* go. The invitation was flattering, and the party would no doubt be fun. After all, how often did an outsider get to take part in something like that? It would be a memory to treasure forever, after he was gone....

Nicky toyed with his second waffle and fidgeted in his chair. He looked around the room, kicked his feet against the table's pedestal, and at least once every three minutes asked if it was time to go.

Chase murmured, "I'm sorry. This wasn't such a great idea, was it? Obviously I shouldn't have said the word 'park' till we were there."

Amanda laughed and put her napkin down, signaling to the waiter. "You're catching on to the fine points."

She went back to her apartment to change, and when they met again in the lobby a few minutes later, she began at once to smooth sunscreen onto Nicky's arms and legs, over his protests. Chase perched on the arm of a wing chair nearby and watched. Amanda was fairly sure it wasn't the sunscreen he was interested in, but the way her floral-print playsuit fit. When she'd bought it, she hadn't even questioned if it might be too brief, but suddenly she felt as if she were wearing a bikini.

One of the inn's permanent residents came in from his regular morning walk and stopped at the registration desk to buy a Sunday paper. He paused when he saw Amanda and Nicky, and scratched his head. "Is this your little boy, Miss Bailey?"

Amanda rubbed her sunscreen-laden hand across the back of her neck. "He's just borrowed for the occasion, Mr. Pierce."

He frowned. "Borrowed?"

"Yes. Just like all the rest of my little friends."

"Oh…of course." His face cleared, and he crossed the lobby to summon the elevator.

Amanda sighed. "He's been getting a bit confused in the past few weeks," she said to Chase as soon as they were safely outside the building. "I'm worried about him. I wonder if he's seen his doctor lately."

Chase shot her a look. "Your job is a lot more than keeping the building running, isn't it?"

"Well, someone has to keep an eye out for the residents. Mr. Pierce doesn't have any family."

"Don't get defensive, I wasn't making judgments. In fact, I admire you for your involvement. You adopt orphaned parakeets and sick kids…"

"Well, it wasn't Floyd's fault Mrs. Henderson died, any more than it was Nicky's fault he got sick."

Nicky, skipping along beside her, said, "But I'm all well now."

"You're much better, yes."

"Largely," Chase said, "thanks to you."

The simple compliment did funny things to her breathing. She shook her head. "I did what anyone would have done, Chase." Her voice came out a little lower than usual, and she cleared her throat and quickly changed the subject. "Let's take my car."

"Car? But isn't the park right over there?" He pointed toward the center of town, where the rich green of the central square beckoned.

"I thought you wanted the best playground."

"Well…"

"The one I have in mind has the highest swings and a tall curlicue slide. It's a good thing you put on jeans, by the way."

"Why?" Chase said warily.

"Because someone will have to take Nicky down the slide. He's too little to go without an escort."

"The joys of fatherhood," Chase said.

The park was already crowded, and the playground was teeming with kids from toddlers to teenagers. Nicky hung back a little, clinging to Amanda's hand, wary of the bustle.

A girl of about eight, with pigtails and a missing set of front teeth, called from a swing, "Hey, Mandy! Watch me!" and pumped herself higher into the air.

The name seemed to be a signal; half a dozen children stopped their activities and converged on Mandy.

"What are you?" Chase muttered. "The Pied Piper?"

Nicky's eyes widened, and he pressed closer to Amanda's side as she dispensed smiles and one-armed hugs to the other children.

"I'll bet if you ever turn up here with a baby of your own there'll be a mutiny," Chase said.

A baby of her own… The very thought nibbled at the

corners of her heart and made it ache. "Of course not," she said stoutly. "They know I'll always love them all, even if there're a hundred children in my life."

"Now *that*—" Chase began.

Nicky interrupted. He tugged at Amanda's playsuit and demanded, "Mandy, play with me!"

"It figures," Chase said. "Mine would be the jealous little brat."

Amanda smiled at him and led Nicky off to an empty swing, next to the one the girl with pigtails was using. She slowed down till her swing matched the easy arc of Nicky's and soon hopped off. "Let me push him, Mandy."

"Gently," Amanda warned.

"I know," Katie Kendall said impatiently. "I haven't dumped my little brother out of a swing yet, no matter how much I'd like to."

Nicky eyed his new source of propulsion with trepidation, but eventually he relaxed a little and even started to giggle as Katie teased him.

"I'll be under the oak tree keeping an eye on you," Amanda said finally. "Bring Nicky back whenever you get tired of entertaining him."

Katie nodded, and Amanda retreated to the shade of the huge old oak at the edge of the playground. Before long she was surrounded by kids.

Nicky hopped off the swing and came running, worming his way in among the others till he was pressed against her side. "Hey," Amanda whispered. "It's all right. I haven't forgotten you."

One group went off to the teeter-totters. Another pair disappeared toward the jungle gym. A third group eventually persuaded Nicky to come along to climb on the big old fire truck.

Chase dropped to the ground beside Amanda. "Nobody asked us to play," he said mournfully.

"Ha. That must be because they're all aware of how famous and important you are, and so they're scared you'll cut them dead if they make a friendly gesture."

"You don't treat me like that."

"Didn't you know, Chase? I'm absolutely in awe of you." She looked up at him, her eyes wide with what she intended to be mock hero-worship. But when her gaze met his, something turned over inside her.

He picked up a lock of her hair and used it like a paint-brush to trace her profile. "Right," he said dryly. "So you're saying if I make the first friendly gesture, people will be more likely to take me into their hearts?"

"Yes. In fact, that's a really good…"

He leaned closer. She thought he was going to whisper something he didn't want anyone to hear, so she leaned toward him, too. The scent of his after-shave made her nose tingle, and she hoped he wouldn't notice her madly jumping pulse.

He kissed the corner of her mouth, long and softly, and relaxed once more against the tree, obviously pleased with himself. "How was that as friendly gestures go?"

Amanda had to swallow hard before she could smile at him. "I didn't mean toward me," she said finally. "I was thinking more about asking the guys who are playing volleyball over on the sand court if you could join them."

"Oh, I see. You're sending me out to play to get me out of your hair. So much for awe," he complained, and went off to join the volleyball game.

Amanda herself got involved in a game of hide-and-seek, which was interrupted by Nicky throwing a tantrum. He was red-faced and screaming because another child had a ball he wouldn't share, but mainly, Amanda was convinced, because he'd had a little too much of a good thing. "Come along," she said, and led him back to the shady spot under the big tree.

Chase appeared within half a minute. "We'd better go."

"Just time for a rest, I think." Nicky put his head down in her lap, and she stroked his dark hair. "It would be a shame to take him back inside. He needs the fresh air. Would you get the blanket out of the back of my car?"

Chase complied, and when he returned, said, "You're prepared for all eventualities, aren't you?" He spread the blanket right beside her and helped ease Nicky onto it. Even in his sleep, the child clutched a fold of Amanda's playsuit.

Chase did not go back to the volleyball game as Amanda had expected he would. He lounged beside her, instead, stretched almost full length on the grass.

Watch out, Amanda told herself. She could easily get used to having him there. And as for the way he was behaving—as if she were an attraction more spellbinding than anything else in his life—well, it was time to remind herself of reality. "Have you hired a nanny yet?" she asked softly.

Chase grimaced. "No. I'll call the registry again tomorrow and see what they've found. If they've got someone, she could be on her way tomorrow afternoon."

"What are you going to do with Nicky in the meantime?"

"I don't have to be on the set till noon." He chewed a stalk of grass and looked at her, big brown eyes pleading. "But after that... I hate to ask you, Amanda. But if I could impose on you for another half day..."

"Of course."

There was a pause, and then Chase said, "He's been so happy with you, Amanda. I can't thank you enough."

She looked down at Nicky. She hadn't even been conscious of it, but her fingertips were stroking his hair as he slept. She was already so deeply attached to this child that it was going to break her heart when he left. Nothing could make that any worse. And Chase was right. Nicky *was* happy with her.

"Why not just leave him with me?" she said. "Until it's time for you to go."

Chase's hesitation was obvious. "Nicky would be thrilled. But you've done too much for us already."

Amanda shrugged. She wasn't going to beg, that was for sure, even if she wanted to.

"Of course," Chase went on slowly, "if it doesn't work out, all you have to do is let me know. I can always make other arrangements. And it's only a couple of weeks more."

He said that as if it was an advantage, Amanda thought, or as if he was trying to convince himself that it wouldn't last forever. She could understand how he felt; to Chase, a few weeks in Springhill must seem like a lifetime. But to her, two weeks with Nicky—two weeks with Chase—was like the blink of an eye.

Still, in two weeks, if she tried very hard, she could store up a whole lot of memories to keep her warm for the life-time that would follow after they were gone.

CHAPTER SIX

WHEN AMANDA CAME DOWN to the lobby the next morning, Tricia said with a smile, "I can't believe it. Are you free at last?"

"For the moment." Amanda picked up the morning's mail and flipped through it. "Is the new chambermaid I hired here yet?"

The desk clerk inclined her head toward Amanda's office.

"I'll take her upstairs and start training, then. Unless there's something else needing my attention?"

"No," Tricia said. "We've all gotten pretty good at handling things without you."

Amanda laughed. The inn was apparently running as smoothly as ever, and she congratulated herself; her policy of delegating responsibility wherever possible was working out well.

Training the cleaning staff was always more difficult when there wasn't an empty room to practice on, and so it was nearly noon when Amanda came back to the lobby. The first thing she saw was Chase, sitting at a table next to the glass wall of the little restaurant with a coffee cup cradled in his hand. He looked preoccupied, as if he was already thinking about the afternoon's work ahead. Across from him, still toying with a grilled cheese sandwich, was Nicky.

The child scrambled to his knees when Amanda approached. She gave him a hug, then extricated herself from his slightly greasy grip. Chase pulled out a chair for her and suggested with a smile, "Everybody needs a hug sometimes, so if you have an extra for me, Amanda…"

She let herself think for one long moment about putting her arms around Chase and allowing her body to melt into his as completely as the cheese in Nicky's sandwich had melted into the bread. But she sat down, instead, and tried to keep her voice light. "Do you want to blow every fuse in Springhill's gossip network? The kiss in the park yesterday was bad enough, thank you. Nicky, we have booster chairs if you'd like one."

Nicky shook his head.

"He's too grown-up for things like that," Chase said.

"Of course. I must have lost my mind even to suggest it."

"You know, I think you have. What do you mean, the kiss in the park yesterday was bad enough? It was a very nice kiss—chaste, friendly and unexceptional." His eyes began to sparkle. "Unless that's exactly what you had against it. In that case, I could try a different sort of—"

She shushed him as the waitress brought her coffee and refilled Chase's cup.

"Thanks, Kathy," Amanda said. "I think I'll try the corn chowder today, too, while Nicky finishes his lunch."

"He was very disappointed that you weren't here when we came down," Chase said. "I thought for a while he was going to stage a sit-down strike in the lobby to wait for you."

At least, Amanda thought in relief, they were off the subject of kisses! She tugged gently at one of Nicky's curls and tucked his napkin a little tighter. "You're beginning to need a haircut, young man."

Nicky dragged a carrot stick through a puddle of melted cheese and took a bite. "Where did you lose it?"

Amanda was completely at sea. "Lose what?"

"Your mind. Can we look for it this afternoon?"

Chase started to laugh, tried to swallow the sound and ended up almost choking. "I think perhaps I'd better go to work," he said to no one in particular. Nicky gave him a kiss and turned expectant eyes back to Amanda, still waiting for an answer. Chase tousled Nicky's curls and raised a hand to Amanda's head as if he wanted to do the same thing to her flaxen hair. But he settled for patting her cheek. "See you tonight, but I don't know when."

A woman at the next table leaned over as soon as he was gone. "You have such a nice little boy," she said. "I'm so glad to see a mother who teaches real manners."

Amanda smiled uneasily. She ought to correct the woman, but what difference did it make? She wasn't one of the coffee shop regulars; in fact, Amanda had never seen her before.

Besides, it might be better for Nicky if not everyone knew who he was. Safe in her small-town world, it hadn't occurred to her to ask Chase about security. Had Nicky's nannies been bodyguards as much as baby-sitters?

So she settled for thanking the woman for the compliment and hurried through her soup. When she stopped at the cash register to pay her bill, Kathy shook her head. "Mr. Worthington told me to put anything you wanted on his account. Room service and all." She grinned. "So if you're hungry for a piece of pecan pie for a snack this afternoon, I'll save it for you."

"No, thanks. That's the last thing I need. Well, Nicky? How about an hour in my office so I can get the bills paid?"

She'd had enough foresight to dig out a large set of

wooden blocks—cubes and arches and rectangles—and he played on the floor at her feet, building castles and bridges and giving her a running commentary of his progress until the last check was written, the last receipt filed, and the calculator and account books put away.

"Let's take a break and go pick dandelion leaves in Central Park," Amanda suggested.

Nicky made a face. "Why?"

"Because Floyd likes to eat them."

He gathered up his blocks, after only a little prompting. "Floyd's funny. I wouldn't eat dandelion leaves."

"You might be surprised."

Nicky stopped stacking blocks, and his eyes rounded as if he half suspected she'd slipped some into his grilled cheese sandwich.

Amanda laughed. "No, dear, I'd tell you what you were eating."

As they crossed the little park, she noticed a couple of men setting up chairs on the freshly painted bandstand. She had forgotten there would be a concert tomorrow evening; perhaps if Chase was late, she'd bring Nicky. The band was composed of enthusiastic amateurs, but the music was lively, and surely Nicky wasn't experienced enough to be a critic.

The workers paused as she and Nicky climbed the steps. "I'm going to pick a few dandelion leaves from the flower beds if you don't mind," she said. "Nothing precious, I promise."

"Take every one you find," one of the workers told her. "You'd be doing us a favor, believe me."

They crossed the expanse of grass to the elaborate, colorful flower beds, and Amanda showed Nicky how to find the dandelions, which were sometimes concealed under other, more desirable plants, and pick the smallest, most tender leaves. A couple of minutes later he brought her half a dozen and said, "I like you lots, Mandy. You're funny."

Her eyes stung a little. Don't be silly, she told herself. It had been a careless compliment, definitely nothing to cry over.

"Do you wish you had a little boy sometimes?" he asked.

Amanda knelt in the bark mulch at the edge of the flower bed, heedless· of the hem of her hunter-green skirt, and smiled into his earnest hazel eyes. "Yes, Nicky," she said softly. "Sometimes I wish I had a little boy just like you."

He smiled at that. His face almost glowed, and dancing lights appeared in his eyes, exactly like the careless teasing sparkle she had seen so often in Chase's. But she didn't have a chance to know what he might have said next, for a voice behind her said, "Well, look who's here."

Amanda recognized the careless drawl. She sprang to her feet and put a protective hand on Nicky's shoulder, drawing him close as she turned to face the tabloid reporter.

"Mr. Smith," she said coolly.

"I'm flattered you remember me. That's Chase Worthington's kid, right?"

Amanda nodded. It would be pointless to deny the fact; there were too many ways for Joe Smith to check.

"I thought I recognized the shape of the face. Don't you think the resemblance between them is amazing?"

Amanda was instantly on her guard. "Why shouldn't they resemble each other? If you'll excuse us…"

"Oh, I don't want to stop you from whatever you were doing, Miss Bailey. Picking flowers in the park? Isn't that frowned on by the town fathers?"

"We're not picking flowers, just dandelion leaves."

"Well, that's a new twist. For an art project, I suppose? Or are you giving the kid a nature lesson?" He dusted off the end of a nearby bench and sat down. "I heard Chase fired the nanny."

Amanda didn't bother to answer that. For all she knew, he might have heard it directly from the nanny.

He went on thoughtfully, "For obvious reasons, I'd say."

The tone of his voice took her by surprise, and despite her determination to ignore him, she looked up from the dandelion she was stripping. The admiring light in his eyes startled her.

"Yes," Joe Smith said, and his voice was like a careless caress. "Very obvious reasons." His thoughts were so clear he might as well have said, *Because he has you, instead.*

Irritation burned a path through Amanda's body. "Sometimes the things that seem most obvious are actually farthest from the truth." She reached for Nicky's hand. "That's enough leaves to keep Floyd happy, Nicky."

"Who's Floyd?" Joe Smith inquired.

"No one you'd get any hot information from, believe me," Amanda said over her shoulder.

"I'd rather get my facts from you, anyway. If you'd like to talk…"

She pretended not to hear him, and she hurried Nicky away a bit faster than he liked. "Why were you mad at that man, Mandy?" he asked.

One of the park workers came down from the bandstand. "Was he annoying you, Amanda?"

"Yes. But there's nothing to be done about it."

"Oh, I don't know." He thoughtfully flexed his biceps, but Joe Smith was already walking toward the far side of the park.

Amanda laughed a little shakily. Chase hadn't seen the man as a serious threat. So why was she so afraid of him?

NICKY WANTED SPAGHETTI for dinner, so Amanda wrapped him in a red bath towel, instead of tucking a napkin under his chin, and he plunged in with gusto. He'd been eating for almost a quarter of an hour when his father came in.

Chase took one look and said, "Good Lord, Amanda. He's got more tomato sauce smeared on the outside of him than his stomach could possibly hold!"

"But he's having fun," she said.

Nicky grinned. "It's good, Daddy."

Chase sighed. "Well, at least he's washable."

Amanda dished up another plate and handed it to him. "That's a very enlightened point of view. You might share it with the next nanny." Then she bit her tongue. "Sorry. It's none of my business who you hire."

Chase didn't seem offended. "I'll keep it in mind." He twisted up a forkful of spaghetti.

"How did the shooting go?" Amanda asked.

"We finished the house scenes tonight right on schedule."

"Darn, I was hoping to get a glimpse of the shooting while you were at Stephanie's."

"We'll still be working in the garden tomorrow if the weather's fair. Bring Nicky over."

"I might, if I can get away." She looked down at the child. "Are you about to give up on the spaghetti?"

Nicky shook his head and spooned up another bite. "Mandy," he said thoughtfully, "if you want to have a little boy like me..."

Amanda turned almost the same shade as the tomato sauce on her plate, but before she could say anything, the child went on, "Why don't you just get a chosen child like Daddy did?" His tone was matter-of-fact, almost practical.

Amanda swallowed hard. "That's an idea, Nicky," she

said as calmly as she could. "I'll think it over. Now, why don't you tell Daddy what we did this afternoon?"

But Nicky wasn't easily distracted. "Daddy, how did you find me, anyway?"

Chase ruffled the child's hair, but he was watching Amanda. "You're not surprised he's adopted."

She shook her head.

"Did Nicky shock you when he told you the news?"

"Not exactly."

Chase's mouth was a thin line. "I see. You'd read the tabloids."

"I saw the stories, of course, but I didn't believe them."

He seemed to turn that over in his mind before he smiled and said, "Sorry. I should have known you aren't the sort who believes the kind of filth those so-called newspapers put out."

The sudden warmth in his voice sent a tingle down Amanda's spine. She tried to keep her voice level. "It was the article in *Today's Woman* that made me wonder, and the cover picture."

His eyebrows rose just a little.

Amanda said, "Actress or not, Desiree would have had to be a miracle woman to get back into that kind of shape within three weeks of childbirth."

Chase laughed.

Nicky was making hills and valleys with the rest of his spaghetti. "Tell me the chosen-child story again, Daddy."

"At bedtime, Nicky."

"No, now!" He saw the disapproving angle of Amanda's eyebrows and turned back to his father with a hopeful smile. "Please, Daddy?"

Chase looked at Amanda and shook his head as if apologizing for boring her with the details. But she didn't find the story at all boring. It was a simple but absorbing tale, in fact, about two people who wanted a child, and so they had selected this little boy and named him Nicky.

"The first time I saw you," Chase said, "you were three days old. You were lying in a big white basket, and you were wearing a pale yellow sweater with bunnies on it, and you were kicking your feet and just getting ready to start screaming for your bottle. But then you saw your toes, and they fascinated you so much you forgot to cry."

Nicky chuckled.

"When I picked you up, you snuggled your face right into my neck, and you've been my little boy ever since."

Amanda's throat felt tight, and she had to blink back tears. She could picture the scene—the big man and the tiny baby, and the primitive instinct that sprang so suddenly to life and bound them together—and it caught at her heart.

But then, Chase hadn't sounded unaffected by the story, either, so she had nothing to be ashamed of.

Nicky said doubtfully, "Did I really think my toes were funny?"

"Well, it looked to me as if you did. And toes are pretty funny things, when you think about it." Chase leaned down to capture Nicky's foot, then stripped his shoe off and began to tickle his toes. The child shrieked with delight.

Before the mock fight was over, Nicky was so covered with spaghetti sauce, despite his towel-napkin, that Amanda offered to put him straight into the tub. "If you try to carry him upstairs, you'll have it all over you, too," she pointed out to Chase.

He ruefully agreed. "Not that I don't deserve it, tickling him like that. Do you want me to supervise?"

"No. I'll dig out the bathtub toys while the water's running."

In a few minutes, Nicky was splashing merrily in the tub. When Amanda came out of the bathroom, the kitchen floor had been wiped up and the plates put in the dish-washer, and Chase was relaxing in the sitting room.

"Sorry about the mess," he said. "The chosen child is one of Nicky's favorite tales, and he'll go on for hours if nothing distracts him."

"I can understand why he likes it. It's a beautiful story." She cleared her throat. "If you don't mind my asking..."

Chase shrugged. "Feel free."

"Do you know anything about his origins?"

"Not much. We—especially Desiree—didn't want to know the details. It would make him more ours, she thought, if we weren't looking for resemblances or char-acter traits or interests that he might have inherited."

Amanda nodded in understanding.

"And of course we were right in the middle of making *Winter of the Heart* when we learned that a baby might be available soon, so there wasn't a lot of time for asking questions even if we'd wanted to. It was a private adoption, and the lawyer offered to handle the fine points, so we let him."

Amanda told herself she should drop it right there. But she couldn't stop herself from saying, "As busy as both of you were with your careers, I'm a little surprised you went to all that trouble for a child."

She thought he might take offense or simply ignore the question. But he didn't, and when he answered his voice was calm. "Desiree was the one who was set on having a baby. She insisted no woman could be completely fulfilled without one. I was less excited, I must admit, but once I picked Nicky up..." He smiled. "He really did burrow his face into my neck, you know, and his breath tickled and sent shivers down my spine, and from then on he was the only kid in the world as far as I was concerned."

"He's still a snuggler, isn't he?"

Chase said dryly, "Except when he remembers that he's getting to be a big boy, and then just try to hang on to him for half a minute!"

Nicky reappeared, wrapped toga-fashion in a bath towel. He climbed onto Amanda's lap and buried his face against her shoulder. She smiled at Chase over the top of Nicky's head and started to sing a lullaby.

"You'd better let me put him to bed," Chase said. He pushed himself up with reluctance from the couch and lifted the child into his arms. There was a sleepy little protest, but Nicky's eyelids were so heavy that Amanda was sure he didn't really know he'd been moved.

She stayed in her chair, looking up at Chase as he loomed over her, the child cradled in his arms. "Come upstairs for a drink?" he said.

It was early yet, and she wasn't ready for the evening to be over. "All right," she said.

His suite was dim, with only a night-light glimmering in the sitting room. That small bulb was not part of the room's standard equipment, and Amanda wondered if Chase had brought it with him or if that had been one of the matters her staff had handled without consulting her. Not that it was important of course. It was just that she wasn't used to seeing one of the inn's two most luxurious suites lit only by a glowing reproduction of a cartoon character.

"Make yourself at home," Chase said as he carried Nicky into the room with the double beds. But she stayed near the door. It was silly, she supposed, but she felt a bit uncomfortable about being a guest in the suite.

There was a stack of paperbacks on the narrow marble-topped table in the tiny foyer. She shuffled through them, only half-aware she was snooping. He had interesting taste in books; there were several titles she'd been wanting to read herself.

Chase returned and paused in the doorway. "Are you all right, Amanda?"

She ran a finger across the edge of the table. "I'm just checking the housekeeping."

"Oh. I thought perhaps you were wondering how many women I've smuggled up here in the past week."

She laughed. "Of course not."

"Well, that's a relief."

"With Nicky around, you couldn't smuggle anything."

Chase winced. "True, but not flattering." He moved across to the tiny built-in bar and investigated the contents. "How about a brandy?"

"That's fine." She sipped from the snifter he handed her. "Don't misunderstand, Chase. I admire you for wanting to have Nicky with you, but bringing him along on location must complicate your life incredibly."

"You're right." He tipped her face up to his and smiled. "He complicates things in all kinds of nice ways. Take you, for instance. If it hadn't been for Nicky…"

But he didn't finish. He kissed her, instead, long and slowly and deeply, until Amanda's knees were like rice pudding. He tasted like brandy, but not the ordinary sort. This was like an old and rich and smooth vintage, one that went straight to her head and seemed to disconnect every muscle in her body.

But it didn't fog her senses. He drew her down on the couch with him, and as his mouth moved across her cheekbone, to her temple, over her eyelids, she could feel each cell reacting to his touch.

"Amanda," he whispered, "I want to go to bed with you."

And that's what I want, too. To make love with him, to be a part of him, even for a little while. No one else would ever know, but Amanda could forever treasure the memory that once upon a time, however briefly, she had been an important part of his life. Not because he was the sexiest man on American TV—her desire had nothing to do with that—but simply because he was Chase, and because she wanted to share the most intimate details with him....

And if she did, she knew, it would be the biggest mistake of her life. That, however, didn't stop her from wanting. She shook her head a little in a vain attempt to straighten out her brain. "But I thought…"

His arms relaxed a little, and he let his fingers wander through her hair, almost massaging her scalp. "You thought because I haven't been harping at you about it, I'd given up the idea? Not at all. I figured when you were ready you'd let me know—one way or the other." His fingertips slid down across her cheek, outlining her face. The contact was like lightning dancing from nerve to nerve.

"No," she said. Her voice was barely audible. It was the most difficult thing she'd ever had to say.

He didn't stop the gentle tracing of her features. "Do you mean no for all time, or no for right now?"

She looked at him with something close to panic in her eyes. I can't say it again, she thought. And I can't even begin to explain. If he asks why…

Chase smiled. "You don't have to tell me."

"I'd better go," she managed. She put the snifter down.

Chase followed her to the door. Almost against her will, she turned to him, with one hand on the knob.

He kissed her again, softly, almost tenderly, on the forehead. "Good night, Amanda." There was a wry note in his voice. "I only hope you sleep as badly tonight as I expect to."

STEPHANIE'S FRENCH revival mansion looked ethereally beautiful as Amanda and Nicky walked up the street toward it late the next morning. Set on a couple of acres of rolling lawns in the middle of Springhill's best residential neighborhood, the big brick house with its ivy-covered tower, bright slate roof and wrought-iron gates was a perfect setting for a movie. Amanda didn't know much about the script, but from the bits of information she'd picked up, it was no surprise to her that the location manager had chosen this house for *Diamonds in the Dew*. But though the house looked quietly elegant, like a lady waiting patiently for her cue, the once-quiet neighborhood was no longer peaceful. The streets were cordoned off and blocked by trucks and tents and equipment vans, and cast and crew bustled back and forth across the manicured lawn. Two young men were busy with cloths, wiping off a red Porsche that sat in the driveway just outside the massive front door.

Amanda paused across the street, not sure how close she was allowed to come. Despite the hectic activity, nothing much seemed to be going on at the moment, and though there were cameras and lights and microphones, she couldn't get a glimpse of Chase anywhere.

She did, however, see Stephanie, sitting in a lawn chair at the edge of the grass, so she crossed the street to her. "Is this spot reserved for the owner or may we join you?" she asked.

"Of course you can. They're between takes, but there'll be some excitement again in a few minutes. I think there's an extra chair somewhere." Stephanie waved a hand vaguely toward a row of trees that separated the gardens from a ravine full of wildflowers.

"Oh, we'll just sit on the ground. I doubt we'll be staying long." Amanda settled onto the grass with a swirl of her khaki skirt. Nicky stood beside her, bashfully eyeing the small boy on Stephanie's lap. "That's Zack," Amanda told him. "Don't you remember him from the park?"

Zack fixed wide blue eyes on Nicky. He was a little younger, and his face still carried the slight pudginess of babyhood, but he was a born leader. "Let's play," he said, and squirmed to get down.

"Not on your life," Stephanie warned. "Any noise, and we'll have to leave."

Zack frowned as if he didn't think that was fair at all. Amanda didn't blame him; after all, it was his home, and his lawn.

"Has Zack just had a haircut?" she asked. "Where do you take him? I need to ask Chase if he wants me to get Nicky's hair trimmed."

"At my regular salon. It doesn't seem as scary as the barbershop." Stephanie shifted Zack to her other knee. "I thought you said there was another nanny in the wings."

Amanda ran her hand through Nicky's curls so she didn't have to look at her friend. "Oh, it just seemed less complicated for me to keep him for a few more days." She tried to keep her voice calm. "I bet it'll be nice to have your house back again."

Though Stephanie's elegant eyebrows rose slightly, she went along with the change of subject. "You have no idea how many hours I've spent in my car this week running back and forth from the lake. If it isn't swimming lessons, it's play group, and if it isn't the kids' activities, it's my own. Eventually I just gave up the whole idea of work for the duration. But it'll be worth all the hassle just to be able to tell everyone who visits us that this is the very bedroom where Chase Worthington seduced Jessamyn Arden in *Diamonds*— Oh, here we go."

There were calls for silence, and the bustle in the front lawn died to stillness.

The bedroom where Chase Worthington seduced Jessamyn Arden. Amanda hadn't heard about that particular bit

of the script. Not that it bothered her, of course. It was only
a script, and even if there was more to the story than that,
it wasn't any of her business.

The camera had moved into place, and the massive front
door swung wide. Chase came out, briefcase in hand, and
walked around the Porsche to open the driver's door. The
way each footstep struck the pavement said he was both
furious and in a hurry.

Nicky sat up straight. Automatically Amanda reached for
the suspenders that held up his shorts, just in case he forgot
the talk they'd had earlier and went running to his daddy.

Jessamyn Arden, in a silky pale green negligee, appeared
on the threshold, shouting angrily. Chase answered, his
voice cold and wrathful. Then Jessamyn tripped over her
next lines, and the director called, "Cut." Chase and Jessamyn went back inside, and the two workers reappeared
to dust the car—to remove any fingerprints Chase might
have left, Amanda supposed.

Nicky tugged at her sleeve. "Why's Daddy mad at the
lady?"

"He's not, darling, not really. Do you ever play Let's
Pretend?"

Nicky nodded.

"Well, that's what Daddy's doing today. He's told you
about it, I'm sure."

In the next half hour, she watched in fascination as they
did the scene three more times. Once Chase fluffed his lines
and started to laugh; Jessamyn was obviously not amused.

Zack was squirming restlessly on Stephanie's lap. "Just
a few more minutes," she said. "Then we'll pick up Katie
at dancing class and go to the lake for the rest of the day."
Another take started just as she said to Amanda, "I hear
you're going to the director's party with Chase."

Where had Stephanie heard that? Must have been the

grapevine again. Amanda tried to sound casual. "Well, not if I can't find a sitter for Nicky. I've tried everyone on the inn's list of baby-sitters, and no one's available then."

"Bring him here."

"You're a glutton for punishment, Steph."

Stephanie rolled her eyes heavenward. "Not me, darling. I'm going to the party, too—it's a reward for all the effort I've put into this production. But I'm arranging a get-together for the younger generation, and that's why you can't find a sitter, because I've hired every one I could find to keep the urchins in order."

"You'll probably need them all."

"Well, one more child won't upset the balance. If you're free this afternoon, bring Nicky out to the lake house to play. He'll be more comfortable Sunday if he gets to know Zack a little better first."

Amanda agreed, and Stephanie gave in to the inevitable and took the restless Zack off down the street.

The next take went all the way through, and the director, apparently satisfied, ordered a break and a shift to the next scene on the shooting schedule. Crew members swarmed over the lawn, moving the Porsche out of the way and relocating cameras and sound trucks. Amanda watched as Jessamyn Arden, still wearing the silky negligee, tripped up to Chase, put one hand on his arm and looked up into his eyes. She couldn't hear what the woman was saying.

Chase shook his head and waved a hand to where Amanda was sitting. Jessamyn turned and stared at her, eyes narrowed, and then went off to her mobile dressing room, parked on the side street.

Chase started across the lawn, heading straight for Amanda and his son. "Come on, Nicky!" he called, and held out his arms. The child was off like a shot, and his father swung the child up onto his shoulders, then continued toward Amanda.

She sat there on the lawn with her feet pulled up under her, one hand spread against the cool grass to support herself, and watched him as he approached.

For the past several years, curiosity and admiration had made her follow his career and consume every word written about him. The moment she met him, however, curiosity and admiration had given way to a deeper and more personal attraction, which had in turn grown into longing and desire.

And then—slowly, quietly and inevitably—longing and desire had shifted into something deeper yet. Something she did not want to admit, but could no longer deny.

It had turned to love.

And as he came nearer, Amanda wished with all her heart that he was seeing not just a kind young woman who had befriended a child in need, not an attractive woman to help pass a few lonely weeks, but a woman he could love for all time, as much as she loved him.

CHAPTER SEVEN

ADMIRATION AND CURIOSITY—who would have dreamed that those things could possibly lead to a lasting love?

But they hadn't, Amanda admitted. She'd been intrigued by Chase Worthington, that was true, but from the moment they'd met, it hadn't been the star she'd found so fascinating, but the man. That overwhelming presence of his—the vibrancy, the sensual aura—caused a subdued throb of excitement to pulse through her whenever he was around. But it was strongest at the moments when he was simply being himself.

She deliberated about it all during the half-hour drive up to Sapphire Lake that afternoon.

She supposed she should have expected something like this to happen. Under the circumstances, thrust together as they had been at all hours, in all kinds of intimate situations, it was perfectly reasonable that they had begun to think of each other in physical terms.

Chase was a normal virile man, caught up in an unexpectedly domestic situation. In the limited space of a hotel suite, with Nicky next door and the whole of Springhill watching, he could hardly be anything but discreet, and so it was quite natural that he had started to look at Amanda with interest. But that was all it was for Chase. He'd said he wanted to sleep with her, but that was far from an invitation to spend a lifetime together.

But for Amanda, well, it was different. This was no pass-

ing attraction, no minor fling. This was a summer to treasure, a few weeks stolen out of time, to hold close to her
heart forever—

"Are we almost there?" Nicky asked plaintively.

Amanda wondered if, caught up in her own thoughts,
she'd been ignoring him. "Almost. Tell you what—let's
see who can spot a cow first."

Nicky peered out the window and almost immediately
shouted in triumph. They played games the rest of the way
to the lake, and when the car pulled up beside Stephanie's
summer home, on a choice lot directly on the shore, he
sighed with disappointment. "I didn't get to see a pig."

"We'll start with that on the way home," Amanda said.
"Remind me, all right?"

Stephanie was on the big deck at the back of the house
that overlooked the lake. A stack of snapshots and a big
piece of poster board sat on the table in front of her.

"What on earth are you doing?" Amanda said. "A kindergarten art project?"

"I'm making a collage of pictures of all the houses
we've sold in the last six months for an ad to run in the
newspaper next week. You know, sort of a 'Look how well
we're doing' kind of thing." She pushed the photos away
with a sigh. "Sounds dumb, doesn't it?"

"No, it's a great idea. Everyone wants to associate with
a winner."

"I know, but I'm not patient enough to do the cutting
and pasting, I'm afraid. And people think kids have life
easy because all they have to do is learn to cut on the
lines.... Iced tea?"

"Please."

"How about a lemonade for you, Nicky? Zack's down
in the sandbox if you'd like to go play with him now and
have your drink later." She pointed over the deck rail. In

a fenced area a few steps down from the deck, Zack was industriously loading sand into a dump truck that was almost as big as he was.

Nicky nodded shyly, and Mandy took him down. When she came back to the deck, her iced tea was waiting and Stephanie was trimming the photograph of a ranch house, trying to leave just enough border to make it stand out. Her scissors slipped and she put them down in disgust.

"Well, at least you can color inside the lines," Amanda said cheerfully. "You did almost as well as Nicky the other day."

"Thanks a heap, friend."

Amanda leaned back in her chair. The breeze ruffled her hair as softly as Chase had caressed her temple last night....

Enough of that, she warned herself, and sat up, looking over the rail to check on Nicky.

"He'll be all right," Stephanie said. "They're perfectly safe down there. The fence is tight, so they can't escape to the lake."

"I know. You're too careful with your kids to take chances like that. Still, it's a bit different for me."

"Since you're just baby-sitting? I don't know. A little benevolent neglect can be good for kids."

"You might be right. Nicky said his nannies never let him get dirty."

Stephanie eyed the two little boys in the sandbox. "He obviously isn't having any trouble remembering how. Besides, leaving kids alone a bit lets them learn to entertain themselves and work out their own social conflicts."

Amanda teased, "Always assuming they don't know where the black crayons are hidden."

Stephanie winced. "You had to remind me of that, didn't you? Why *are* you baby-sitting, anyway?"

Amanda sipped her tea. "I told you. It just seemed easier."

"For Chase, no doubt. But you?"

"It's working out fine. I take Nicky to the office with me, and on my inspection tours. What I can't accomplish with him around, I do after Chase takes him back to his suite for the night."

Like last night, she reflected, when she had been up till the wee hours balancing the inn's books. Though to be perfectly fair, she had to admit that it wasn't bookkeeping that had occupied her mind so completely, but that kiss.

Stephanie shook her head.

"You think I'm crazy, don't you?" Amanda asked.

"Not exactly. But I think you're walking a tight rope. For one thing, you're developing a king-size soft spot for Nicky."

"Wouldn't anybody?" Amanda glanced over the rail at the two little boys, heads close together over the big dump truck. The sunlight caught Nicky's curls, giving them a golden glow.

"All right, I admit he's a whole lot sweeter than I thought he could possibly be. Still...it's dangerous, Mandy."

"Because no good can possibly come of it?" Amanda knew she sounded almost bitter. "I know that, Stephanie. Two more weeks and they'll—he'll—be gone. But—"

"But you'd rather have the two weeks and heartache to follow? Oh, Mandy, why Chase? There are a dozen men right here in Springhill who would be better for you."

"Are you thinking of the sales manager?"

"Maybe. Who knows? You certainly don't—you haven't even given him a chance."

Amanda was glad when rapid footsteps sounded on the deck stairs and Katie came into view. "Mom! Where's my— Oh, hi, Mandy.'' She dispensed a hug. ''Mandy, come to my room and listen to my new tape. It's the best group ever!''

Amanda laughed. ''Katie, I think I'd better stay—''

''Oh, go along,'' Stephanie said. ''I'll keep an eye on Nicky, and if the Sapphire Lake Monster carries him away I'll even explain it to Chase.''

Once plunged into Katie's world, it took a while to extract herself again, and when Amanda returned, Stephanie was in the kitchen pouring them each a fresh glass of tea. ''I'd really better get back,'' Amanda said.

''Oh, don't rush. You haven't helped me decide how the pictures should be arranged in my collage.''

At least maybe, Amanda thought, there wouldn't be any more lectures about the foolishness of letting herself care for Chase and Nicky.

''Well, the bigger ones at the bottom of the ad, of course, and scatter the really nice houses around...'' They stepped onto the deck once more.

Nicky was perched on a corner of a chair, and Zack was standing beside him, wielding Stephanie's scissors. Around his feet was a pile of soft dark curls, and as Amanda watched in horror, too paralyzed to move, Zack neatly snipped another lock of Nicky's hair and let it fall. Then he turned around with a grin. ''I'm making Nicky handsome,'' he announced. ''Just like me.''

''Good Lord,'' Stephanie whispered. She snatched her son up and wrenched the scissors out of his hand. ''Zack Kendall, you're incorrigible!''

Zack started to wail. ''But Mandy said...''

Amanda closed her eyes in pain. ''I said that Nicky needed a haircut. Oh, Steph, he was only trying to help.''

''With this kind of helpfulness,'' Stephanie said grimly, ''the kid is going to be locked in his room till he's twenty-one! No, I won't punish him for cutting hair. But taking my scissors is a different matter, because he knows very well he's not supposed to touch sharp instruments.''

"In the meantime," Amanda said, "what are we going to do about Nicky?"

Nicky was shrieking now, too, and she gathered him up and tried to get a look at the damage. Zack had gotten only halfway around, that was one blessing, but in places his head was almost scalped.

Katie leaned against the deck rail and bit into a juicy nectarine. "He looks weird," she observed.

Nicky screamed all the harder.

It took a while for Amanda to get him calmed down, and even then he sobbed quietly as she and Stephanie combed and clipped and tried to cover the worst of the damage. By the time they were finished, Nicky's hair was almost even once more, but there was a whole lot less of it.

Stephanie gathered up handfuls of dark hair from the deck. It was hard to believe Nicky could have had so many curls. "Do you suppose Chase will want these as a memento?"

Amanda shrugged. "I'll take them just in case."

"So much for my theory of benevolent neglect. Nicky looks like he's ready to join the marines. Mandy, I am so sorry."

"You only took your eyes off them for a couple of minutes. I know how it feels, Stephanie. Don't forget I was supposed to be watching Katie the day she ran into the tree while she was flying a kite and gave herself a concussion."

"Yes, but nobody had to explain that one to Chase," Stephanie said drearily. "Look, I'll come into town with you and tell him how it happened."

"No. I have no idea when he'll be home—" she caught herself and hoped Stephanie had been too preoccupied to notice what she'd said ''—when he'll be off the set tonight. There's no sense in your sitting around waiting for him.''

And if I have any luck at all, she thought, Nicky will be out of sight when Chase arrives, so at least I can warn him before he gets a glimpse of the damage!

She left Nicky in the tub till he was wrinkled, but Chase didn't arrive. So she used the blow-dryer on his hair, which added a little fullness and body. In fact, she decided, it wouldn't have been too bad if it wasn't for the bare spot behind his left ear. Nicky, who couldn't see the bare spot, seemed to think his hair was all right; he even admired himself in her hand mirror.

At the last minute she decided to take him to the concert, after all. Hiding in her apartment was cowardly. Besides, the evening was warm and beautiful, and she could hear the lilting music drifting all the way from the park. Why not go and enjoy it? The odds were that the concert would be over long before Chase left the set.

But in fact, the band had just struck up a medley of Broadway show tunes when she spotted Chase at the edge of the park. He must have opted to walk back to the inn.

Reluctantly she raised a hand to catch his attention. He might not have seen her if she hadn't, for she and Nicky were sitting in the shadow at the verge of the park, as far from the bandstand as they could be. But even if she avoided him now, the reckoning couldn't be postponed for long; she might as well get it over with.

He stopped at the edge of the blanket Amanda had spread on the grass and stared down at Nicky with an expression she'd never seen on him before. It wasn't horror, exactly, and yet it wasn't mere surprise, either.

''He's half-bald,'' Chase said. He sounded as if someone had hit him in the stomach with a baseball bat. ''What happened to my kid?''

"I meant to ask you about cutting it," Amanda began.

"You sliced off all his hair without even consulting me?"

"But before I had a chance, the kids got hold of some scissors and..." She ducked her head miserably. "I'm sorry, Chase. I didn't have much choice, you see. He looked a great deal worse before I evened it up a little."

Nicky was biting his lip, his eyes wide, as if he knew there was big trouble somewhere and he was simply waiting for the roof to fall in.

"I turned my back for just a few minutes," Amanda admitted. "It's entirely my fault. I know Zack Kendall is dangerous, but I didn't even think—"

"Nicky looked worse than *this?*"

Amanda whispered, "I wouldn't blame you if you want to take him away from me entirely."

"Daddy?" Nicky said uncertainly. "Don't you think I look nice?"

"Once you get used to it," Amanda said hopefully, "it's really not so bad. It's the contrast that makes it such a shock."

Chase sat down on the blanket as if he was folding up in slow motion, propped his elbows on his knees and put his face down into his hands. He sounded as if he was choking; Amanda wondered if she ought to slap him on the back.

Nicky patted his father's arm.

"I saved his curls for you," Amanda said.

Chase raised his head, and she saw that his eyes were wet.

Tears? But that was ridiculous; it was only hair, after all, and it would grow back. She almost said so, before she realized Chase was laughing.

He lay back on the blanket and pounded his fist on the

ground. "Oh, Nicky," he said finally, "you're absolutely guaranteed to give me a lift!"

The clouds on Nicky's face dissipated in an instant. "And Amanda, too," the little boy said loyally. "She helped."

"Thanks a lot for the recommendation, pal," she muttered. She held out a small envelope.

Chase sat up and looked at it warily. "What's that?"

"What was left over after Stephanie and I finished the job."

He glanced at the contents and tucked the envelope into his shirt pocket. "Did you say her little demon was in on this?"

Amanda nodded. "And there's worse."

"Hit me with it. At least I'm sitting down."

"I can't find anyone to take care of Nicky on Sunday, so Stephanie invited him to come play with Zack during the party. And I said yes—before this happened."

"Well, at least we know one thing they won't be doing." Chase sounded awfully cheerful.

"What do you mean?"

"They won't be cutting any more hair, because there isn't enough left to get a grip on." He pulled Nicky down to sit between his knees.

"You mean he can go?"

He tipped his head to one side. "Unless we skip the party to do something else and take Nicky along."

It sounded like a wonderful idea to her. The party itself had never been a big attraction; spending another afternoon and evening with Chase had been what she found appealing. With Nicky or without, at the party or not, or doing nothing at all, it wouldn't matter, as long as she was with Chase.

She kept her voice steady. "I don't think the director would like it if you cut his party."

She was glad the evening light was fading; the street-lights hadn't yet started to come on, and at the edge of the park the shadows were thick, so Chase wouldn't be able to see the longing in her eyes.

THE DIRECTOR HAD LEASED the entire country club for his party, not only the clubhouse itself but the grounds. On the first tee a rock band was playing, and people were dancing on the fairway. Inside the building the bars were in full operation, food tables groaned under the load of savory dishes, and a second band was pounding in the ballroom.

It was not Amanda's kind of party. The best thing she could say about it was that the people were interesting. Though she knew most of the faces from the inn, there hadn't been time to learn about their jobs or what other movies they had worked on; if it had been a little quieter she would have enjoyed talking to them. As it was, however, within a couple of hours she was fighting a headache.

Chase brought her a tall glass of tonic water and noticed the wrinkle between her eyebrows. "You look miserable," he said.

She tried to smile. "It's just the noise. I'll be all right. And I keep thinking about Nicky."

"Wondering if he's still all in one piece, or if Stephanie's house is?" The room was crowded, and the chair he pulled up next to Amanda's was so close his thigh brushed hers.

"Zack's not a bad kid, you understand, just overwhelmingly curious. He's almost scientific about it."

"Now there's a thought. I'll give Zack a chemistry set as a token of thanks for Nicky's haircut."

Amanda shuddered. "He can do enough damage with

the stuff he finds in the pantry, thank you. And the way Nicky soaks up information…"

"Is that why you're worried about him tonight? Because of what he might learn from Zack?"

Jessamyn Arden strolled up, her low-cut cocktail dress and absurdly high heels making her stand out even in the crush of the crowd, and leaned over Chase's shoulder. A man across the table swallowed hard and averted his eyes from the display of cleavage. "What a shame, Chase darling," she murmured. "In the midst of a lovely party, you and the nanny are talking about Nicky." She smiled sweetly. "Too bad you haven't anything else in common." Then Jessamyn moved on, her hips swinging provocatively.

Chase's mind was obviously still on Zack Kendall. "I hadn't thought of what habits Nicky might pick up. Swallow your drink and let's get out of here."

"Don't you have to stay?" asked Amanda. "I mean, you're the star."

"Why? It's not my party."

It took another half hour to work their way through the crowd, chatting with people nearby and waving to those too far away to speak to, so it wouldn't look as if they were running away. But as they walked down the long drive to where Chase had parked his rented car, Amanda was still thinking about Jessamyn's comment. It was true, in a way—the main thing they had in common was Nicky. It was natural for Jessamyn to think it was the only thing they shared. But it was almost funny how the actress seemed to resent that fact.

"Now I know why you bring Nicky on location," Amanda said almost to herself.

"Because he's armor against she-cats like Jessamyn?"

She was startled at his matter-of-fact tone. "That's not

quite the way I'd have put it. And I'm sure that's not the only reason."

"Of course not. He also makes a great excuse to ditch a dull party." Chase reached for her hand. "Where do you want to go when we've retrieved the kid? Or better yet, let's leave him for a while and do something else."

"I thought you were worried about him."

"Not at all. Besides, he wouldn't like being dragged away from all the games and snacks Stephanie promised. Are you in the mood for a walk?"

"Of course." Unlike Jessamyn, she almost said, she had worn sensible shoes.

The country club bordered a park, and under the ancient trees the air was fresh and moist. There was just enough breeze to make the leaves stir in a gentle rustling symphony, and it was cool, so the insects hadn't come out to feed. The full moon bathed the park in silvery light—or was Amanda seeing that soft glow because of the contentment filling her heart?

I have never been quite so happy as I am right now, she thought. And even though that happiness was guaranteed not to last, surely it wasn't wrong to enjoy it for the moment.

Her hand rested comfortably in his, as if it had been made to lie there. And when they reached the farthest, most private section of the park, and Chase turned her toward him and put his arms around her, their bodies seemed to fit as neatly as two spoons nestled in a drawer.

He didn't ask her again to make love with him. He didn't need to put it into words; his kiss held both longing and the promise of a joy sweeter than anything she could imagine.

And the fear that had kept her from giving him the answer he wanted—the fear of sharing herself fully—gave way to a new certain knowledge that she must seize this opportunity or regret it forever. The joy he promised would be brief, a few short days, stolen from a lifetime—a mere pocketful of summer. That was all she could have, and she knew it. But it would be better than nothing.

And so she would share with him everything she could and hold the rest always in her heart....

Chase's hands slid slowly from her shoulders down her spine, and he let her go. "Maybe we'd better pick up Nicky." His voice was gruff. "Or I, for one, will forget all about him."

Amanda knew he was right, but for one awful instant she had to fight the urge to cling to him and beg him to love her, in the physical sense at least, if nothing else was possible. When she had finally come to understand her needs, when she had gathered the strength to take what she might and accept what she couldn't have, it was just too difficult to have that promise of joy—however fragmentary—snatched away.

They walked slowly back to the car, his arm around her shoulders, hers around his waist. By the time they reached Stephanie's house the rambunctious games had given way to quiet stories. Some of the kids were already asleep, and Nicky's eyelids were heavy as Chase carried him to the car.

Amanda started to say good-night to them both in the lobby, but Chase reached for her arm, and Nicky roused enough to protest. "I want Mandy to tuck me in," he murmured.

Chase looked down at her. "Would you mind?"

Mind? She'd missed Nicky's bedtime—when he was warm and sleepy and wanted to be cuddled—most of all. But she realized, as she looked up at Chase, that she was being asked for much more. There was a warm glow in his

eyes—uncertainty mixed with desire—and she wet her lips.
"Of course not."

By the time she found Nicky's pajamas in the bureau
drawer, he had collapsed against his pillow, his stuffed rabbit held tight. Amanda managed to uncurl him enough to
take off his shoes and socks and slide him under the blankets. She stood beside his bed for several minutes, watching
the way his long lashes lay against his cheeks, and the soft
rise and fall of his chest, and the small hand curved around
the stuffed animal, before she switched off the light.

When she returned to the sitting room, the lamps were
dim. Her first thought was that the chambermaids must be
using the wrong wattage. Then Chase pulled the cork from
a bottle of champagne, and Amanda forgot the lights. She
forgot everything but him.

"That didn't take long," he said.

"He didn't stay awake long enough to get into pajamas,
so I just left him in his shorts and shirt."

Chase shrugged. "I imagine he'll survive." He handed
her a slender flute. "I hope you realize I put him up to
this."

She choked on her first sip, then saw the twinkle in his
eyes and laughed. "You talked Nicky into luring me up
here to your lair so you could ply me with champagne? I
don't think so."

His eyebrows rose a fraction. "Don't you believe I'm
capable of using a four-year-old in a seduction scheme?"

She curled up at the end of the couch. "It's not that. I
just don't think you could get him to go to sleep on command."

Chase sighed and sank down beside her. "I knew there
was a flaw in that plot." A husky note crept into his voice.
"This is driving me crazy, Amanda. Every time I touch

you, I want you more.'' He drew a line with the tip of his index finger down the side of her neck just under her ear.

Amanda wouldn't have been surprised if the contact had left scorch marks. Her heart was pounding in slow, almost painful thumps.

Just don't get any illusions about forever, she reminded herself. If a week or two was all the time she could have, she would accept that gift gladly, and cherish it forever....

''You don't need to scheme at all, Chase.'' Her voice was low, and she had to clear her throat before she could finish. ''All you have to do is ask.''

She saw his eyes grow brilliant, and his hand slipped to the back of her neck and drew her close. He didn't put the question into words, because it wasn't necessary. The way he kissed her—and the way she responded—said it all, and when he gently pulled her to her feet and led her toward his bedroom, she did not hesitate.

She had dreamed of what it would be like to make love with him. But in fact no dream could have matched the reality. She had anticipated the gentle sensuality of his touch, but not the impact on her as each separate nerve tingled and rasped and ached with delight. She had expected that he would be as concerned about her pleasure as his own, but she had not imagined how incredible that pleasure could be.

And even after passion had burned itself out and left her lying almost paralyzed in his arms, her body seemed to vibrate with the memories.

''Oh,'' she said. Her voice shook. ''Oh, Chase.''

Chase raised his head and smiled at her. His eyes were bright with an expression she couldn't quite interpret. It was more than contentment, and less than triumph....

''Yes,'' he whispered. ''That's just about the way I feel, too.'' He laced his fingers through hers and whispered against her lips, ''Mandy, do you know how very beautiful you are?''

She felt beautiful, that was for sure. She was smiling when he kissed her, and that kiss of course led to another....

She almost told him she loved him. She didn't know what stopped her—the last tiny fragment of common sense, perhaps, or fear of what she might see in his face if she made that declaration.

And in the small hours of the morning as she lay beside him and watched him sleep, she knew there was nothing to be gained by complicating things that way. Telling him would only lead to pain.

He was lying on his side, one arm across her, his hand tangled in her hair because he had fallen asleep while he was running his fingers through it. She couldn't move—not that she really wanted to, but she couldn't even turn her head to see the time on the bedside clock.

She didn't know how long she lay that way, her mind drifting. But after a while she became convinced it must be nearly dawn. The idea jolted her out of her tranquil mood. The inn would soon be stirring. Worse, Nicky might rouse....

She tried to ease herself away from Chase, but the moment she moved he stirred and opened his eyes. For half a second, it was almost as if he didn't recognize her. Then he smiled, and his arm tightened and drew her down beside him once more. ''Running away?'' he said softly.

''I don't think it would be smart to bump into any of my staff in the halls, and if I wait any longer...''

He propped himself up on one elbow and looked at the alarm clock. ''It's early yet.''

''Not all that early.''

''Only a little past three.''

"Really?" She tried to twist around to see. "I thought—"

But he didn't seem interested in what she thought right then. He kissed her, and Amanda felt her body tighten like a perfectly tuned violin string, waiting for the virtuoso's touch.

And in the other bedroom, Nicky screamed.

She had heard him scream before, but in anger and frustration, never in terror. She was out of bed in an instant, shoving her arms into the sleeves of her dress, blessing the designer for making it easy to get into. She was still fastening buttons when she pushed open the door of Nicky's bedroom.

The night-light cast only a dim glow across the bed, but it was enough. Nicky was sitting bolt upright, his eyes wide, his body rigid, his face contorted, and even when Amanda reached him he didn't seem to realize she was there. She carefully put a hand on his shoulder, and when he didn't shrug it off, she slipped her arm around him. "It's all right, Nicky," she soothed. "I'm here."

Chase came in, still tying the belt of his robe. He sat down on the edge of Nicky's bed, but he didn't try to touch him.

Abruptly the stiffness went out of Nicky's body and he nestled against Amanda's side. He still wasn't awake, she thought, but that was just as well. Perhaps he would slip back into sleep without even realizing he'd had a nightmare. "Does this happen often?"

Chase seemed to have relaxed, as well. "Depends on what you mean by often. Once a week or so." He stroked Nicky's hair with a fingertip. "Four-year-olds," he said with gentle irony.

Amanda remembered what he'd said once before, about how children Nicky's age seemed to have an instinctive ability to interrupt at the worst possible moment. She colored a little and gathered Nicky even closer.

His eyelids fluttered, and he looked up at her. "Mandy," he said sleepily, and yawned in the middle of the word.

Chase said, "Do you realize how much that sounds like 'Mommy'?"

Amanda tensed. She tried to tell herself that it had been no more than an idle comment. But she couldn't stop herself from looking up at him. Her eyes were wide with panic.

Chase sucked in a deep breath. "That's who you are," he whispered. "My God. That's who you are."

She didn't know what had given him the key. It couldn't have been Nicky's slurred use of her name; Chase had heard that a hundred times before. She didn't think it had been her own startled reaction, either, for on some level Chase had already seen the truth or he wouldn't have made the comment.

Perhaps it had been the way the dim light fell across the two faces, hers and Nicky's, so close together. Chase's job was to study expressions and resemblances, but of course he had never had a reason to look at the two of them quite that way. And so he had not seen till tonight that despite their superficial differences, the green-eyed flaxen blonde and the dark-haired child with hazel eyes looked a great deal alike. In fact, the bone structure of the two faces was not just similar, it was identical.

Amanda had seen it, too, on that first afternoon in the hotel lobby—the afternoon she saw Nicky Worthington for the first time in four years. The first time, in fact, since he was three days old, when she had dressed him in a handmade yellow sweater with bunnies knitted into it and then kissed him goodbye and given him to the lawyer who had arranged his adoption.

There was no hiding the fact anymore, that was obvious.

Chase's voice had held a note of certainty. And in any case, she would not lie; she would not deny her child.

Nicky gave a tiny snore. Amanda eased him back against his pillow and waited till she was certain he was fully asleep before she slid cautiously off the edge of the bed.

Chase's voice was low and hard. "Where do you think you're going, Amanda?"

"Out to the sitting room. Or would you rather discuss it right here and wake him up for real?" She didn't turn around, and she didn't wait to see if he followed her.

He did, of course. He paced around the sitting room, turning on every lamp, as if darkness was more than he could bear. The lights seemed much brighter now than they had over the champagne glasses just a few hours ago, Amanda thought. They looked like the light an Inquisition torturer would have shone on the accused's face.

"Well?" His voice was like a whip. "Are you going to tell the truth for a change?"

Amanda moistened her lips, then raised her head and looked him straight in the eye. "I never lied to you, Chase. You never asked me before."

"Dammit, there was no reason to ask!"

She ignored the interruption. "But you're quite right. I am Nicky's birth mother." Her voice was trembling, and her knees felt no more substantial than rubber bands.

And what, she thought, *are we going to do now?*

CHAPTER EIGHT

CHASE SAT DOWN suddenly on the end of the couch like a puppet whose strings had been cut. He looked as if, even though he had made the accusation himself, he hadn't quite believed what he'd said, and that the confirmation of his fears had knocked the breath from his body.

Amanda stood in the center of the room, barefoot, twisting her hands together, and watched him. Her breath was coming quickly through parted lips.

"How long have you known?" His voice was flat, almost expressionless.

She started to breathe a bit easier. At least he wasn't angry. If they could just talk this out… "Always," she said, almost eagerly.

He looked at her sharply. "That damned shyster of a lawyer promised to keep it secret. You should never have known."

"The attorney didn't tell me who the adoptive parents were, Chase, just that he'd arranged a wonderful home for my baby."

Chase said something under his breath she was glad she didn't catch. But there was an edge to his voice; it seemed she had overestimated Chase's calm.

Amanda ran the tip of her tongue over her dry lips. "To be perfectly accurate, I haven't known *always*. Just since the day I saw Nicky's picture on the cover of *Today's Woman* with Desiree, when he was three weeks old."

"You recognized him, I suppose?" Chase sounded sarcastic. "Out of all the babies in the world, you just knew this one was yours?"

She didn't blame him. "It does sound a bit foolish, doesn't it? But I did. He looked exactly like my pictures as an infant."

Chase shook his head in disbelief. "Don't you think it's a pretty steep coincidence that you just happened to run across that magazine?"

"No. I'd been following the progress of the movie, you see." He didn't answer, and after a moment, Amanda went on almost tentatively. As long as he was listening... "Even though I wasn't here in Springhill, it was pretty exciting to read about you and Desiree and *Winter of the Heart,* and know it was all happening in my hometown. And I didn't have much else to do that spring but watch television and read."

He looked at her coldly, without a hint of empathy or understanding. But then, what had she expected?

She cleared her throat. "At any rate, if you remember, Desiree gave all the details about the baby in that interview."

"Proud mother that she was."

"Yes." Amanda's voice was hollow. "At first I couldn't believe it—it *did* seem too much of a coincidence. But the fact that she'd worked all the way through her supposed pregnancy and managed to keep it a secret from everyone just didn't ring true. And his birth date checked out, and his weight and length, and the little mole on his shoulder. Then I compared that photograph with my baby pictures..."

"And you convinced yourself that Nicky must be yours."

Amanda looked at him in disbelief. He sounded as if he

was going to argue the fact now, after he'd spotted the resemblance himself.

"I can give you the attorney's name. I'd bet even the tabloids have never heard of Luther Bain."

Chase sighed and shook his head, then paced across the room and stared out at the darkness. "When were you planning to drop this bombshell on me, Amanda?"

She shook her head—uselessly, because he wasn't looking at her. "I wasn't."

"Not even when you decided to sleep with me?"

"No. I knew you'd go out of my life soon."

"Of course you did." His tone was dry.

She didn't understand why he was being sarcastic, but something deep inside her said it was very important that he believe she was telling the truth. "I know it's confusing, but—"

"That is the only thing you've said so far that I can wholeheartedly agree with!"

She tried again. "But you see, I swore when I gave him up that I would never contact him, or you. I took that vow seriously, Chase."

He wheeled on her then, and his face was etched with rage. "Dammit, don't expect me to believe this trash about your ethics! Or about the lawyer's, either. He must have tipped you off. Did he also share the finder's fee with you? It's illegal, you know, under the laws of this state, for a birth parent to profit from an adoption. Or didn't you care if you were breaking the law?"

She was stunned. Did he honestly think she had sold her baby? She'd never given it a thought before, though she hadn't trusted Luther Bain. If it had been up to her she'd have ditched him a dozen times over. But if the attorney's finder's fee had been a large one—and she suspected he would have calculated it to fit the Worthingtons' wallet—

she could see why Chase might believe she had profited, too.

Still, the idea that he actually thought she had sold her baby to the highest bidder made her more furious than she had been for years, and she lashed out at him without even pausing to think.

"If you were an adequate parent," she said tightly, "you would never have known who I was."

Chase took two steps toward her. "What the hell? How dare you imply I'm not! There's nothing he lacks!"

"Not if you're talking about *things*, no. But you didn't even notice when he was sick."

"That's what the nanny was for."

"Oh, yes, the nanny. And what a wonderfully responsible young woman she turned out to be!"

Chase scowled.

"I'd have kept my distance if I'd had a choice," Amanda went on. "I never intended to interfere. I gave him up absolutely, and I expected never to see him again. But when you brought him here, and he was lonely and spoiled and neglected—"

"Dammit, Amanda!"

"Yes, neglected!" She was shaking with fury. "And so I did what I would have done for any child."

"You seized the opportunity to make him fall in love with you. You planned this, didn't you? You'd do anything to get your hands on him."

"No!"

Chase gave no sign of having heard. "So what's next, Amanda? Are you going to try to overturn the adoption and sue me for custody? Or are you just going to try your case in the tabloids?"

Amanda sucked in a shocked breath.

"So that's it." His voice was soft, but there was nothing

gentle about it. "Now that I think about it, no wonder you said so comfortingly that you didn't believe the tabloid stories of Nicky being my illegitimate son—you knew damned well he wasn't." He came toward her, and Amanda stepped behind a chair. "I'm amazed you haven't sold your story yet. Don't you realize what it's worth?"

"I would never take money where Nicky's concerned."

"You expect me to believe that? There must have been something in the deal for you. Or perhaps you've been saving your story till you could add my second folly to the package? Is that why you've been throwing yourself at me since I walked through the door of this dreadful little inn?"

"Throwing myself? I have not—"

There was a sleepy little cry from the bedroom. Chase wheeled around to listen for a moment, but there was no further sound; apparently Nicky had subsided into sleep once more.

Chase looked at Amanda. "Get out," he said curtly. "I'm not going to explain this to him."

There was nothing else she could do. She didn't even bother to go back to his bedroom to get her shoes; she simply stumbled down the fire-exit stairs till she reached the safety of her own apartment. She sank onto the floor in her sitting room, ignoring the soft cushions of the couch to pillow her head on the flat-topped trunk.

How could things have gone so abominably wrong? All she'd wanted to do was care for a child in need. The fact that he was her own child had been a secret little curl of delight in her heart. She had never expected it to become a stick of dynamite that would destroy her.

If she had told Chase right away that she was Nicky's mother...

But no, that would have made things no better. He'd probably have snatched the child out of her arms and rushed him back to California. Nicky would have been up-rooted once more and left behind before he even had a chance to adjust to yet another new nanny.

She'd made the only choice she could. When she'd first taken Nicky into her care, there was no reason for Chase to know the truth; to have told him would only have caused problems. But it wasn't as if she had lied, either. She was simply carrying out the solemn promise she had made four years ago—a promise she had made as much to Chase himself as to the court that had approved Nicky's adoption. Couldn't the man understand that she had taken her vow seriously?

And how very seriously she had thought through that decision to give her child up irrevocably and forever. She had agonized over it for months, though in truth she'd had little choice. With no possibility of support from her parents, with her education only half-complete, already in debt for her tuition and with no way to make a living for herself, much less bring up a child, her options had been cruelly limited.

In the end, for the sake of her baby, she had sworn away her rights to see him, to talk to him, to watch him grow, to comfort him, because it was better for Nicky to have parents who were financially secure and married and emotionally stable. She had made her sacrifice out of her love for her baby.

Even Desiree's death had not erased Amanda's promise—and nothing ever would. Chase had asked if she would sue for custody, but even if she wanted to, she knew better than to try. No court would overturn the adoption. Even if the finder's fee Chase had paid had been far above the norm, it had been legal—she was certain Luther Bain had stayed within the letter of the law.

And despite the harsh accusations Amanda had flung at

him, Chase was not a careless or inadequate parent. Even if she could reclaim Nicky, she wouldn't. Chase was the only father Nicky had ever known; she couldn't tear him away from that.

And so the only thing Amanda could do was fade out of the picture as gracefully as possible. If in the secret corners of her heart she hoped that sometimes Nicky might remember the funny lady with the silly parakeet, well, no court in the land could forbid hope.

She raised her face from the trunk. The action took effort; her head felt as heavy as a cannonball.

She opened the trunk and took out the bright-colored quilt and the scrapbooks. This time she didn't pause to look at the pictures. Instead, she inserted a fingernail into an almost hidden slit in the cloth-covered bottom of the trunk, and when she pulled, the false panel lifted out.

The hidden compartment was shallow, no more than three inches deep. But then, she didn't have much to hide there. Only the few small souvenirs left to her of Nicky's first three days of life—when he had still been her son, not Chase Worthington's.

A blurry photograph, snapped in the nursery when he was just an hour old. A plastic identification bracelet that said Baby Boy Bailey. A small ball of yellow yarn, the bit left over from the sweater she had knitted for him in her final month of pregnancy.

She spread the items carefully out on the top of the trunk. It was a pitifully small group of mementos, and she stared at them for a long time before she put her head down once more.

She didn't cry. She had done most of that long ago, before he was born.

But it was even harder this time to say farewell in her

heart to the child she had carried, because now she was also saying goodbye to the man she had loved.

AMANDA HAD NO IDEA what time it was when the banging started on her door. She didn't care, either. Sooner or later it would stop.

She was correct about that—but a few minutes later she heard the click of a key in the lock and felt a surge of air as the door opened. She looked up, only mildly curious, as Stephanie rushed in.

Behind her was the bellman. "I don't know about this, Mrs. Kendall," he was saying. "I'm not supposed to use my key except when I have orders, and—" He spotted Amanda on the floor and he gasped. "Are you hurt? Did you fall? Shall I call an ambulance?"

Stephanie's shrewd gaze rested on Amanda's face for a moment. "I think you can go back to work now. Thanks, John." She didn't move until the door had closed behind him. Then she crossed the room quietly and sank down on the floor beside Amanda. "Want to tell me about it?"

Amanda shook her head.

"This was outside your door."

Amanda looked at the brown paper bag Stephanie held out. The top of it was tightly folded to keep the contents private, but she had no trouble guessing what was inside. Her shoes and the rest of her clothes. She wondered why Chase had bothered to bring them down. He could have just thrown them in the wastebasket.

Then she answered her own question. If he had discarded her things, Nicky was likely to see and ask questions.

Nicky…

She had never given her child a name, for she had known almost from the start that he could not be hers to keep, and she thought it might be a little easier that way. But when she had seen him in the magazine and learned what Chase and Desiree had called him, she had hugged the knowledge to her heart. The name fitted him so perfectly.

"What's going on?" Stephanie asked lightly. "Chase called me at an absolutely ghastly hour this morning, wanting the name of my day-care center. Are you sick?"

"No."

Stephanie put a gentle hand on the back of Amanda's neck and started to rub the taut muscles. "Then what happened? You looked so happy last night when you left the party."

"That was last night."

"Tell me."

"I can't."

There was a trace of irritation in Stephanie's voice. "Amanda Bailey, what the hell do you think friends are for, anyway? You're always here for all of us, but now that you need someone…"

She stopped rubbing Amanda's neck, though her palm still rested, warm and comforting, against the soft skin, and stretched her other hand out to pick up the tiny plastic band that lay on top of the trunk.

Amanda waited.

Stephanie gave a long, deep, discouraged sigh. "Baby Boy Bailey," she said. "I had no idea."

"You weren't meant to. No one in Springhill knows."

"When did this happen?"

"My junior year in college."

Stephanie calculated. "Four years ago?"

"Just a little more. He was born early in June."

"And you told Chase you'd had a baby, and he reacted badly?"

"You could say that. But I didn't tell him. He guessed."

"Guessed?" Stephanie shook her head in confusion. "I don't get this at all, Mandy."

Amanda reached for the tiny bracelet and stroked it as if it was Nicky's curly hair. "My baby…" She paused. It was hard to say the words; she had never before acknowledged him like this. It had been different with Chase, because he had already known what she was going to say. "My baby is Nicky Worthington." The words were painful, but there was a sort of relief, too, almost like the instant after he'd been born and her exhausted body could rest awhile.

Stephanie's hand stilled. "I see." There was a long silence, and then she stood up.

Amanda wasn't quite sure if she was afraid of being left, or of where Stephanie might go, and what she might say. She surely wouldn't confront Chase, would she? "Stephanie, please—"

"I'm not going anywhere. I think both of us could use a cup of tea, that's all." She gave Amanda's shoulder a quick squeeze. "Did you think I was going to walk out on you? It's a surprise, yes, but now that I think about it, Nicky's got some of your mannerisms. I guess I thought he'd picked them up in the last week, but there's the smile, too, and the shape of his chin…"

By the time she came back with two steaming mugs, Amanda had managed to pull herself together somewhat. She cradled her tea between her palms and stared down at the amber liquid.

Stephanie gestured toward the pile of scrapbooks. "May I?"

Amanda shrugged. "Help yourself."

Stephanie leafed through the top book, pausing to look at the magazine cover where Nicky had first been introduced to the world. "Four years," she mused. "They were making *Winter of the Heart*.... But you weren't even here then, so how did you meet Chase?''

Amanda was puzzled. ''I never did. Not till he came back this summer.''

''But...'' Stephanie flushed a little. ''None of my business, of course.''

It was only then she realized that Stephanie thought the tabloid stories had been true, after all. ''Chase isn't Nicky's father, Steph.''

Once the ice was broken, Amanda's story flowed out—of the young man she had met in the college drama department, and how much her parents had disapproved of him. ''If it hadn't been for that,'' she said, ''I might have seen for myself how selfish he was. But it wasn't till I told him I was pregnant, and he said it wasn't his problem...''

''Oh, Mandy. Why didn't you share this with anyone then?''

''I didn't have too many friends. Not the kind I could trust with this, that's for sure.''

Stephanie nodded. ''Your parents were awfully particular about who you associated with, weren't they? Those of us who were older and considerably wilder would never have passed muster.''

''You actually remember me from those days?'' Amanda was honestly surprised; she'd been several years younger than Stephanie's crowd and not nearly as popular.

''Of course. I remember thinking that if you stopped being such an awful prig and developed a sense of adventure, you might be fun. But you weren't at all like I thought, were you?''

Amanda smiled ruefully. ''I wasn't a prig, really, I was just awfully shy. And I didn't want to find out what my parents would say if I did things like slide down the inn's grand staircase using a pizza pan as a sled.''

Stephanie winced. "I'll never be allowed to live that down. You know, I seem to remember thinking one summer that you looked pale and wan and sick."

"That would have been afterward. After Nicky was... gone."

"I thought you'd had mononucleosis or something. Oh, Lord, how I wish I'd talked to you then. Keeping this bottled up inside you all these years—it's a wonder you're sane." She hugged Amanda close, and the tears came once more. Only after Amanda was calm again did Stephanie ask gently, "Why did you give him up?"

"I didn't want to. But when I told my parents..."

Stephanie sighed. "I guess they were no help."

"They were mortified. I'd disgraced them, and when there was no chance of getting married in a hurry and hushing it up, they sent me to Mother's sister. I stayed there till Nicky was born. I was supposed to be taking some classes that weren't available at my college."

"And they insisted the baby was to be put up for adoption?"

Amanda nodded. "If I kept him, they said they'd disown me. I could have lived with that, but how would I have managed? On my own, I couldn't have supported myself and a baby, much less finished my education. Things would never have gotten any better, and I'd have been condemning my baby to a life of poverty. The lawyer they sent to talk to me—"

"Who sent him? Your parents?"

Amanda nodded. "He kept harping at me about that, and telling me how much better it would be for the baby if I gave him up." She sipped her tea. "Eventually I listened, and I signed the papers."

"And the lawyer contacted Chase and Desiree, and they adopted him."

Amanda nodded.

"And now Chase brings him back here." Stephanie sighed. "What a mess, Mandy. What are you going to do?"

"Nothing. I have no place in Nicky's life. I never expected to, though." She picked up the blurry photograph of her hour-old child and said wistfully, "He's a great little boy, isn't he?"

"He's the best, sweetheart."

"And I'm glad I got to know him just a little. Not every birth mother gets to see firsthand that her child is happy and well...." Her voice was trembling. "I'll concentrate on that."

Stephanie nodded slowly. "Amanda...what about Chase?"

"Chase?" For a moment she sounded as if she'd never heard the name before.

"I know I said before that you were crazy to allow yourself to care about him, but I'd really started to believe that it could work out. You seemed so happy together, Mandy, and I thought you were getting serious about each other."

Amanda forced herself to laugh. At least Stephanie didn't know about last night. If she was lucky, no one would ever know just how enormous a fool she was. "You're a world-class romantic, Steph. Oh, it might have been a summer fling if he hadn't guessed about Nicky—but nothing more than that, believe me." She drank the rest of her tea. "What time is it? I have to go to work."

"After nine. You're sure you're up to it?"

"I have to be. Thanks for coming. For caring."

Stephanie's forehead was furrowed as if she didn't want to leave, but nevertheless she stood up. "Call me anytime. And come for dinner tonight. You shouldn't be alone."

Amanda managed to smile, but her face hurt as if she

was forcing muscles to move in ways nature hadn't intended. "I don't know. Can I call you later about that?"

Just standing in the shower hurt her body; the spray felt like needles against her supersensitive skin. Odd, she thought, how a purely mental and emotional experience could translate itself into physical pain. Chase hadn't put a hand on her this morning, but if he had beaten her senseless she couldn't feel more bruised.

She stood in front of her open closet door for long minutes, unable even to decide what clothes to put on. Her mind felt as if it had split into two pieces; the one that controlled normal daily functioning was numb and paralyzed, while the part that felt emotion—the part she would have anesthetized if she could have only found a way— was very much awake.

She shouldn't be alone, Stephanie had said. It was a gentle way of saying she was afraid of what Amanda might do to end her grief.

But the fact was, Amanda knew, she had always been alone. She ought to be used to it by now.

The only child of parents who had been in their forties when she was born, she had grown up by herself, a solitary, dreamy, imaginative child. Her parents weren't uncaring, but in their inexperience they had tried too hard to keep her safe. The other children were too undisciplined, Amanda's mother thought, too wild, too likely to lead her astray. And so Amanda took part in few of the youthful activities of Springhill.

After high school, her parents wanted her to take a secretarial course. They felt it was an appropriate profession for a woman, at least while she waited to be married. They didn't understand that Amanda's generation was far removed from what had been acceptable in their youth. But for once Amanda had stood up to them. Instead, she worked at the hotel for two years, saving every penny, and then she went away to college.

It wasn't till her second year, when things had settled down a little and she was sure she could keep her grades up, that she discovered the joy of pretending on stage—and it was then she had met Eric.

Amanda supposed, as she looked back with something like disbelief at her younger self, that she had been an accident waiting to happen—a naive girl, young for her years, pretty and eager to please. Eric had said she was beautiful, with a fresh and fragile radiance. And she had believed he was as much in love with her as she was with him.

But for once, her parents had been right—she had been a fool. And yet, out of that ill-fated relationship had come a precious little boy called Nicky.

She sat down in the wicker rocker in her bedroom and picked up a tiny envelope from the table next to her bed. Carefully she opened it and extracted three soft, dark brown curls of hair. She had given the rest to Chase, but he would never miss these.

She stroked a soft curl, wrapping it around her fingertip. He had been born with a lot of hair, dark and soft and curly. He had been a beautiful baby.

She had called him her snuggle-bunny. He had craved contact and body warmth. It was almost as if he knew from the moment of his birth that he would not have his mother for long, and so he'd nestled close, and he'd whimpered whenever he was put down. She had not been surprised at Chase's story of picking the child up for the first time. Of course Nicky had cuddled up against him.

She smiled a little as she reflected on how many new memories she had of Nicky now. Those memories would get her through the tough times, just as she had managed so far by keeping alive in her heart the first precious seventy-two hours of his life.

Finally she got dressed and went to put her treasures safely away. The photograph, the bracelet, the bit of yarn. This time, almost ceremonially, she added the tiny envelope of hair. And she took a crayon drawing off the refrigerator door—the picture Nicky had drawn of himself, with an exaggerated case of chicken pox—and laid it to rest in the bottom of the trunk, as well. These few things were all she had left for concrete remembrances, and she wanted to make certain they were close by and safe.

She was on her way out the door when she remembered the parakeet. She pulled the cage cover off, and Floyd untucked his head and eyed her with interest as she refilled his food and water dishes. His daily bath would have to wait; she was already dreadfully late, and there would be enough questioning looks as it was.

Floyd cocked his head to one side and said tentatively, "Say Nicky?"

Amanda's lower lip started to tremble. "No, Floyd," she said. "Not anymore."

"Strike one," Floyd said. He sounded almost sympathetic.

She took the elevator, since even going down the stairs seemed to require more energy than she possessed. But it seemed slower and noisier than usual; she had plenty of time to read the notice posted on the wall, and realized that it was time for the annual inspection. She'd have to see if she could put it off for a few more weeks, till the movie crew departed. She couldn't take the only passenger elevator out of service for half a day with the inn full.

The elevator doors opened, and she almost bumped into Chase. He was alone. Had he already sent Nicky back to

California, then? No, Stephanie had said something about daycare....

She stepped outside, and the heel of her shoe caught in the gap between the lobby floor and the elevator car. Chase steadied her, his touch impersonal. He didn't look at her, though, and as soon as she had regained her balance he released her, stepped to the side and punched the control panel. The doors closed with a whoosh.

Neither of them had said a word.

Amanda was trembling. Last night they had been lovers; today they could not even exchange polite remarks. "Thank you for catching me" and "I hope you're all right."

But she had one thing to hang on to, she told herself firmly. One thing for which she could be forever grateful. At least she hadn't told him she loved him.

CHAPTER NINE

STEPHANIE CALLED in midafternoon to renew the dinner invitation, and Amanda agreed to go. It would have been easier to creep back to her quiet apartment that evening and sit with her memories, but she hadn't gotten through the last four years by being a coward, and she wasn't going to start now.

It didn't occur to her that she might not be the only guest until she saw an unfamiliar car parked next to Stephanie's black Jaguar behind the Kendalls' mansion. She was almost annoyed for a moment; Stephanie hadn't said a word about this being a party, even a small one.

But of course if there were other people present, the conversation could not center on Nicky and on Amanda's pain. Perhaps that was why Stephanie had arranged it this way, knowing instinctively that right now Amanda needed laughter and distraction, not a further dissection of her troubles.

There was nothing she could do about Nicky but accept the facts; rehashing the situation wouldn't change anything. And though she had no intention of making a wholesale announcement, the sooner she faced her friends and picked up the threads of her life, the easier it would be in the long run. She had learned four years ago that life was a carousel that didn't stop just because one person's plans went astray, and the sooner one ceased standing on the sidelines and climbed back aboard, the less painful the transition was.

At least the car in the drive wasn't the one Chase had rented. Stephanie wouldn't do that to her, and facing anyone else would be a picnic in comparison.

Amanda took a deep breath and knocked at the kitchen door. Katie answered it, a stack of plates clutched in one arm. "Oh, good, you're just in time to help me set the table!"

"Katie," her mother intervened, "Mandy's a guest."

"No, she's not. She's family." Without checking to see whether Amanda was following, Katie headed for the breakfast room just off the big kitchen and started distributing plates with a nonchalance that bordered on the haphazard.

Not an elegant guest, then, Amanda deduced, or they'd be using the formal dining room and good china, instead of the breakfast room and pottery.

Stephanie was running a fingertip down the page of a cookbook. "Teriyaki sauce, honey, pineapple juice— Oh, I forgot the chives. How are you doing, dear?"

Amanda shrugged. "As well as can be expected. Who else is here?"

"No one. Why?"

"There's an extra car in your driveway."

"Oh, Jordan brought it home for me to try. I'm thinking of trading in the Jaguar." She stirred chives into the sauce simmering atop the stove and raised her eyebrows at Amanda. "What did you think I was doing—matchmaking?"

"I hoped you hadn't picked tonight to introduce me to Jordan's new sales manager."

Stephanie looked offended. "Not that I wouldn't like to, you understand, but give me credit for a little sensitivity."

Amanda managed to smile. "Thanks, Steph."

Jordan Kendall came in from the front of the house with

Zack riding on his shoulders. He put the boy down and gave Amanda a hug. "I haven't seen you for a while," he said. "You've been too busy with the movie crew, I understand."

Amanda eyed him a bit warily.

"They're shooting up at Sentinel Oak tonight. Maybe after dinner we should go and watch."

Stephanie didn't look up from her sauce. "Why don't you take the kids?" she suggested. "Maybe Amanda and I'll go for a walk, instead."

"Take the kids to Sentinel Oak? By myself? You've got to be joking, Steph."

"Why? You take them everywhere else."

"I was hoping to sneak a kiss, at least. After all, it's the most notorious lovers' lane in six counties."

Stephanie blushed. Amanda was amused, till she remembered that under other circumstances she might have been going up to Sentinel Oak tonight herself and taking Nicky....

If Chase was working tonight, who was taking care of Nicky?

But that was no longer any of her business. As a matter of fact, it never had been, and she'd be a lot better off if she remembered that.

Amanda complimented Stephanie's pineapple chicken even though she managed to eat just a few bites, and after dinner she duly admired the new wallpaper in the formal drawing room and wondered aloud whether the house would be recognizable when *Diamonds in the Dew* was broadcast in the fall.

"I haven't any idea," Stephanie said. "Furthermore, even though I watched them film, I still don't have the vaguest notion what the movie's really about. What I saw was so far out of sequence that there was no making sense of it.''

''We'll have a party when it's broadcast,'' Jordan added. ''Maybe if we all put our heads together we can figure it out.''

Amanda almost turned the invitation down right then. She knew very well she couldn't bear a party. In fact, she didn't know if she could sit through the film at all, or even enjoy the views of Springhill and Stephanie's house and Sentinel Oak without drowning in her memories of a stolen bit of summertime.

Katie was pulling her toward the stairs. ''I'll give you the rest of the tour, too. They used my room, and the guest room, but not Zack's.'' She made a face. ''Too many toys. It would have taken a steam shovel to clear them all out, Daddy says.''

Stephanie intervened. ''I'm not sure Mandy cares for the details.''

''Oh.'' Katie seemed to chew on that. ''Well, all right. Can I come and stay overnight with you, Mandy? We haven't had a slumber party yet this summer.''

Had Katie's mother put her up to that question? Amanda wondered. Was Stephanie honestly afraid to let her be alone?

''I don't think—'' Stephanie began.

''Yes,'' Amanda said. She intercepted Stephanie's quizzing look and added quietly, ''I have to pick up my life, Steph. I can't just sit and wait for something that isn't ever going to happen.''

Stephanie nodded. ''I know.''

''Maybe I should think about a change,'' Amanda said almost to herself.

''Leave the inn, you mean?''

''Leave Springhill.'' She hadn't consciously thought

about it before, but the words, once spoken, seemed to have a life of their own. "Maybe it's past time. I only came back here because my father was ill, and I did that grudgingly. I'm not sorry, of course, because we settled our differences before he died."

"You mean he actually apologized?"

"In his own way. He was unenlightened and painfully conservative and old-fashioned, but he wasn't deliberately cruel." She swallowed hard. It had not been easy to put those ghosts to rest. "And I'm glad I stayed. At least I was here to get to know Nicky."

And Chase, of course, though she couldn't bring herself to say his name. It was one thing for Stephanie to know about Nicky; it was something else altogether to bare her heart and expose the hopeless helpless love she felt for Chase.

Nevertheless, she was glad to have had him in her life for this short while, even though at the moment her heart felt as if it had been assaulted with a dull dental drill. The hurt would ease with time; she of all people knew that. And after a while, when the worst of the pain was past, she would treasure the memories of that single night with him—one brief night in which she'd been certain that she mattered, that he truly cared just a little for her.

Jordan Kendall had been so quiet Amanda had almost forgotten he was there. "If you decide to make a change," he said, "let me know. I could use you myself in personnel. But if you really want to leave Springhill, I've got a lot of contacts, and someone's sure to need a businesswoman with lots of experience in managing people."

Amanda nodded. "Thanks, Jordan." She felt better knowing there were always possibilities.

But she didn't have to do anything just yet. She couldn't simply walk out, anyway; she owed it to the absentee owners of the inn to give them proper notice. She'd have to stay until the rush was over, until the movie was finished....

Until Chase and Nicky were gone.

THOUGH AMANDA SAW Chase occasionally over the next four days, she didn't come face-to-face with him. In the limited space of the inn, with all traffic intersecting in the lobby, that wasn't easy to do—which simply meant that he was being as careful to avoid her as she was to avoid him.

She caught only glimpses of Nicky—mostly from her sitting-room window in the early mornings as he left the inn with his father on the way to daycare. She told herself that she shouldn't watch for him, but she couldn't help herself; she started to take her coffee onto the tiny terrace every morning, sitting there till she had seen them safely on their way. Sometimes, when she missed them, the dregs in the bottom of her cup were cold and bitter before she gave up the wait. She had a good excuse for her vigil, of course—she was watching solely to avoid the consequences of running headlong into Nicky some morning in the lobby. It would be better for all of them to avoid that kind of embarrassment, and so she waited till she was certain he was safely out of the way before she left her apartment.

The truth was she didn't want to think about how she would feel if she bumped into Nicky and he didn't seem to care.

She thought he looked tired and cranky as he dawdled along beside Chase, dragging his stuffed rabbit by the ear. Not that she could really tell, from such a distance and from that angle; she could only see the way his head drooped sometimes. Of course, there were many explanations for that, all of which her imagination insisted on embroidering.

And, of course, there were the tantrums.

Amanda didn't hear Nicky's tantrums firsthand, but she

heard about them—from chambermaids, from John the bellman, even from Katie Kendall, who gave her an account in minute detail of how Nicky had screamed one entire afternoon at the day-care center, until he made himself too hoarse to yell anymore and finally slept from sheer exhaustion.

Amanda told herself she had no reason to feel guilty about his behavior no matter how terrible it was. She had not provoked this protest; she had not led Nicky to believe he might have her always. Indeed, to be brutally honest, she had no reason to think his bad temper had anything at all to do with her; it was no worse than what he had done before she'd ever become involved.

But she quickly learned that guilt didn't have to be logical, and every time she heard another tale, one more tiny piece of her heart was carved away. If only she hadn't made things worse....

She ought to have had no trouble keeping her mind occupied, for she had plenty of work to do. The unseasonably cool summer had given way to an old-fashioned Iowa heat wave, and the inn's air-conditioning was working at capacity and barely keeping pace. The heat and humidity told on personal relationships, as well as on mechanical systems. The guests bickered at the chambermaids and each other, and Jessamyn Arden growled at everybody.

"She told me yesterday that she considered going to work a blessing compared to staying upstairs in her private sauna," Tricia told Amanda one morning, and pushed a stack of mail across the registration desk. "You know that sweet way she has of sticking a knife in and then twisting it?" She gave Amanda a sidelong glance. "She also implied that she was seeing a great deal of Chase off the set, as well as on."

Amanda wasn't listening. She was staring at the top en-

velope on the pile—a pristine white linen, expensively en-
graved with a return address in a businesslike block-style
type: BAXTER AND BAIN, ATTORNEYS AT LAW...

It was like a voice from the grave. It had been well over
a year since she'd attended Luther Bain's funeral, but of
course his firm was still in existence. That was where Chase
would have gone with any unfinished business about
Nicky's adoption—back to the firm that had arranged it. If
he wanted to ask questions or issue warnings or make
threats, he would have contacted Tom Baxter, the remain-
ing partner.

Her hands trembled as she picked up the stack of mail
and carried it into her office.

She wasn't exactly surprised, though she wouldn't have
expected Chase to do anything as clumsy as putting warnings or threats in writing. Of course he could simply be
preempting any move she might be considering by making
certain she understood how little right she had to interfere
in Nicky's life. But he'd made himself perfectly clear in
person....

She slit open the envelope and unfolded a polite note
from Tom Baxter asking if the inn's facilities would be
available on the first weekend in October for a local bar-
association meeting.

She had worked herself into such a pitch that she stared
at the letter for a couple of minutes before she tossed it
onto the desk blotter and put her head down in her hands.
What an idiot she was! After that gibe about selling her
story, why on earth would Chase give her anything else to
sell?

THE HEAT WAS GETTING to everyone. Even in the coffee
shop, its effects were felt every time the street door opened
and a wave of blistering hot air rolled in. Kathy's smile

had lost some of its eagerness and her uniform much of its starch, and Amanda's coffee wasn't waiting for her as usual when she took her late-afternoon break.

"I knew we should have put in the deluxe cooling system," Amanda muttered as she took a stool at the counter. "On days like this, nothing makes much difference."

A few minutes later the door from the lobby opened again, and Amanda groaned when she saw who was standing there. Joe Smith smiled and put his hands in his pockets as he crossed the restaurant. "May I?" he asked, and didn't wait for an answer before he took the stool beside hers. "I've been trying to catch you for several days, Miss Bailey."

"Well, obviously you haven't found the right bait," Amanda said coolly. She picked up her coffee mug. "Talk to you later, Kathy."

"Want me to sweep him out of here?" Kathy asked.

"Wait a minute," Joe Smith said. "You can't evict me. I'm wearing shoes and a shirt, I've got money, and I'd order something if there was a decent waitress in the place." He gave Kathy a toothy smile. "Lemonade and a piece of rhubarb pie."

"Rhubarb?" Kathy sniffed. "Where'd you acquire a taste for that?"

"I always make it a point to sample the native delicacies wherever I go. Such as they are." He turned to Amanda. "You might be interested to know that I've talked to Chase Worthington's ex-nanny."

"Oh? Which one?" Then she bit her tongue. There was no need to give him any information.

"The last one. She's by far the most interesting." He cut the tip off the wedge of pie Kathy set before him and impaled it on his fork. "Also, I heard some very interesting speculation the other day."

"I'm sure you hear a lot of that. It doesn't make it reliable."

"Very true. But the speculation I hear isn't usually *this* interesting."

"Thanks for the tip. I'll keep an eye out for your paper next week. If a copy turns up in the garbage bin, I can read all about it."

He smiled sweetly. "The nanny says we were right four years ago about the little boy being adopted."

Amanda settled back on her stool again. The story of the chosen child, she thought. Naturally, Nicky's nanny would have heard all about it. And it was equally certain that once the woman had been dismissed she'd have told everything she knew—for a price.

Joe Smith looked satisfied. "I thought that might get your attention."

Amanda shrugged. "It's old news."

"Ah, but there's a twist that brings it right up to date. If he was Chase Worthington's love child, which we've also speculated, and not Desiree's, after all, then who was his mother?"

"Why ask me?"

"Because I think you might know, Miss Bailey."

Amanda tried to pretend that cold shivers weren't playing tag up and down her spine. "Sorry. I can't help you."

"That's where our latest interesting speculation comes in—about how attached you and the little boy are to each other and how cozy you are with his daddy. And just how long it's been going on. A few weeks? Or maybe a few years?"

"If you're threatening to publish a story about Nicky and Chase and *me*…"

"Just one happy little family."

"It's not true." At any rate, not all of his speculations

were true, she thought. And even if what she said was on the margins of telling a lie, at least she had good reason.

"It's still a good story," Joe Smith said pensively. "We could put together a photograph of you and the boy and airbrush it till it would make even you believe he's your kid."

Amanda's smile held a trace of real amusement. "What talent!"

There was a thoughtful pause. "Of course, I'd be willing to keep that one to myself."

"For a price, I'm sure?"

"Oh, not money. You could tell me what really happened instead."

Amanda's eyes widened in mock surprise. "You'd be interested in the truth? Now that's incredible news."

"Who was it, Miss Bailey? You can trust me."

The desk clerk came in. "Amanda, the elevator's stuck on three, and John's inside it."

Amanda didn't bother to excuse herself. She also didn't bother to scan the lobby before she dashed across it toward the grand staircase, and so for once she didn't see Chase in time to turn her back and escape into her office. In fact, she almost ran straight into him.

He let go of Nicky's hand in order to steady her. He'd just come in from outside, and he was still wearing sunglasses, so she couldn't see the expression in his eyes. The set of his mouth, however, made it clear he wasn't precisely tickled to see her.

At least he hadn't spotted her with Joe Smith. Seeing her talking to the reporter would really have been the last straw.

"Sorry," she said breathlessly. "I didn't mean to bowl you over. The elevator's stuck, and I—"

"Mandy!" Nicky's voice was almost a wail, and he flung himself at her, his arms clutching her waist, his head buried so tightly against her ribs that she couldn't draw a full breath. "I missed you!"

Despite her best intentions, her fingers smoothed his hair. In just these few days it had already started to grow back; even the bare spot Zack had created behind his left ear was decently covered now. "I missed you, too, Nicky."

He raised his head and looked up at her, his big hazel eyes tear-drenched. "Daddy says you're too busy to have time for me."

She was furious—and yet what else could Chase have told him? Nothing that would have made things any easier. Nothing that could have been a satisfactory explanation to a four-year-old. And at least what he had told him had the veneer of truth.

"Oh, my darling," she said helplessly.

Chase put both hands on Nicky's shoulders. His fingertips brushed Amanda's waist, and she shivered just a little at the contact. "Come along, Nicky. Amanda has to take care of the elevator."

She'd forgotten for a moment that the bellman was stranded.

Nicky sobbed once more, but he allowed himself to be peeled away. With his warmth gone, icy cold settled into Amanda's bones.

"I don't know how long it'll be before it's back in service," she apologized. "And I'm afraid the freight elevator isn't available at the moment, either. John's the one who usually runs it, and since he's stuck..."

Chase didn't bother to answer. He led Nicky toward the grand staircase and paused at the bottom, looking up with a sigh. Amanda didn't blame him; six flights was a good climb, and he'd probably end up carrying Nicky.

Amanda went to her office to telephone the repairman.

When she came out, Joe Smith was leaning on the reception desk, chewing on a toothpick.

No doubt he'd seen the whole episode in the lobby. Why on earth had she thought putting glass walls in the coffee shop was such a brilliant idea?

"My editor would happily pay for *that* story," he said.

"He couldn't afford it," Amanda snapped. She headed for the service stairs and took the first two flights at a run. By the time she got to the third floor, the inn's handyman had the foyer doors unlocked and the shaft exposed to show the bottom third of the elevator car. But John was still inside, and the doors of the car itself stubbornly refused to move.

The fireproof doors to the stairwell were propped open, and she heard Nicky before she saw him. "I don't *want* to play that I'm climbing a mountain," he complained.

"Then we'll pretend we're rockets shooting off toward the stars," Chase said.

"Rockets don't get tired, Daddy."

"I wouldn't bet on it."

Nicky spotted Amanda and his fatigue seemed to vanish as he ran toward her. "I don't want to walk, Daddy. Why can't I just go to Mandy's, instead?"

"Because Mandy's here, and she's too busy to look after you."

Nicky started to look sulky.

Chase waved a hand at the bustle around the elevator door. "How long is this likely to continue?"

"I don't know," Amanda admitted. "The repairman's on his way, but he'll be a couple of hours getting here. So unless we can get it running ourselves—"

"A couple of hours? I thought you worked miracles with repairmen!"

"That *is* a miracle, Chase. Springhill doesn't have

enough elevators to keep a repairman occupied, or hadn't that occurred to you? Sometimes when it isn't an urgent matter, it's days before he gets here.''

''Oh, how reassuring,'' Chase drawled. ''Break's over, Nicky. Let's go.''

''I don't want to go,'' Nicky protested. But their footsteps retreated up the stairs, and Amanda pressed her hands against her temples and tried to reason herself back to some sort of calm. The sarcasm in Chase's voice had torn at her just as sharply as a personal attack—and perhaps, even if he hadn't realized it himself, that was exactly what it had been. She didn't blame him exactly; his life must have looked very simple before he'd come back to Springhill.

Almost an hour had passed by the time they managed to force the doors open enough to let John slide out of the car and down to the foyer, and once he'd taken a drink of water and a few deep breaths, Amanda said, ''I hate to ask you to do this, John. But the only way to get people up and down is the freight elevator, and since it's not exactly self-service…''

John, who hadn't yet regained his normal color, turned another shade paler at the idea of getting straight into another elevator. ''All right,'' he said gamely. ''Just let me sit still a minute first.''

''Great. I'll go down to the lobby and tell people they don't have to walk.''

The lobby was full of people milling about and going up and down. Most of the crew seemed to consider the event high adventure. Jessamyn Arden, on the other hand, shuddered at the idea of subjecting herself to the rigors of a freight elevator. ''I'll wait,'' she said tartly, and crossed one elegant knee over the other. ''And it had better not be long. I'm overdue for a rest.''

It was all Amanda could do to keep from saying that like

any other child, Jessamyn showed the effects of missing her nap. Instead, she got a spare key from her office. "If you'd like to use my apartment in the meantime, Miss Arden, it's on the second floor. There are cold drinks in the refrigerator, and books and magazines everywhere. Feel free to use them."

Jessamyn considered and graciously inclined her head. "That would be acceptable, I suppose."

As soon as Jessamyn was out of hearing range, Tricia muttered, "The woman's a viper."

Amanda pretended not to hear. With everything else that was going on, the last thing she had time for was lecturing her staff on the proper attitude toward troublesome guests—especially when privately she agreed with the staff's point of view.

A few hours later, she signed an enormous repair bill and went upstairs to tell Jessamyn that the elevator was back in service. She wasn't surprised to hear her television set blaring while she was still twenty feet down the hall. She also wasn't surprised to see a litter of dirty dishes scattered throughout her sitting room.

But she was astounded and furious to see that Jessamyn was entertaining herself by paging through the scrapbooks that had been safely buried under the quilt in the flat-topped trunk.

Worse yet, Jessamyn didn't even apologize. "This is fascinating reading," she said, waving a hand at the neatly clipped stories. "That's quite a little infatuation you have for Chase, isn't it?"

"That is private material, Miss Arden." Amanda's voice was shaking with anger. "It was in a closed chest."

Jessamyn's eyes widened. "But my dear, you invited me to read your books." She turned another page. "No wonder you flung yourself at Chase. And no wonder he took you up on the offer. This sort of adoration can do wonders for a man's ego. Never lasts, of course. Wide-eyed worship gets tiresome after a while. But while it's fresh..."

Amanda moved across the room. "The elevator is operating normally now, so you can go to your own suite."

Jessamyn pouted. "I don't know that I dare ride it alone anymore."

Amanda wanted to say that if she was alone, Jessamyn would have every molecule of oxygen inside the elevator all to herself if it got stuck again. And as far as Amanda was concerned, she could stay there till it ran out, too. But she managed to say reassuringly, "It's fully repaired and perfectly safe."

She closed the door behind Jessamyn and leaned against it, her hands clenched into fists. How dare the woman pry into her private things?

Don't think that way, she told herself. She should be glad Jessamyn had found only the scrapbooks and not the contents beneath the false bottom.

A knock on the door seemed to vibrate through her bones, and she jumped a foot. She stared at the doorknob as if it were a snake. Jessamyn must have forgotten something and returned to claim it. Amanda would have to face the woman, for Jessamyn knew she was there....

She opened the door and looked unbelievingly up at Chase. He had changed clothes since she had seen him in the lobby; the casual shirt and jeans made him look even taller than usual.

She swallowed hard, blinked and tried to close the door, but he'd put his foot in the opening. There was a determined light in his eyes.

"If you came here to accuse me of putting Nicky up to that little demonstration in the lobby," she began, "I assure you—"

He shook his head. "If he'd been seeing you all along, it would have been a different sort of scene. Nicky's no actor. He sees what he wants and he goes after it."

The answer should have been a sort of relief—at least he didn't think she'd been sneaking around behind his back—but it wasn't. Amanda didn't quite know why.

"May I come in?" he asked.

"Where's Nicky?"

"I bribed one of the assistants in the art department to keep him corralled for a while so we could talk."

Reluctantly she moved out of the doorway. "I can't imagine what you think we have to talk about."

He slanted a look at her. "Can't you?"

Amanda settled on the edge of a straight chair and then wished that she hadn't sat down at all, for Chase hadn't. He didn't stand still, either; he paced the small room like a panther in a cage.

"Would you stop?" she said finally. "You don't have to be afraid of me, Chase. I could have told Nicky today that you'd lied to him...."

He turned sharply and faced her. "What do you mean?"

"You did, you know, when you told him I was too busy for him and made it sound as if I didn't want to see him."

"Dammit, Amanda—"

She hurried on, unwilling to be interrupted. "But I won't undercut you like that. I won't do anything to diminish his respect for you."

He stared at her silently for half a minute. His eyes held an expression she didn't recognize—it wasn't doubt precisely, and it wasn't cynicism. He looked almost puzzled, and it made her nervous. He was wondering why she would go out of her way to preserve Nicky's opinion of him—and he was apt to jump to uncomfortable conclusions.

She leapt up from her chair. "I didn't make that resolution for your sake, Chase. I made it for Nicky. Under-cutting you would only confuse Nicky and make him more unhappy.''

"And heaven knows he's unhappy enough as it is.''

Amanda bit her lip. "I know. And I'm sorry about it.'' Her voice was barely audible. "I didn't set out to make him love me.''

Chase looked as if he had his doubts. "So what do you plan to do about it now?''

There was no mistaking the challenge in his words, and Amanda lifted her chin. "I don't see that there's anything I can do. I gave him up long ago, and whether you believe it or not, I stand by my promises. Even if I could overturn the adoption, I wouldn't do it. It would only upset Nicky more.''

She was talking as much to herself as to him, trying to convince herself that she had looked at every option, that there were no loopholes, that she was doing the only thing she could.

"You don't have to give him up, Amanda.''

For a moment she thought she hadn't heard him correctly. "You'd let me see him sometimes?''

"More than that.'' Chase braced his hands on the back of the couch. "Come to California with us.''

"And take care of him?'' Her voice was wary. "I'm not a nanny, Chase. I can't be professional when it comes to Nicky.''

"I'm not asking you to be a nanny.''

"Then what do you have in mind?''

"An arrangement. A permanent arrangement, for Nicky's sake.'' He straightened to his full imposing height. "I'm asking you to marry me.''

CHAPTER TEN

IT WAS EVERYTHING Amanda could have asked of life. Chase and Nicky, wrapped up in an inseparable package, forever hers. And yet…

A permanent arrangement.

There was something almost chilly about the words. Only then did she realize that Chase had said nothing about love, nothing about caring—except where Nicky was involved. And though he had told her he wasn't asking her to be a nanny, what else was this but a long-term, cold-blooded, very logical way to be certain that Nicky got the attention and care he needed? What better person to give it to him than Amanda? She wouldn't fuss about the hours or the travel, or quit at an inopportune time.…

"Why?" she said.

"Oh, Amanda." He sounded almost sorry. "Don't you think I know how this has torn you up? I was stunned at first, I admit, and angry—and afraid you'd only put yourself back into his life for personal gain. But when I calmed down, I know you didn't. You're too honest for that."

She said stiffly, "Thanks for that much at least." Unable to face him, she crossed the room to the long windows and stared unseeingly out at what passed for Springhill's skyline. *So Chase does care about me in a way,* she thought. *At least, he cares enough to feel sorry for me.* But sympathy and compassion weren't the things she needed him to feel.

Chase crossed the room to her. "When I thought it all

out, well, it's the only way I could see. Nicky wants you. He needs you, Amanda.''

''He obviously needs some stability in his life.'' She was hardly aware of what she was saying. ''Something and someone he can depend on who isn't working twelve-hour days.''

''You can give him that.'' His hands came to rest gently on her shoulders.

And you, Chase? What can I give you? What do you want from me?

She stood rigid, trying to ignore the warm weight of his hands, trying to forget the other times he had touched her like this. ''You're suggesting a marriage of convenience, I suppose?''

''What do you mean by that?''

''Separate bedrooms.''

He was obviously startled, for he didn't answer right away. ''Well, no, actually, I wasn't. Don't be a prude, Amanda. It's not as if we haven't—''

She didn't wait for him to finish. She couldn't bear to hear him dissect the single night they had shared. For her it had been magic; if he made it sound ordinary, it would hurt beyond bearing.

''So we could call it a marriage of almost-convenience,'' she said. ''Or perhaps the best way to put it is a marriage for your convenience.''

He let her go and moved back a step. ''I got the impression that you'd enjoyed yourself in my bed.''

The cool note in his voice made her even more furious. ''You get a nanny with a lifetime contract—didn't you say once that was something you longed to have?—and a bed partner who's handy whenever you feel the urge. Not a bad combination from your point of view.''

''You don't have to make it sound like I'm...'' He

paused. "It makes sense, Amanda. You have to admit that."

She turned to face him. "Oh, no doubt about it from where you're sitting."

"It's not as if there wouldn't be advantages for you."

"I'm sure there would be. To be the wife of the sexiest man on American TV.... I suppose I should be grateful. It's positively noble of you to make the sacrifice and actually offer me marriage, Chase. And I can't help thinking if Nicky's been good armor against the Jessamyn Ardens of the world, how much handier it'll be for you to have a wife tagging along, too."

"Have you quite finished, Amanda?" His tone was level, almost dangerously so. "I was under the impression that you'd do anything for Nicky, but of course if that's not the case…"

Her heart gave a painful lurch. *Nicky,* she thought. *I can have Nicky....*

If only she could feel the same way Chase did, if she could put Nicky first and be as cool and logical as Chase seemed to be, then perhaps this marriage of almost-convenience would actually work. Even if all it ever could be was a…a business partnership, at least she would have Nicky. And with time and patience it might actually develop into something more. Once, they had started to be friends, and that wasn't a bad sort of foundation....

But friendship had passed them by, poisoned by sarcasm and suspicion and doubt, and she didn't think it likely they could ever find their way back along that twisted route.

And probably down the road lay jealousy, as well, and the bitterness it would bring. By nature, she wasn't a jealous sort, and if she could be confident of his feelings for her, Chase's work wouldn't bother her, no matter how many gorgeous women he encountered.

But when the only place for her in his life was in the shadow of uncertainty—not exactly an employee, but not quite a wife, a lover who was not loved—she didn't think she could calmly stand by and not be fearful of the inevitable woman who would be more important to him than she was.

To live with Chase, to love Chase and to know that he didn't care about her, to understand that he slept with her because it was pleasant and convenient, but that he didn't love her… Not even the joy of having Nicky could make up for that, because in the long run her bitterness and pain would hurt the child, as well.

"I would do almost anything for Nicky," she said. "But not this."

She wasn't looking at him. It would have been too difficult to meet his gaze and then send him out of her life. She knew Chase watched her for a long moment before he turned away, and though he walked almost as softly as a wild animal, she knew he paused halfway across the room as if he was thinking. She braced herself, gathering what little strength she still had against what he might say. Would he strike out at her? Or would he try persuasion?

He did neither. The door shut softly behind him.

In the wire cage at the corner of the room, Floyd sidled back and forth on his perch and observed sagely, "Strike three!"

"You're right, Floyd," Amanda said quietly. "And this time, the game's over."

BUT IT WASN'T OVER, for the movie wasn't completed. The filming went on relentlessly, and no matter what Amanda did, it seemed she couldn't stay out of Chase Worthington's way. One morning she patiently waited till she saw him leave before she went downstairs to work, but Nicky had forgotten his stuffed rabbit and insisted on coming back for it, and they met in the lobby. She couldn't help herself; she stooped over Nicky to retie his shoes and said how much fun the day-care center must be, with all the other children.

"It's not so awf'ly bad," Nicky said, and added with a hopeful look at his father, "but I'd rather stay with you."

She didn't look at Chase, and he didn't comment. So Nicky went to daycare.

The next day was as gray and somber as she felt, and she postponed her rounds of the inn to an hour when she knew Chase absolutely had to be on the set. Instead, she found him in one of the large meeting rooms, reading the newspaper while Nicky ran races against imaginary opponents. "I hope you don't mind," Chase said. "But shooting was canceled because of the rain. It's too wet to be outdoors, but Nicky needed to use up some energy."

She bit her tongue and said it was fine with her, and after that she peeked around the corners of rooms before she entered them.

A couple of days later, she took Zack and Katie Kendall to the park, and Chase and Nicky were there playing catch. Katie shepherded the boys off to the swings, and Amanda stared at the second button on Chase's shirt—a knit pullover in the same rich warm brown as his eyes—and said, "Please stop using Nicky this way."

"Using him?"

"I don't understand why, but you have to be doing this on purpose. Running into me no matter where I go."

He didn't deny it. "I'm showing you what you're missing."

You're showing me all the wrong things, she wanted to tell him. If Nicky was the only thing that mattered, she'd never have made the choice she had. If she could just believe that Chase cared about her in even the smallest of ways... But feeling sorry for her didn't count.

After that, however, he stopped putting himself in her path. She saw him only once in the next few days—on the afternoon when he came down to the registration desk, with Nicky and the stuffed rabbit and John the bellman with a loaded cart, to check out.

Amanda was startled. She had thought she had another week at least to prepare herself for this, a few more days to gather her strength for this parting. "But the movie—" she said, before she thought better of it and stopped.

"The rest of the cast and crew will be here for another week," Chase said. "But my scenes are finished. Why do you ask? Are you going to miss us, Amanda?"

Nicky tugged at his father's arm, and Chase lifted him to the edge of the desk. "Are you going to miss me, Mandy?" the child asked.

It's not fair, she thought, and closed her eyes against the pain.

"I'll miss you," Nicky confided. "And Floyd and Zack, too. But 'specially you, Mandy."

Her voice was rough-edged and her eyes were wet. "And I'll miss you, sweetheart."

He hugged her long and tightly, and then, after due deliberation, he handed her his stuffed rabbit, the one Chase had bought for him on their first afternoon in Springhill. "Keep him for me," he said. Then he jumped down and ran out to the waiting limousine.

"You don't have to say goodbye to him," Chase said.

Amanda stroked the rabbit's crushed fur. "Please don't do this to me, Chase."

He didn't answer. He signed the bill, and then he was gone. She stood in the lobby, watching as he crossed the sidewalk to the car. She saw how the light played on his hair, turning it to spun gold. And she held Nicky's bunny to her heart in the futile hope that the stuffed toy might help to fill the emptiness there.

AS EACH SEGMENT of *Diamonds in the Dew* was completed, a few more members of the cast and crew, with their jobs finished, checked out of the inn and left Springhill behind. The day Jessamyn Arden left, the staff held an impromptu party; Amanda called a halt to it as soon as she realized what was going on, but she privately admitted that she, too, was glad to see the last of the woman—just as she was when Joe Smith finally left town.

The production people would stay awhile longer, returning borrowed property and tying up other loose ends, but the interlude was over, and Springhill was once more just a quiet little town.

Too quiet by far, Amanda found herself thinking. She had too much time on her hands, and too many memories that rushed in to fill her unoccupied moments.

She began to think seriously of leaving. It wasn't that going somewhere else would take the memories away, but at least there would be fewer reminders of Chase and Nicky. As it was, everywhere she went something brought one or both of them to mind. Even a dandelion peeking out of a flower bed in the park had the power to bring tears to her eyes.

So she started working on her résumé, and one Sunday afternoon when all her qualifications and experience were down in black and white, she called Jordan Kendall to ask if she could get his opinion on the best way to present herself to prospective employers.

"I'll stop by later," he said. "Right after the softball game."

She left the résumé on the flat-topped trunk and started

to make oatmeal cookies. They were Jordan's favorite, and adding a little extra incentive never hurt a deal, Amanda had found.

The first pan of cookies was just coming out of the oven when she heard a knock at the door. Jordan was early. He must have decided to come before the game. She called out, "Come in!"

The door opened, but there was no hearty answer. She finished lifting the cookies from the baking sheet and turned off the oven; she'd finish the job later. She pulled her apron loose and draped it over the edge of the sink.

"Jordan?" she said as she came around the corner of the kitchenette into the sitting room carrying a plate of cookies. "I baked your favorite extra-crispy—"

Chase was standing just inside the door, his hand still on the knob.

Amanda felt the plate tip, but she couldn't stop it. She watched as it slid from her hands in what seemed like slow motion and spun toward the floor, cookies flying in all directions. "You," she whispered. "You came back."

Chase crossed the room to her, and for a moment she thought he was going to put his arms around her. Instinctively she took half a step backward, and he looked down at her for a very long moment before stooping to gather up the worst of the mess.

Amanda put her hand to her throat and watched as he picked up the shattered pieces of the cookies and set the plate on the edge of the breakfast bar. She was an idiot to dodge away from him like that, when he'd probably never intended to touch her at all.

She moved toward the center of the room. "What brings you back to Springhill?" she asked, trying to sound bright and cheerful and friendly.

He didn't answer, and finally she looked at him. His eyes

were darker than usual, without a trace of humor. "I thought you'd had long enough to think about all this, without Nicky constantly underfoot. I thought you'd be able to see the logic."

Her knees were trembling. She took hold of the back of a chair to brace herself and hoped he couldn't see the way she was shaking. It wasn't fair; she'd been through this whole tormenting scenario before, and she had made her decision. Wasn't once enough?

"I haven't changed my mind." She congratulated herself; her voice wasn't so terribly wobbly. Chase might not notice.

His gaze didn't shift from her face. "Why won't you marry me, Amanda?"

She tightened her grip on the chair. "I've seen people try to hold damaged marriages together for the sake of the children. It doesn't work, so I don't think starting out that way would be a good idea."

He nodded quietly. "I see what you're saying. Since the only thing we have in common is Nicky..."

The matter-of-fact note in his voice almost broke her heart. But he was right of course; she'd always known that loving him didn't mean he felt anything similar. She nodded. "It wouldn't work, Chase."

He moved a little closer. "But you see, I think you're wrong there."

"You actually believe it would work?" She shook her head. "You haven't really thought about it, then. In the end it would hurt Nicky even more. I love him too much to tear him apart like that. If he wants me in his life, I'll always be there for him, but—"

"That wasn't what I meant at all, Amanda. I think you're wrong about Nicky being the only thing we have in common."

She shook her head in confusion. "I don't know what you're talking about."

"I mean your scrapbooks."

Amanda felt as if little chunks of ice were coursing through her veins. How did he know about the scrapbooks? From Stephanie, perhaps? Nicky hadn't seen them; they'd never been anywhere in sight when Chase himself was around....

Or had they? She'd almost forgotten about Jessamyn's snooping the afternoon the elevator broke down. Had she put the books away by the time Chase arrived, or had they still been spread on the trunk when he had proposed to her? And if so, would he have noticed them, or had too much else been on his mind?

"What about them?" she said warily.

"Did you keep all those stories and photographs all these years only because of Nicky?"

She shrugged. "Why else?"

He didn't speak for long seconds, and finally she dared to raise her eyes to his. Then she wished she hadn't, for his gaze was level and direct, and he seemed to be seeing into her heart.

But he said, "Stephanie was wrong, then. She told me it looked to her as if you've been half in love with me for years."

"Stephanie should mind her own business." To her dismay, she began to choke up. "Dammit! She had no right to tell you—" She stopped abruptly, horrified at what she had almost said, and started over. "She was most certainly wrong. She shouldn't jump to conclusions."

Chase moved closer. "I've only loved you for a few weeks," he said softly. "But if you'll give me years, Amanda, I'll work hard to make it up."

The floor seemed to rock under her feet, but the delicate

ornaments on the shelves weren't sliding around. The earth-quake she was experiencing was inside her. She fumbled her way to a chair and sat.

He would do anything for Nicky, she reminded herself. He hadn't said it in so many words, but the implication had been clear. And if Chase thought that her presence was the only thing that would make Nicky happy, he would take whatever steps were necessary. "I can't," she whispered. She propped her elbows on her knees and let her face drop into her hands.

"What can't you do? Believe me?" He pulled a hassock around and sat down facing her, his hands warm on her wrists. "I don't blame you. You see, I was going to propose to you that night—the morning, actually—you spent with me, and then Nicky had his nightmare, and the world came apart at the seams."

She remembered the way he'd looked at her that night, with a sort of lazy triumph in his eyes, and against all reason a glow of hope sprang to life in her heart, like the first tiny flicker of flame in a pile of kindling.

"I was so angry right then, Amanda, I honestly thought I never wanted to see you again. At the same time I was hurt that you hadn't told me, that you hadn't trusted me. And I was afraid you only found me attractive because of Nicky."

"No," she whispered.

"It wasn't till later I decided I didn't care about that. Even if you only married me because of Nicky, maybe sooner or later it would turn into more. I told myself you couldn't have been pretending all the time—you'd enjoyed yourself with me a little, at least. Hadn't you?"

She nodded.

"But the doubts were still there, and when I proposed to you I did it very clumsily." He sighed. "When you turned me down, I was furious that even for Nicky's sake you wouldn't try to put up with me. You would give up any chance of having Nicky, even of seeing him, rather than share my life. It was like a blow to the gut to think you could dislike me that much and conceal it. But what other reason was there? And what could I do but accept your decision?'' Very gently he pulled her hands away from her face. ''But then as I was on my way to the door I saw your scrapbooks, and I realized that it wasn't only Nicky you'd been watching all these years. It couldn't have been only Nicky, was it?''

Amanda whispered, ''It sneaked up on me, I suppose. I was interested in you of course. But when I met you, and I realized how crazily head over heels I'd gone... I never meant you to know.''

''Is that why you wouldn't marry me? Because you love me?''

She nodded a little. ''It sounds stupid, doesn't it?''

''Oh, no. Not when I'd just offered you the least-romantic proposal of the century. And I could have kicked myself for it. But I could hardly turn around right then and say, 'By the way, this isn't just for Nicky, I'm in love with you, too.' You'd have hit me with the nearest vase.''

She made a sound, half laugh, half sob. ''Probably.''

''Every time I saw you after that, I was more convinced that it wasn't only Nicky—either that or I was the world's greatest fool, deluding myself that you cared about me. I wasn't sure which—and you didn't give me an opening to find out. If you saw me coming, you ducked out of the way.''

''I didn't want Nicky to be hurt any more than he already was.''

''I know. That gave me some hope. There isn't much you wouldn't do for him, is there?''

She shook her head.

"So I disappeared in the hope that when I came back you'd give yourself away. Betray some kind of happiness to see me. And if you hadn't—"

"Did I?"

"Oh, yes. It was in your eyes for just a moment, and then you shut me out again. Amanda…"

Tentatively he put his arms around her, and she huddled close to him, her face buried in the softness of his shirt. "I thought I'd never see you again," she whispered.

"I didn't go very far," he admitted. "Just up to Sapphire Lake to the Kendalls' cabin. When you called Jordan this afternoon and told him you'd be at home, well, I decided you'd had enough time to think. And I knew I'd waited absolutely as long as I could. I had to know. Amanda, I do love you so."

He drew her up out of her chair and over to the couch, where she nestled against him, safe in the circle of his arms. His kiss was long and deep and somehow comforting—and also the most terrifyingly exciting sensation she had ever experienced. By the time he raised his head once more, Amanda's whole body felt like clay—warm and mellow and eager for the sculptor's touch.

He smiled down into her eyes and brushed a knuckle over her nose. "Most women use powder on their faces. But I kind of like the flour you're wearing."

"You would." She rubbed futilely at her nose. "So I baked Jordan's favorite cookies for nothing?"

"We could invite the Kendalls over to hear the news. Unless you still think Stephanie should mind her own business?"

"Well…"

She recognized the look he gave her—it was partly the lazy triumph she had seen before, mixed with a healthy dose of desire—and suddenly she had no interest in anything but the two of them. But ultimately something else began to nag at the back of her mind. Something she'd almost forgotten.

"Speaking of Nicky..." she managed finally.

"Were we?" Chase said unsteadily. "Must we?"

"Where is he?"

"Upstairs with a sitter—just in case I needed backup."

"You wouldn't use him like that!"

"Don't count on it. A desperate man will do almost anything, Amanda." He rubbed his chin against her hair. "I actually considered the idea, if you turned me down again, of leaving him with you."

She pulled away and looked at him in disbelief. "Leaving him? You mean permanently?"

He nodded. "I thought about it long and hard. You looked so unhappy and he's been miserable. But I couldn't do it. I couldn't give him up. And it was then I really understood what a wrenching sacrifice you'd made—when you first gave him up, and then again when you didn't try to take him back from me—because you felt it was best for Nicky."

"I didn't want to give him up." Her voice was so low that Chase had to bend his head to hear.

"Why did you?"

She told him about her parents, and the disgrace they felt she had brought upon them, and the pressure she had been under. "But I didn't sell him, Chase. I never saw a dime of your money. The attorney paid my expenses—that was all."

"I believe you. I'm sorry I accused you of that."

The last little knot of fear, deep in the pit of her stomach, loosened. "How can you know?"

"Because a woman who could sell her baby to the highest bidder wouldn't have bothered to dress him in hand-made clothes before she gave him up. If I hadn't been so angry, if I'd stopped to think, I would have remembered that little yellow sweater.''

''Thank you for believing in me.''

''My pleasure. Besides, I have to admit I didn't know much about the legal niceties at the time.''

''What do you mean?''

He sighed. ''Desiree could have offered you the earth and I'd have been the last one to know about it. I think I told you she was the one who really wanted a child.''

Amanda nodded.

''I don't know why she felt so strongly about having one. Possibly because she thought she might need a weapon someday, and a child would fit the description.''

''What?''

''That sounds pretty awful, doesn't it? I honestly loved her when I married her—at least I loved the person I thought she was. And when I found out she wasn't like that at all, well, I still intended to stick it out. If she thought a baby would make her happy, it was all right with me. It wasn't till later that I began to wonder about her motives. To be perfectly honest, I figured this craze would pass, too—Desiree wasn't known for her patience.''

Amanda settled a little closer against his shoulder.

''She made the rounds of the agencies, of course, but they didn't give her much hope of getting a baby soon. So she got the idea of a private adoption—where, I don't know, and I never did find out how she made connections with that sleazy attorney of yours.''

''Not mine, actually. My father hired him.''

''And paid him, no doubt? I wouldn't be surprised if he was making money on both ends of the deal. At any rate, I didn't realize what kind of finder's fee Desiree had agreed to pay until after I'd seen Nicky. I'm almost sure she planned it that way—or the attorney did.''

"Oh," Amanda said softly. ''That's when he snuggled right up to you.''

Chase nodded ruefully. "Of course once I'd held him, well, no amount of money would have been too much.''

"I'm glad it worked out that way.''

He ruffled her hair. "So am I, all things considered. But for a while... Once Desiree had her live baby doll, she decided he wasn't really as much fun as she thought he'd be. She'd smother him with attention one day and ignore him the next. The truth was, Nicky was mine and mine alone—right up to the minute I caught Desiree with her lover and told her I wanted a divorce.''

Amanda's eyes widened. "That never made the news. Or even the tabloids.''

"She was discreet, I'll say that for her. Not that I was watching very closely. The marriage had been over for all intents and purposes for quite a while. We were still talking about terms when her plane crashed. Nicky had been the sticking point—I wasn't about to give him up, and Desiree knew he was the only thing I cared about, so naturally she demanded custody. I don't think she'd have pressed the point once she got everything else on her list, but in the meantime, she even wanted to take Nicky with her on location.''

Amanda shivered. If Desiree *had* taken him that last time...

"But he had an ear infection, and at the last minute she decided she didn't want to be bothered.'' Chase saw Amanda's lower lip tremble and steadied it with his fingertip. "It's over, sweetheart. And because of Nicky, we have each other, too.''

She gave herself up to the joy of touching him, the sheer

delight of allowing her fingers to toy with his hair, of stroking the soft skin at the corners of his eyes, of kissing him with every ounce of passion he had roused in her....

The doorknob turned very quietly. A detached little corner of Amanda's brain heard the slight creak and told her that she ought to pay attention. But before she had managed to pull herself together, a small voice asked, "What are you doing, Daddy?"

Amanda turned to look. Nicky's head was all that showed around the edge of the door; the rest of him was still in the hall.

Chase didn't move. "I'm kissing Amanda." He sounded as if he was having trouble getting his breath. "What are *you* doing, Nicky?"

Nicky pushed the door wide and stopped just inside the room, shifting his weight from one foot to the other. "You said I could see Mandy later."

"Yes, I did."

Amanda said quietly, "You were that sure of yourself?"

"I wish I had been," Chase whispered against her lips. "But in any case, you wouldn't have refused to see him, would you?"

She shook her head. "I couldn't."

"Well, that was a long, *long* time ago," Nicky pointed out.

"Half an hour at least," Chase agreed. "Almost an eternity, in fact. So you sneaked away from the baby-sitter and came down on your own?"

Nicky nodded. "You said I could see Mandy," he repeated hopefully.

"I know I did. Close the door and come here, Nick."

Nicky's hug was almost the sweetest sensation Amanda had ever felt. His curls tickled her face, and she closed her eyes and rocked him a little, savoring the scent of him.

Far too soon for her liking, he wriggled away. "I have to say hello to Floyd, too," he said, and bounded across the room. "Say Nicky, Floyd!"

The parakeet looked at him slightly cross-eyed and observed, "Home run."

Nicky came back in disgust. "He'll probably never learn my name."

Amanda smiled. She wouldn't tell him, she decided. She'd let him have the thrill of discovery.

"Daddy's going to teach me to whistle," he announced. "Do you still have my bunny?"

"Of course I do." Amanda opened the trunk and lifted out the quilt and the scrapbooks. She hesitated a moment, feeling silly, and darted a look at Chase before she pried loose the false bottom and handed Nicky the stuffed rabbit. He tucked it under his arm and cuddled close to Amanda's side.

Chase leaned forward and studied the items in the bottom of the trunk. When he turned to look at Amanda once more, the warmth in his eyes was intense.

"You'd better call the sitter before she has the whole hotel out searching for Nicky," she said finally.

He nodded and reached for the telephone. "I was wrong, you know."

"About what?"

"You. I've loved you much longer than the last few weeks."

"How could you? You didn't know me."

"Yes, I did." He reached into the bottom of the trunk and picked up the tiny ball of yellow yarn. "I knew the very special woman who knit a sweater from this, and dressed a baby in it, and gave him up because she cared for him so much. I think I've loved you since the day I first held Nicky in my arms."

Nicky sat up straight. "Are you going to marry Mandy, Daddy?"

"Yes, Nick."

"And that means we can always keep her?"

"For ever and ever." Chase was looking at Amanda as he said it. He was smiling a little, but the steady light in his eyes was like a solemn vow.

"That's good." Nicky put his head down on Amanda's shoulder again. "Does that make me your chosen child, too, Mandy?"

Chase told the baby-sitter to take the remainder of the day off and put the telephone down. "Do you want to hear the rest of that story, Nicky?"

"Will I like it?" the child asked practically.

"I think you will," his father said. He slipped an arm around Amanda and settled her comfortably against his side, with Nicky in her lap. "In fact, I can just about guarantee it."

Sharon Kendrick was born in West London, and has had *heaps* of jobs which include photography, nursing, driving an ambulance across the Australian desert and cooking her way around Europe in a converted double-decker bus! Without a doubt, writing is the best job she has ever had and when she's not dreaming up new heroes (some of whom are based on her doctor husband!), she likes cooking, reading, theatre, listening to American West Coast music and talking to her two children, Celia and Patrick.

Look out for:
SURRENDER TO THE SHEIKH
by Sharon Kendrick
in Modern Romance™, July 2001

PART-TIME FATHER
by
SHARON KENDRICK

This book is dedicated
to the talented and beautiful
Daniella Trendell.

CHAPTER ONE

'MOTHER! *Mother*!' Out of breath from running at top speed up the path following her mother's urgent summons, Kimberley dropped her suitcase on to the cold tiles of the flagged floor and listened.

Silence.

Fear gripped at her heart like a vice, and a note of uncertainty crept into her voice. 'Mother?'

She heard the scrape of something in the small sitting-room, and, striding over in the shortest time possible, she threw open the door to see her mother just moving the small stool which stood in front of the sofa, on which she'd obviously been resting her feet.

Thank heavens! The unacknowledged fear, ever present when your elderly mother lived on her own, immediately subsided. 'So *there* you are!' said Kimberley in relief.

Her mother pushed her spectacles further back up on her nose and looked at her only child, a small smile lighting her still shapely mouth which was so like her daughter's. 'Where did you think I'd be?' she enquired mildly. 'Robbed and left trussed up in the attic? Kidnapped by modern-day pirates and heading for the coast?'

Kimberley giggled. 'You *are* outrageous, Mother! Your imagination is much too vivid, and those crazy adventure stories you read don't help.'

'And you don't read enough of them!' commented Mrs Ryan sternly. 'You're far too serious about that job of yours.'

Kimberley decided to ignore that—for who wouldn't be obsessively career-minded when their love-life was a total non-starter? And whose fault is *that*? mocked a tiny inner voice.

Ignoring that too, she went over to plant a kiss on her mother's forehead, then perched on the other end of the sofa. 'Why did you need to see me? I was coming down soon for Christmas anyway. You are OK, aren't you? What are you doing lying down in the middle of the day?' And then her attention was caught by the bandage which was tightly tied around her mother's ankle. 'Oh, heavens—whatever have you *done*?' she exclaimed in horror.

'Kimberley, please,' said her mother calmly. 'There's absolutely no need to panic.'

'But what have you *done*?'

'I've sprained my ankle, that's all.'

'But what does the doctor—?'

'He says it's *fine*, I just need to take it easy, that's all…' Mrs Ryan's voice tailed off. 'The only problem is—'

'What?'

'That I can't work.' Mrs Ryan leaned back against the cushions piled on the sofa and surveyed the immaculately dressed form of her daughter, who was at that moment letting a frown mar her exceptionally pretty features.

Kimberley gave a little click of disapproval. 'Then give the job up, Mum,' she urged. 'I've told you that

I earn enough to send you what Mrs Nash—' she said the name reluctantly '—pays you.'

'And I have told you on countless occasions that I enjoy the independence which my little job gives me, and I have no intention of relinquishing it.'

'But, Mum—must you do a *cleaning* job?'

'You, Kimberley, I'm ashamed to say, are a snob,' said Mrs Ryan reprovingly.

'I am *not* a snob. I'd just rather you didn't work at all, if you must know.'

'You mean,' said Mrs Ryan shrewdly, 'that you'd rather I didn't work in the big house which you almost became mistress of?'

Kimberley's mouth tightened, but she felt tiny beads of sweat break out on her forehead. 'That's history,' she croaked.

'You're right. It is. In fact, I've some news for you.'

'What kind of news?'

'He's getting married. He's engaged!'

The beads of sweat became droplets. Kimberley heard her heart pounding in her ears, felt the blood drain from her face. 'He is?' she croaked, dry-mouthed. 'That's wonderful.'

'Isn't it? Dear Duncan,' said her mother fondly.

'Duncan?' asked Kimberley weakly.

Her mother gave her a strange look. 'Yes, of course Duncan. Your ex-fiancé, the man you were going to marry—who else could I have meant?'

Surreptitiously Kimberley wiped the back of her hand over her sticky forehead, and then, terrified that her mother might notice and comment on her pale complexion, searched around for a distraction. 'How about some tea? I'm absolutely parched. Shall I make some?' she asked brightly.

'Best offer I've had all day!'

Kimberley quickly left the room and filled the old-fashioned kettle with shaking hands, reacquainting herself with her mother's tiny kitchen, pulling biscuits out of the tin with trembling hands as she tried to put her thoughts in order. She wondered what her mother would have said if she'd known that Duncan had been the last person in her thoughts; she had thought she'd been talking about Harrison.

Harrison Nash—her ex-fiancé's brother. The man with the cold grey eyes and the hard, handsome features and the lean, sexy body. Harrison Nash—who had changed the whole course of Kimberley's life without even realising that he was doing so...

It had been one bright and beautiful summer's evening, with the setting sun pouring like golden honey into the red drawing-room at Brockbank House where Kimberley had been waiting to conduct what was obviously going to be a difficult and painful interview with Duncan, her fiancé. Because, after much thought and many sleepless nights, Kimberley had decided to break off the engagement which had followed their whirlwind romance.

Duncan and his mother had recently moved into Woolton village's most imposing building—the historic Brockbank House, left to the Nash family by a distant relative who had died without leaving an heir. Kimberley had met Duncan when she'd been visiting her mother in the village, on one of her brief but regular forays from London, where she lived.

From the first meeting he had pursued her avidly, and, flattered by his charm and his persistence, Kimberley had allowed herself to believe that she had fallen in love at long last. Already in a strong and powerful position at work, where her male colleagues tended to fear and revere her, Kimberley had been charmed by Duncan's healthy irreverence and his ready agreement to let *her* set the pace physically.

He didn't leap on her and he respected her somewhat old-fashioned view that she wanted to wait until they were married before consummating their relationship. At twenty-four she thought that she'd found the perfect gentleman—and she *had*.

Kimberley sighed.

It just wasn't *enough*. Quite apart from the fact that she was three years older than Duncan, and that he was still at university while she had already established a successful career for herself in London, there was one even more important reason why she could not marry him.

She simply didn't love him—or rather, she did, as the dear, sweet person he was, but not in the way that he said he loved her, and to marry him under those conditions would simply not be fair to him.

She had decided to tell him as gently as possible, but Duncan was young, good-looking and the best fun in the world. He would get over it, of that she was certain.

Kimberley sighed as she perched nervously on the edge of one of the large chairs in the red drawing-room, brushing one hand through the thick abundance of raven-black hair and pushing it off her high-browed face so that it spilled in shiny soot-dark waves down her back.

She wondered how one went about breaking off an engagement. She would have to tell her mother and Duncan's mother—both widows. She herself had no other relatives, and Duncan very few. She wondered briefly whether the older brother in America had been informed—the rich, successful one, who Duncan and his mother both seemed slightly in awe of.

Probably not. They'd only become engaged last weekend—hardly time to make it properly official.

As Kimberley stared out of the window at the magnificent grounds of Brockbank House she heard a soft noise behind her. Not a footstep exactly, it was much too subtle for that, but she suddenly experienced the unease of being watched. She turned round slowly, to discover who her silent scrutineer was, feeling her skin ice with some unknown fear as she stared at the dark, silent man who stood before her.

She had seen photos of him before, of course—various portraits of him scattered around the house and, latterly, newspaper clippings from gossip columns—but Kimberley would have known without being told that this was Harrison. Harrison the rich, the powerful, the blessed older son. Not that he looked in the least bit like Duncan, although the familial similarities were there.

But this man was Duncan's very antithesis. Where Duncan's eyes were soft, smiling, this man's were hard and crystalline and bright. Where Duncan's mouth was full and kissable, this man's lips were a thin, hard line. Cruel lips, thought Kimberley wildly, and tried but failed to imagine them kissing her, her cheeks flaring red as she saw those same lips twist into a contemptuous curve.

For one frozen moment Kimberley sat staring up at him, unable to move, to think, to speak, unable to do anything other than acknowledge the dark and potent and sensual rush of desire which flooded over her with the heavy pull of a tidal wave. She stared into eyes which no longer looked grey but black as the night, she saw the heated flare of colour which scorched along his high, perfectly chiselled cheek-bones—and she felt dizzy with a shameful longing.

Unnerved by that still intense scrutiny, and by his silence, Kimberley scrambled to her feet.

'You must be Harrison,' she blurted out, in nothing even resembling her usual calm, confident manner.

'And you must be the fortune-hunter,' he observed caustically, withering contempt written all over his face.

For a moment Kimberley thought that she must have misheard him; it was just not the sort of thing which one expected to hear, certainly not in civilised company, but there again, with that raw, scornful censure blazing from those amazing eyes, this man didn't look in the least bit civilised. He looked...

Kimberley shuddered.

Almost *barbaric*.

She forced herself to remain calm, because some instinct told her that if she responded on his level she would live to regret it. She raised her eyebrows fractionally. '*What* did you just say?' she queried, quite calmly.

'Oh, dear,' he said mockingly, and sighed. 'I should have guessed that it was too good to be true—you couldn't possibly have brains as well as beauty. I called you a fortune-hunter, my dear. It's an old-fashioned term, whose meaning is quite simple—'

'I'm well aware of what it means,' Kimberley cut in, but her voice was shaking with rage, and deep within her a seed of hostility blossomed into rampant life. 'How dare you?'

He shrugged his broad shoulders. 'Quite easily. You see, you might find this peculiar, but I happen to be rather protective of my kid brother. And what else am I supposed to think when I hear that he's about to marry someone he hardly knows, who happens to be years older—?'

'Only three,' she interrupted furiously. 'And what difference does that make? Lots of men marry women older than them.'

'Do they?' His look was cool, assessing. 'And do lots of older women marry inexperienced college-boys, who stand to gain huge inheritances? Is that what turns them on—*Kimberley*?'

She shivered with some dark nebulous recognition as he said her name, the way his tongue curved round it making the very act of speaking into the most sensual act she had ever encountered.

'I don't have to stay here and listen to this,' she said shakily, but her feet were rooted to the priceless Persian carpet and she was incapable of movement as she gazed into mesmeric grey eyes.

'But stay you will,' he ordered silkily. 'And listen.'

She watched, horrified, as his eyes dropped to her body and lingered insolently on the lushness of her breasts beneath the thin cotton T-shirt she wore, and Kimberley was powerless to stop what that appraising stare was doing to her.

She felt a dart of something which was a combination of pain and acute pleasure, felt her breasts grow heavy, hard, swollen. She saw his mouth twist with derision as he observed the blatant tightening of her nipples, and at that moment she felt utterly cheap.

He nodded his head, as though satisfied by something. 'Yes,' he said thoughtfully. 'As I imagined. A hot little body and a face like a madonna—quite exquisite, but unfortunately they are such ephemeral assets. And, wisely, you've decided to capitalise on them. But I'd prefer you to do that with someone other than my brother. Understand?'

Kimberley bit back her rage, her normally sharp mind in dazed turmoil because he was still staring at her breasts, and her nipples were torturing her with their exquisite need to have him take each one into his mouth, to suckle slowly and lick and...

Horrified, she stared back at him, her body's appalling reaction to his scrutiny stinging her into defending herself. 'I don't have to capitalise on any assets I might have, actually,' she retorted. 'Because I happen to have a very successful career in a merchant bank.'

'And how did you get it?' he queried insultingly. 'On your back?'

His hostility rode every other thought out of her

mind. 'Why are you doing this?' she whispered incredulously.

He shrugged. 'I told you. I'm looking out for my brother—and he needs shielding from women like you.'

'Women like you'.

Her face flaming, Kimberley lifted her hand and slapped him hard—very hard—around the face. She should have been shocked at her violent reaction but she wasn't; it was the most satisfying thing she had ever done in her life. But he didn't flinch. Only the angry spark which glittered ominously from the grey eyes betrayed his emotions.

'In a minute,' he said calmly, 'I shall respond to that. But first I want you to listen very carefully to what I'm going to tell you.'

'I don't have to listen to anything you tell me. You insulting—'

'Spare me your misplaced anger and shut up, *Kimberley*,' he said in a voice soft with menace, and Kimberley felt a shiver ice its way down the entire length of her spine. 'My brother is on the threshold of his life. Emotionally he is immature. If he marries now it will be a huge mistake. He is not ready for marriage.'

And neither was she, though Harrison Nash did not know that. She saw the grim determination on his face, the arrogance and the dominance. A man used to getting his way at all costs. How far, she wondered, would he go to prevent her from marrying Duncan?

And Kimberley suddenly knew an overwhelming and very basic urge to get her own back for his insults, for that sexual scrutiny which had had her responding in a way which sickened her.

All at once she was filled with the most tremendous exhilaration, exultant with the sense of her own power to anger this man. 'You can't stop us marrying!' she told him coolly.

The grey eyes narrowed calculatingly as he registered her change of mood. 'No, you're quite right. I can't.' And here he paused, so that there was a brooding, forbidding silence before he resumed speaking. 'But what I *can* do is to withhold any of the financial hand-outs from my company to which Duncan has quickly become accustomed. This house is legally mine, although I have always intended to transfer the deeds to my mother and Duncan, since I have enough homes of my own. However, I *could* change my mind...' He gave her a questioning look. 'I imagine that Duncan's attraction might wane if he didn't come with all the trappings you'd expected?'

Kimberley had met many cynical, ruthless men during her years in the City, but this one, this dark and cruel stranger, made the others look like amateurs.

She lifted her head proudly. 'If I wanted to marry Duncan, then nothing *you* could say or do would stop me,' she said truthfully. 'So you've lost, haven't you?'

'I never lose, Kimberley,' he contradicted her softly. 'Never.'

She fixed him with a look of mock-polite disbelief, fascinated in spite of herself to know just how far he would go to achieve what he wanted. 'Oh, really?'

'I have a proposition to put to you.'

'Go on,' she said, very quietly.

He spoke with a certain reluctance. 'I'm prepared,' he said heavily, 'to offer you a financial incentive of your own if you agree to call the wedding off. If, on the other hand, you refuse and the wedding goes ahead, then I'm warning you that you will receive nothing from Duncan's inheritance unless I am satisfied that the marriage is a good one, and one with solid foundations. Do you understand?'

The grey eyes were so hard and so cold, making a mockery of the rugged perfection of his features, and another shiver of apprehension sent icy claws scrabbling all over Kimberley's skin. 'It isn't just because I'm older, is it?' she whispered, shaken by his venom, her desire for revenge for his insults momentarily forgotten. 'Or even because you think that I'm marrying Duncan for his money? You really don't *like* me, do you?'

He went perfectly still, so still that he might have been carved from some unforgiving stone. 'No,' he said eventually. 'I don't think I *do* like you, if liking can be gauged after such a short acquaintanceship, but you are correct in your assumption in one way—your age and your greed are not the real reasons why I want you to call the wedding off.'

'Why, then?'

'It's simple. Because you are not the right woman for him.'

Stunned by the sheer unremitting force with which he spoke, Kimberley stared into his hard, cruel face.

'What on earth gives you the right to say that?' she whispered.

'This does,' he said, in a voice which was brutal with some unnamed emotion, and he caught her by the waist and bent his dark, savage face to kiss her.

Something happened to her—something irrevocable and mind-blowing. Something which was to change her life forever. What the hell had he done to her with just one kiss? she wondered desperately. Because sexual desire, fiery and hot and potent as life itself, began blazing its way through her veins as his mouth found hers.

Oh, God, but it was heaven.

Heaven.

She opened her mouth to him as though she had waited all her life for that sweet, punishing kiss. She found herself trembling, almost swaying, now wanting more, much more than his kiss. She wanted him to touch her where no man had ever touched her; she wanted those long fingers to remove her T-shirt, to kick away her jeans. She wanted him to lay her down on the floor and make love to her right there...

But then reality crashed in with a sickening sensation as, distantly, somewhere in the house, she heard the sound of someone shouting. She felt his hands drop from her waist, felt, too, his tongue withdraw from her mouth, where it had been inciting her with provocative little movements which had mimicked what no man had ever done to her.

She gave a kind of automatic protest as he lifted his head up and stared down at her dazed face, and she read the contemptuous look in his eyes.

'I rest my case,' he said insultingly.

Kimberley straightened her spine and stared back at him, hiding her shame behind the frosty glitter in her blue eyes.

In her eyes sparked the hatred she felt for him. To illustrate his point he had treated her no better than a whore, and in a way she had responded no better than a whore. The way she had felt in his arms had frightened her with its intensity, so that all her carefully fought for self-control had vanished like the wind. She was the vanquished, he the victor. He had all the power, and she had none. And she never wanted to see him again, not as long as she lived.

Never.

But then Kimberley discovered something else. She could see that behind the contempt which distorted the angular features there remained a hunger—a savage, sexual hunger which made his eyes glitter blackly and beat a frantic pulse at the base of his neck. He wants me, she thought, yet he despises me. And he's a man who gets exactly what he wants.

Oh, my God, thought Kimberley weakly. He'll come and find me. And what if I can't—what if I just *can't* resist him? What will a man who despises me offer other than instant heartbreak?

Unless she somehow contrived to make him despise her so much that he'd leave her alone forever.

She gave a small, smug half-smile, and allowed the kind of cold, calculating look which she knew he would be expecting to come into her eyes.

'This—er—financial incentive you're offering,' she purred. 'How much are we actually talking about?'

Some light in his eyes died. If she had thought she'd read scorn and derision there before, it was nothing to the look which now replaced it. He looked at her as though her very presence contaminated the air surrounding him.

He mentioned a sum, and she allowed a rapacious little smile to curve her lips upwards as she nodded. 'I'll do it,' she told him. 'On one condition.'

He shook his head, the contempt hardening his mouth into an unforgiving line. 'No conditions, sweetheart,' he drawled coldly. 'Unless I make them.'

She shook her head. 'I won't do it unless you agree not to tell Duncan *anything* about what's happened here this afternoon. I want to tell him—to break things off—in my own way.'

He stared at her incredulously. 'Do you really think I'd hurt my brother like that? And, much though I'm tempted to tell him about his lucky escape, I'm really not cruel enough to disillusion him with the knowledge that he fell in love with a cheap little tramp. Do I make myself clear?'

'Perfectly.' She held out a slim white hand, which was miraculously free from tremor. 'And now, if we can conclude our *business*.'

She saw his barely concealed shudder of distaste as he took a cheque-book out from the inside pocket of his suit and began to write.

What she hadn't expected was that it should hurt quite so much...

Kimberley raked her hand roughly through her hair, as if the frantic movement could somehow magically dispel the image of Harrison which burned on her mind's eye as if it had been branded there. After more than two years, she thought despairingly, it shouldn't be quite so vivid. She wasn't naïve enough to have expected to forget a man like Harrison Nash, but surely by now just the merest thought of him shouldn't be enough to make the heat rise up in her blood with its slow, insistent throb?

She picked the tea-tray up to carry it back through into the sitting-room where her mother was waiting.

Why remember all that now?

Because she remembered it every time she came home; it was one of the reasons why her visits were more infrequent than either she or her mother liked. This place was tainted with memories of Harrison Nash and that one fateful kiss.

The day after he had kissed her she had done several things. Firstly, and most importantly, she had gone to Duncan and gently given him back his ring. He had not railed or argued with her; he had quietly accepted her stumbling explanation, saying that deep in his heart he had not been completely surprised.

The following day Kimberley had fled to stay with an aunt in Scotland, where she had remained for a fortnight, quietly licking her wounds. She had also cashed the cheque which Harrison had given her and given the money to charity. More importantly, as she'd handed the huge wad of money over to the bemused representative of Save the Children, she had made a solemn vow. That she would put Harrison Nash out of her mind forever.

And so far, at least, it hadn't worked.

'Kimberley!' came her mother's voice. 'Where's this cup of tea you promised me?'

'Just coming!' Fixing a smile on to her face, Kimberley took the tray and biscuits in, and poured out two cups.

The Earl Grey tea was deliciously refreshing, but Kimberley, though hungry, took only one bite out of a biscuit then left it—still ruffled about remembering that extraordinary day.

Forcing her mind back on to safer subjects, she offered the plate of biscuits to her mother. 'How are you going to manage with your foot bandaged?'

'Oh, I expect I'll be all right,' her mother replied unconvincingly.

Kimberley hid a smile. Her mother, love her, was like an open book! 'Would you like me to come and stay with you until you're up on your feet properly again?' she asked.

Mrs Ryan's smile could have lit up Oxford Street. 'Oh, *would* you, dear? I'd be so grateful!'

Kimberley's mind skipped along. She could telephone her bank later. She was a conscientious high-flyer in the merchant bank where she'd worked for the past five years—she doubted whether they'd mind her taking a break at such short notice. 'Of course I don't mind,' she said. 'But I'll have to drive back up to town to get some clothes.'

'That's fine, dear,' said her mother contentedly as she eyed the teapot. 'Is there another cup in the pot?'

Kimberley poured her mother another cup. 'So, who's Duncan marrying?' she asked, glad that the boy she'd been so fond of had found someone else to love.

'Some girl he met in America—an heiress, apparently.'

'That will please Harrison,' commented Kimberley acidly.

Her mother gave her a shrewd look. 'I don't know why you won't hear a good word said about that man. He's actually very charming.'

'Charming?' About as charming as a snake-pit! Kimberley gave a forced little laugh. 'That's the last adjective I'd use about *him*!'

'But why do you dislike him so much?'

'How can I dislike him—I've barely met the man?' said Kimberley dismissively, then relented. 'If you must know he stands for everything I hate—all that arrogance! He thinks he's God's gift to women—'

'A lot of women tend to agree with him,' cut in Mrs Ryan in amusement. 'Or so I'm told.'

Kimberley resisted the temptation to scream. 'I'd better leave now,' she said hurriedly, in order to stop her mother from regaling her with any anecdotes about Harrison's life. 'If I set off now, I can be in London and back before dark.'

Her mother frowned. 'Well, do drive carefully, won't you, dear?'

'Don't I always?'

'Do you? You're a little too fond of the accelerator, in my opinion!'

But Kimberley was a good, careful driver—though she *was* slightly on the fast side. She made good time to London, and just over an hour later her scarlet sports car drew up outside her delightful honeysuckle-covered cottage in Hampstead.

She phoned her office and spoke to her boss, who told her to take as long as she liked off work.

'Seriously, James?' she laughed.

'No! Take all that back—I'll miss you too much!'

'I'll call you when I get back—I should only be a few days!'

'Call me sooner, if you like. That's if you need a broad, manly shoulder to lean on.'

'I'll bear that in mind, James,' said Kimberley, before ringing off.

James had never made any secret of his admiration for her, but he was confident and rich and handsome enough not to take her laughing refusals to go out on dates with him to heart. She had told him she never dated people she worked with, which was true. Although she actually had a reason for not dating *anyone* who happened to ask her.

She had tried dating, and it didn't work. She couldn't cope with the physical thing. The unfortunate legacy of her brief kiss with Harrison was that no other man moved her in any way that even remotely resembled the way she'd behaved in his arms that day.

Which was a good thing, she reasoned, since she had been so disgusted with herself afterwards. If passion turned you into a wild, mindless creature at the total mercy of your body—then you could keep it! Kimberley would manage just fine with her brain!

She emptied her fridge, cancelled the milk and

switched on the answerphone, threw her suitcase into the back of her MG, and set off back up the motorway.

Her journey was uneventful, save for the episode when a low, black and infinitely more powerful car than her own forced her to move over into the middle lane and then roared off spectacularly into the distance. For Kimberley, who took some pride in her driving and was fiercely competitive, this proved irritating.

Obviously a man, she thought, slightly unfairly. Probably someone who's into phallic symbols to compensate for his own weediness.

She saw the car again, parked outside the one really up-market restaurant in the village, which was a few miles from her mother's house and well off the beaten track—not a tourist trap at all. And she wondered vaguely who, round here, was driving such an expensive piece of equipment.

She arrived back at her mother's, unpacked and then concocted some supper from the food she'd brought with her. The two women were just enjoying a quiet glass of wine when Mrs Ryan dropped her bombshell.

'Er—Kimberley?'

How well she recognised that voice! Kimberley felt a bubble of amusement welling up inside her. 'Mother?'

'I'd like to ask you a favour, dear.'

'I somehow thought that you might. Go on—ask away.'

'Er—it's a little difficult to know how to put it.'

Obviously a very *big* favour, thought Kimberley. 'Mmm?'

'You know I mentioned that Duncan's got engaged?'

Kimberley smiled. Mothers could be so transparent! 'Yes, Mum—and I don't mind, honestly!'

Mrs Ryan gave her a severe look. 'I wasn't imagining for one minute that you did—since you were the one to break it off. Still, better before the marriage than after, I always say.'

Kimberley sighed. 'You were saying?'

'Oh, yes. Well, the thing is that he's due to arrive in a couple of days' time and, with my leg and all, there's no one to get the place ready for him...'

Kimberley put her wine-glass down on the table and looked incredulously at her mother. 'I'm not sure what you're getting at, exactly.'

'Well, I was wondering if you could help me out?'

'Help you out?'

'Just stand in for me—until my leg is better.'

'You mean—*clean* Brockbank House for you?'

'That's right, dear.'

Kimberley shook her head. 'I'll pay someone from the village to stand in for you.'

Mrs Ryan shook her head. 'But I doubt you'd get anyone at this short notice, and so near to Christmas. Besides, you know how fussy Margaret Nash is—she won't let just anyone near all those antiques.' She caught a glimpse of her daughter's expression. 'You wouldn't have to do much, darling,' she said hastily. 'Just hoover the place and flick a duster around. And the kitchen floor could probably do with a bit of a wash. I mean—' she gave Kimberley another stern look '—look on it as a kind of atonement, if you like.'

Kimberley blinked in astonishment. '*Atonement*?'

'Mmm. It would be rather a nice gesture, wouldn't it—after jilting Duncan? Getting the house nice for him. Unless, of course, you're not being entirely truthful with me. Perhaps you *are* a tiny bit jealous…?'

Kimberley stared at her mother very hard, before throwing her head back and laughing loudly. 'You know, Mum, for sheer cheek you're world-class!' Then she thought of something else. 'But surely Mrs Nash wouldn't want me near the place?'

'Oh, no, dear—she's quite happy to have you there. She likes you, you know—she always has. She always said that she thought you were quite wrong for Duncan.'

Interesting. She hadn't said a thing at the time. 'Oh, did she?'

'Will you do it, then?'

Kimberley sighed. 'I suppose so! Anything for a quiet life. But only on one condition.'

'Yes, dear?'

'Where's—Harrison?'

'Oh, he's in France or Germany or somewhere. Living there while he takes over another company. His mother says he works himself into the ground. She says—'

'Fascinating as I'm sure you and Mrs Nash find it,' Kimberley interrupted coolly, 'I really have absolutely *no* interest in hearing about Harrison.'

Her mother's face said, Well, you did ask me!—but to her eternal credit she didn't utter another word.

It was just unfortunate that hearing about him was one thing, but trying not to think about him was another—and the moment she set foot over the threshold of Brockbank House more memories of that hateful, scheming man came flooding back to haunt her.

Kimberley wondered how she could have allowed herself to be talked into doing this particularly distorted 'favour' for her mother. She hadn't been near the house, not for over two years, not since that dreadful day when Harrison had given her the cheque.

Despite her mother's assurances she had been dreading seeing Mrs Nash, but Duncan's mother held her hand out immediately she opened the front door. She was a tall, graceful woman, with Duncan's soft brown eyes; Harrison, Kimberley knew, was the image of his father who had been killed in a yachting accident when both boys were quite small.

'Hello, Kimberley,' said Mrs Nash. 'It's good of you to help me out.'

'It's no trouble. Really. Mother insisted I stand in for her.'

Mrs Nash smiled. 'Eleanor's so terribly conscientious. I really don't know what I'd do without her.' There was a pause. 'She told you that Duncan's getting married?'

'Yes, she did.' Kimberley hesitated. 'I'm very happy for him, Mrs Nash. Really, I am.'

Mrs Nash smiled. 'I rather thought you might be.'

She laid her hand on Kimberley's arm. 'Won't you come and have some tea with me?'

Kimberley shook her head. 'Another time, perhaps. I'd rather get started, if you don't mind.'

'I understand.'

Did she? thought Kimberley. Not really. She imagined that even the fairly liberal Mrs Nash would be shocked if she knew the real reason for Kimberley's reluctance to linger any longer at Brockbank House than she needed to. What would she say if Kimberley told her that the sight of that framed silver photograph of Harrison on the hall table was playing havoc with her equilibrium?

She stared at it, trying to view it objectively. It was just a face, after all. The features weren't particularly even—the eyes were too cold and the jaw much too harshly defined ever to be called handsome. The photographer had caught him smiling, but it wasn't a sunny, happy smile. It was nothing but a cynical upward curve of those hard, sensual lips.

Kimberley turned away from the photo, removed her coat, and set to work immediately. She'd tied her hair back and was wearing a pair of ripped jeans with her oldest T-shirt, which seemed to have shrunk slightly with repeated washing. Once black, it was now a sort of washed-out grey colour, and it revealed about two inches of her midriff.

She couldn't find a mop, so she filled up a bucket with hot soapy water and set about cleaning the floor the old-fashioned way—on her hands and knees!

There was something curiously relaxing about seeing the floor clean up beneath her cloth. Her busy life in London meant that she employed someone else to clean her house, but actually it was really quite satisfying to do it yourself, she decided—if you had the time.

She was just about to wring out her cloth when she heard the kitchen door open. Kimberley looked up, expecting to see Mrs Nash, her smile of greeting fading into frozen disbelief as the longest pair of legs she had ever seen swam into her field of vision. She let her gaze wander up into a hard and cruel face.

And the cold grey eyes of Harrison Nash.

CHAPTER TWO

'WELL, well, well—how the mighty have fallen,' came the sardonic drawl.

His voice sounded exactly the same—rich and deep. And as contemptuous as it had ever been. Kimberley dropped the cloth and it splashed water on to the front of her T-shirt.

'Do you know,' he continued, in that same, silky tone which sent prickles of excitement and dread down her spine, 'I rather like to see you in such a *subservient* position, Kimberley? Rather fetching. And, funnily enough, I was never particularly turned on by wet T-shirt competitions—but I can now see that I'm going to have to revise my opinion.'

His cool grey gaze had travelled to her sopping T-shirt, where the water had cruelly outlined the rounded swell of her breasts with detailed precision. Under his gaze she felt the nipples tighten immediately into those exquisitely painful little peaks, and she felt a hot weakness kick at the pit of her stomach. She saw the flash of hunger which darkened his eyes and he moved the tip of his tongue over his lips in a gesture which shrieked pure provocation.

Remember what he did to you.

'What the hell are you doing here?' she demanded as she flung the cloth back into the bucket and scrambled to her feet.

'I really should be asking you that question, don't you think? Are times hard for merchant bankers? Supplementing your income with a spot of charring—'

'My mother happens to do the charring in this house,' she cut in icily. 'God knows why she does it, but she does—and I will *not* have you insulting her.'

'I wouldn't dream of insulting your mother, whom I both like and respect.' His eyes narrowed; she could barely see them. 'Unlike her little madam of a daughter. Tell me, did you hatch a plot to get back into this house, somehow—anyhow? What are your intentions—to try to ruin Duncan's life a second time?'

Kimberley stared at him, wondering genuinely if his memory was defective. 'You're mad! What are you talking about?'

'I'm talking about your motives for being here.'

'My *motives*? You really aren't making yourself at all clear, I'm afraid, Harrison.'

'Then allow me to elucidate,' he said softly. 'My brother is returning from America, where he went after you dumped him, and he's bringing with him his new fiancée. And now you're here. Again. I'm just interested to know what you're up to. Do you want him back? Or do you just want to rub in what's he's been missing all these years? Are you planning to flaunt that beautiful, hot, rapacious little body around him?'

'You *are* mad,' she said scornfully. 'If your memory serves you as well as mine, you will recall that *you* were the one determined to break our relationship up.'

He gave her a ruthless little smile. 'You think so?

If you'd really loved him you'd have told me to go to hell! As a matter of fact, that's what I expected to happen.'

Kimberley's eyes narrowed suspiciously. '*Expected*? Are you telling me that you were calling my bluff? That it was some kind of little test which I had to pass to be allowed to marry your brother?'

He inclined his head. 'If you like. When a rather wild young man—who stands to inherit the kind of money Duncan will one day have—announces he's about to marry, it's wise to put the commitment of *both* partners to the test.'

It was unbelievable! The man was living in the Dark Ages! Kimberley shook her head slowly and incredulously. 'Did your mother know this—that you were conducting this barbaric little experiment?'

He gave her a bored smile as he ignored her question. 'As I said—I expected to be sent away with a flea in my ear. Instead of which you went out of here clutching a big, fat cheque in your greedy little hand. But that was nothing to what you very nearly gave *me*. Was it, Kimberley?' he mocked.

Kimberley blushed scarlet. Only someone as hateful as Harrison Nash would take such pleasure in reminding her of her behaviour that day.

He moved a little towards her and instinctively she stiffened, her head held proudly high, her eyes slitted into glittering blue shards.

'So what did you spend the money on, hmm? Easiest bit of money *you* ever made in your life, wasn't it, Kimberley?' He gave an empty-sounding laugh. 'My God—you stand there so cold and so damned beautiful, as though ice were running through your veins instead of blood, and yet I only have to touch you and you go up in flames—don't you? Tell me, Kimberley, do all men have that effect on you, or is it just me? It could prove quite embarrassing, surely?'

She fixed him with a frosty smile, though her heart was beating like a bass-drum in her ears. 'I rather think you overestimate your own attraction, Harrison.'

He gave a half-smile. 'You think so? Perhaps I do, but I'm pretty confident in your case. Maybe we should put it to the test.'

She saw the hungry intent on his face, and understood his meaning immediately. 'Don't you dare try!'

He came one step closer, totally ignoring what she was saying. 'But you want me to, don't you, Kimberley? We both know that. You hate me, yet you want me...' He pulled her into his arms, not roughly but not gently either.

'If you dare continue, then I'll scream as loudly as—'

There was no scream. Not even the smallest attempt at resistance, which would have left her with some dignity. But there was no resistance, and no dignity. Just an overpowering reaction to him which took all her will away, sapped her strength and her resolve and left in their place the swamping, unbearable cocktail of desire and frustration as she let him kiss her.

And, as she'd done once before, she opened her mouth wide beneath his—so wide because she wanted to eat him up, to lick him all over. She gave a little moan as she found her hands winding themselves around his broad back, and she clung on to him as though she were clinging to life itself.

'Oh, baby,' he murmured into her mouth. 'Yes. Show me. Show me just how much you want me...'

She didn't know what he wanted her to do. She was responding through pure instinct, kissing him back with frantic fervour as though she had never before been kissed. As indeed she hadn't.

Not like this.

'Or shall I show you?' he whispered, and pulled her into him, as close as it was possible to be. She felt his arousal immediately; no garment in the world had yet been designed which could disguise how hard and hot and turned on he was.

Her hips swivelled in instinctive excitement against him, and he gave a low laugh. 'You want that, don't you? Don't you?' He kissed her again, and one hand slid to her back, underneath her T-shirt, and he rubbed his hand sensually against the silky bareness of her skin, a soft, tantalising caress, a tiny circular movement which cajoled an instinctive response, and she felt as though her veins were being transfused with thick, sweet honey.

'Oh, baby.' He dropped his head to whisper against her hair. She felt him shudder—such a wild and uncontrolled shudder of excitement—and it made her realise that he teetered on the very edge of control. She pulled away from him, afraid of what might happen if she didn't. He stopped kissing her immediately, and she almost gasped as he stared down at her, for she barely recognised him, the stark hunger on his face turning him into a stranger.

But he *is* a stranger, she thought. What do you know of Harrison Nash, other than the fact that he represents nothing but a wild and elemental danger?

'You were wise to stop me,' he said, in a flat, deliberate voice. 'Because I'm afraid that if we carried on kissing then I would not have been responsible for my actions. Much more of that and I would have been unable to stop myself from removing every single item of clothing from that beautiful body of yours and taking you right here, because all my reason seems to have deserted me.'

And then he shook his head in some kind of despairing disbelief. 'Dear God!' he exclaimed. 'What am I *saying*? What am I *doing*? My mother could have walked into the kitchen. The gardener's outside—'

She'd had enough of his self-disgusted confession, and every word he uttered only added to her own despair. 'Let me go—'

'No.'

She stared up at him, her mouth quivering, on the brink of tears. 'Harrison, *please*.'

His eyes narrowed at her trembling state. 'Kimberley—this thing between us—'

She shook her head distractedly, as if trying to remove a very heavy burden which simply refused to budge. 'It's sex!' she asserted. 'Nothing but sex! That's all. Just some unfortunate accident of nature— a chemistry between two people who happen to loathe one another. And I *hate* it, if you must know.'

His eyes were bleak with self-loathing. 'You can't hate it any more than I do,' he said bitterly.

She tried to pull away, but he still held her firm, and her determination to escape him was only rivalled, infuriatingly, by the desire to give in—to him, and to herself. To give herself up to the white-hot passion which threatened to devour her. 'Will you please let me go now?' she asked quietly.

'Only if you promise not to run away.'

'I'm promising you nothing. You have no right to ask anything of me.'

'Not even to leave Duncan alone?'

She could have wept. That he could have started to make love to her, yet still think her duplicitous enough to imagine that she would scheme to steal Duncan from his new fiancée. 'Oh, for goodness' *sake*! It's all over! It's history!'

'You mean you no longer care about him?' he asked quietly.

'That's right,' she answered, equally quietly.

'But maybe you never did care?' he challenged, in a voice of pure steel.

She took a deep breath. She wanted him to despise her so much that he would be repulsed by her. To hate her so much that he would never try to touch her again. And if he never touched her again she would be safe from the power he wielded over her. 'Sure, I cared for Duncan,' she said, in the husky kind of voice she'd heard bimbos use. 'But maybe I cared about the money more. You did me a big favour, Harrison. Does that make you feel better?'

His mouth became an ugly line. 'God, you are

nothing but a little bitch,' he ground out. 'And if I ever doubted whether I'd done the right thing in trying to buy you off, you've just convinced me.'

Her cheeks flamed. Knowing that his rejection of her was the only sure route to sanity was one thing, seeing that look in his eyes was another.

'So, was it worth it, Kimberley?' he asked, still in that cold, scornful voice. 'Did the money I gave you compensate for any fleeting regrets you might have had that you'd made the wrong decision?'

She picked up her handbag from the table. 'I think that we've exhausted the whole subject. I'm going now, Harrison. I can't say that it was nice seeing you again, because I'd be lying. I'll leave it to you to explain to your mother why I can't continue with the cleaning. I'm sure you'll think of something.'

His voice was soft; it echoed in her ears as she left the room. 'There's only one thing that I can think of right now, and that's how much I want you, Kimberley. As much as you want me. Whichever way you look at it—there's unfinished business between us.'

She composed her face, then turned. 'In your dreams, Harrison,' she said coldly. 'Goodbye.'

CHAPTER THREE

KIMBERLEY left Brockbank House mixed up, het up and downright angry with herself at the way she'd handled Harrison. To say nothing of the way he'd handled her—both literally *and* figuratively, she thought disgustedly.

She walked home by a circuitous route, and by the time she'd reached her mother's cottage she had calmed down enough to realise that she hadn't hurt more than her pride—and since only one person knew about it, and she wasn't planning on seeing him again, then, so what?

She had managed to avoid him successfully for two years, and if she managed to avoid him for the rest of her life, then the situation need never arise again. He rarely visited Woolton—she knew that. He was only here now, she presumed, because Duncan was bringing over his new fiancée to meet the family, and once he'd celebrated the engagement Harrison would be off again, to France or Germany or wherever it was he lived, pulling off the kinds of huge deals her mother kept harping on about.

The way to avoid him would be simple. She might actually have to come clean with her mother. Not exactly telling her the *whole* truth—that would be far too upsetting—but perhaps explaining to her that for very personal reasons she simply couldn't stand the man, and she would like to be informed if he was planning any trips home. Then she would just avoid setting foot in the village to visit her mother until he was safely on his way again.

And, for the moment, she wished for two things. That her mother's ankle would heal very quickly, so that she could escape from the danger of his close proximity. And that something horrible would happen to Harrison Nash. Perhaps he could go bald and lose all his money?

Kimberley bluntly told her mother that she had no intention of cleaning the Nashs' house while Harrison was there. 'Let him do it!' she declared.

Mrs Ryan had been brought up in a very different generation from her daughter. 'But he's a very important executive, dear,' she said reprovingly.

Kimberley glowered. 'And so am I, Mum. So am I!'

The next couple of days passed uneventfully. She took her mother out for long drives, she cooked meals, and they had companionable chats over a couple of glasses of wine in the evenings.

She saw Harrison just once—when she went shopping one day and spotted him just pulling to a halt in the fiendishly expensive black car which had nudged her out the fast lane on the motorway the day she'd arrived. She should have guessed it was *him* at the wheel of such an outlandishly expensive piece of driving equipment, she thought resentfully.

She saw him climb out. He wore black jeans and a black polo-neck sweater, with a black leather jacket protecting him against the cold of the December day, and he looked suitably diabolical, thought Kimberley. He was unshaven, and the thick black hair was ruffled by the breeze. He glanced up and her heart seemed to still with the sheer physical impact of his presence. It was like being given a solid punch to the solar plexus, robbing her of air and of comfort, and then, suddenly and devastatingly, he smiled.

There was no malice in that smile today, not even desire. Kimberley would have challenged anyone in their right mind to have resisted that smile, and she had to fight hard with herself to maintain the cool, haughty look she was giving him. Yet she couldn't look away; something kept her staring at him.

She felt the wind lift up the heavy silken tresses of her hair, and it tugged at the hem of the short tartan mini-skirt she wore, revealing the slim length of her thighs, encased in ribbed woollen tights. She saw the dark eyebrows rise fractionally, and she turned hastily and almost ran into the local grocery store.

Conversation stilled immediately. It was a small enough village for memories to be long, and Kimberley's inexplicable jilting of Duncan had kept the locals in gossip for a good few months.

After replying politely but in a restrained manner to the curious questions of Mrs Spencer—the owner—she had bought her eggs and her bread, and the fresh fruit her mother had asked for, when the tinkling of the shop-bell behind her announced that someone else had come in behind her. She only had to look at the barely concealed excitement on Mrs Spencer's face to know just who that someone was.

'Can I help you, Mr Nash?' asked Mrs Spencer obsequiously.

'No, thanks,' came the deep voice. 'I came to give Miss Ryan a hand with her shopping.' The grey eyes were shuttered. 'I'll give you a lift home, Kimberley.'

He thought that he had her out-foxed. He was probably assuming that she cared too much for what others thought of her to resist him, that she would meekly agree to the lift.

Well, he was wrong.

'I have my own car, thank you,' she answered coolly. 'I've never had to rely on men for lifts.'

His mouth quirked a little. 'Very commendable. I'm sure that you make a lot of men feel very redundant. And I realise that you have your own car, but you've left it sitting outside your mother's house. It's a small red thing, isn't it?'

Calling Kimberley's beloved MG a 'small red thing' was tantamount to asking her if she knew how to change a plug, and her breathing quickened in temper.

'It's a damn sight better than that ridiculous monstrosity which you drive!' she retorted. 'But then women don't have the need to use a car as a substitute for any areas in which they might be—er—*lacking*.'

She had allowed herself to get carried away, and as soon as the words were out she regretted them— not just because Mrs Spencer was bristling with undisguised indignation, though frankly Kimberley doubted whether she'd actually got the gist of what she'd been saying, but also because Harrison's sickeningly sardonic smirk left her in no doubt that he knew and *she* knew that he didn't have any areas in which he was lacking.

'Are you quite sure you won't change your mind?' he mocked softly, and Kimberley knew that he wasn't just talking about giving her a lift home.

She blushed madly. 'No, thank you,' she reiterated. 'I'll walk.'

She heard Mrs Spencer's sharp intake of breath, as though she was indignant that someone like her, a little Miss Nobody, should have the temerity to turn Mr Nash down—and on more than one occasion!

'You can't walk—it's started to rain.'

He didn't give up, she would say that for him. She knew exactly what he wanted—to get her in his car so that he could begin to seduce her again. At least here, in the shop, she was safe from that. And she doubted that Harrison would be desperate enough to follow her home. Ice-blue eyes were turned disdainfully and decisively in the direction of the grey glitter of his. 'I don't care. I like the rain.'

His eyes flickered over the brief little tartan mini, with its short matching jacket. 'I'm quite sure you do. But, exquisite though you may look, you're hardly dressed to combat the elements,' he said softly.

'Let me be the judge of that!' she answered coolly, and walked out of the shop.

He walked directly behind her, staying her with a hand on her arm, and she had to steel herself not to respond to the fleeting contact. He bent his head close to her face, and she was caught up in the dazzle from those glittering grey eyes. 'I told you,' he said softly, 'that we had some unfinished business to settle.'

'Oh, go to hell!' she said exasperatedly, infuriated when he laughed at her, and she stalked off in the direction of her mother's.

Even so, she wondered if he'd follow her. But he didn't, and she walked home with the steady drizzle slowly soaking the woollen fabric of her suit until it clung to her in a soggy mass. Her hair was dripping, the egg-box was drenched, and the bread was virtually inedible—but her mother hardly noticed; she was bobbing up and down with excitement when Kimberley walked through the door.

'Should you be hopping around on your bad ankle like that?' observed Kimberley mildly.

'Oh—it's almost better, darling. Dr Getty says I'm as fit as a flea. Listen—they've just delivered an invitation from Brockbank. Margaret Nash is throwing a party to celebrate Duncan's engagement tomorrow night. I'm invited—and so are you!'

Kimberley put the shopping on the kitchen table and eyed the invitation her mother was proffering. 'I'm not going,' she said flatly.

Her mother's face fell. 'Oh, Kim—why ever not?'

Kimberley sighed. 'Just think about it, Mum. If I go it'll just put people's backs up—especially his new fiancée. I'm sure that if I were her I wouldn't particularly want his ex-fiancée turning up. People would be bound to make hurtful comparisons—and I don't expect that Duncan would want to see me either. In fact, I'm surprised that I was included on the invitation.'

But she wouldn't even admit to herself the real

reason why nothing would make her set foot inside Brockbank House again.

'You go. You'll have a great time.' Kimberley picked up a towel and began to rub at her sopping hair. 'Will you ring up and RSVP for me?' she asked. 'Please?'

Mrs Ryan's eyes narrowed. 'I've a feeling there's more to this than meets the eye, but, yes, darling—if you're absolutely adamant.'

'I am.' She stared down at her mother's ankle. 'And if you're feeling better now, Mum, then I'll have to think about getting back to London.'

Mrs Ryan sighed. 'I can't say I wasn't expecting it. Such a pity, though—I could quite get used to having you around the place again.'

Kimberley had planned to leave the following afternoon. She had just finished packing after lunch when there was a knock at the front door. Thinking it might be her mother, who had insisted on hobbling next door to see her neighbour, just to prove she could do it, Kimberley opened the door. Before her stood a young woman in her early twenties—someone Kimberley didn't recognise.

She had shiny shoulder-length fair hair, which was cut into a bob, and she wore a superbly cut pair of trousers in an immaculate but very unseasonal cream colour, with a matching cashmere jacket. Gold gleamed discreetly at her ears and neck and she exuded a kind of confidence which only money could give you. And lots of it, too.

'Can I help you?' asked Kimberley uncertainly.

The girl creased her eyes into a frown. 'Are *you* Kimberley Ryan?' Her voice was American—cultured and direct.

'Yes, I am—but I'm afraid I don't—'

'I'm Caroline Hudson—I'm Duncan's fiancée. Would you mind awfully if I came in?'

Kimberley pulled herself together and opened the door wider. 'Of course I don't mind. Do come in.'

The American girl immediately stepped over the threshold.

'Won't you sit down?' asked Kimberley politely, not at all sure about the etiquette of entertaining your ex-fiancé's fiancée. 'And have some tea?'

'Thank you. I will sit down, but I won't stay for tea.' Caroline positioned herself in one of the comfy armchairs and began fiddling with the gold link bracelet at her wrist.

Obviously, thought Kimberley, she wasn't quite as confident as she had initially seemed. She wondered why the girl had come. She strove to say something neutral which couldn't possibly be taken the wrong way.

'That's an absolutely beautiful ring you're wearing,' she managed.

It was obviously the right thing to say, because Caroline smiled as she held her left hand up to the light in the manner of newly engaged women the world over and the mammoth diamond solitaire sparkled and glimmered magnificently. 'Isn't it?' she agreed. 'We bought it in Tiffany's. Duncan wanted me to have the family ring—but I wanted something new. I didn't,' she said deliberately, 'want the ring that you'd worn.'

Kimberley nodded. 'That seems like a very wise idea.' She looked questioningly at the American girl. 'Do you want to tell me why you've come here?' she asked gently.

Caroline nodded, then fell silent before turning her rather spectacular green eyes anxiously to Kimberley. 'You aren't in love with Duncan any more, are you?'

Kimberley was so surprised that she almost laughed aloud, but then, realising that that could be taken as offensive, shook her head emphatically instead. 'Heavens, no! Hand on heart. That was over a long time ago, and to be quite honest I think that was the best thing for both of us.'

'So do I,' said Caroline firmly. 'Duncan's told me about you. I know you're brighter than he is, and I know you're ambitious—it would have meant that he would always have been competing against you, and he couldn't have coped with that—not in the long run. He needs someone like me. I don't care about making my mark on the world and I've more than enough money through my trust fund—and if that sounds awful, then I'm sorry, but I can't help being rich. I'm quite happy to be Duncan's woman, to support him. That's what I want to do with my life.'

'Lucky Duncan,' said Kimberley faintly. 'But I don't quite see—'

'Duncan loves me—I know that. But—' Caroline lifted her hands up in the air and the bracelets at her wrist jangled like wind-chimes. 'How can I put it? I guess it's just that you're a ghost he's never put to rest. And everyone else here knows that you dumped him.' She saw Kimberley's expression. 'I'm sorry— I didn't mean to insult you.'

Kimberley shook her head. 'Of course you didn't. Please carry on.'

'It's just that if you don't come to our party tonight, it's going to become like a sort of *thing*—you know how people are. They'll say that you couldn't bear to see him, or that he couldn't bear to see you. Maybe they'll think,' she finished miserably, 'that he's still in love with you.'

Kimberley looked at the girl who sat, her shoulders hunched up now, in her mother's sitting-room. Young, beautiful, rich—and bogged down by all the insecurities of love. Damn love! she thought vehemently. 'What is it that you want me to do?'

'Come tonight,' urged Caroline. 'To the party. And show there's no hard feelings—nothing bottled up.' She looked up at the ceiling, then down again, swallowing convulsively as she did so. 'I need to see Duncan. With you. Do you understand what I mean?'

Kimberley nodded. It seemed that Caroline needed to put her own ghosts to rest. 'Of course I do.'

'Then you'll come?'

Kimberley thought of Harrison, and of music, imagined him in a dinner jacket, looking superbly at home in the ravishing surroundings of Brockbank House. She put the thought firmly away. 'I won't stay very long,' she promised. 'But, yes, I'll come.' I owe Duncan, after all, she decided.

The heavy velvet drapes had been left undrawn and the lights of Brockbank blazed out, shimmering and sparkling from their costly chandeliers, to spill glorious light on to the gravelled drive leading up to the big house.

Kimberley drove, even though the distance was short enough to walk, but she wasn't planning to drink anything, not tonight, and with her car there she'd be able to make a hasty getaway. She had packed her suitcases and loaded them in her boot, and planned to drive straight to London from the party. 'And if I leave before you do,' she told her mother, 'then you can always get a taxi if you don't get a lift from anyone else.'

Kimberley had deliberated for ages over what to wear. There were so many things she didn't want to look like—a *femme fatale*, for one thing, or a defiant ex-lover who was pulling out all the stops to show how good she could look. On the other hand if she dressed like a total frump, for what was obviously going to be quite a smart do, it would be oddly out of character—and quite bad manners.

In the end she wore her black dress, which had seen her through just about every social occasion imaginable, and had never yet let her down. It came to several inches above the knee, but apart from showing some leg it covered everything else, with its high neck and long sleeves. The beauty of it was in the cut and the material. It was made of butter-soft silk, which rustled like a whisper as she walked.

Her hair she wore piled high upon her head, with several black corkscrew tendrils teased out to frame her face. With black kid slippers and pearls at her ears and wrists, she felt that she could withstand an hour or so at the party. And surely, in a crowd, it would be easy to avoid being alone with Harrison?

At first she saw neither brother. She was greeted at the door by Margaret Nash—who thanked her profusely for her help with the house—and by Caroline.

Caroline looked stunning—and nervous. She wore a slithery sheath of a dress in gleaming scarlet satin. She immediately took Kimberley to one side and took her wrap. 'Duncan's gone to order more champagne,' she whispered. 'I want to be here when he sees you.'

An awful, until now formless fear manifested itself. 'He does know that I'm coming?' asked Kimberley.

Caroline looked her straight in the face, her mouth a thin, determined line. 'No. He doesn't.'

Dear God, thought Kimberley despairingly, wondering how on earth she could get out of here.

'I couldn't see the point of telling him,' continued Caroline, apparently unconcerned by Kimberley's shocked silence. 'And neither could his mother.'

'His *mother*?'

Caroline nodded.

'I think you'd better explain,' said Kimberley faintly, feeling more and more divorced from reality by the second.

'His mother suggested it. Like me, she thinks it's a ghost he ought to lay to rest. You see, young love is very, very intense—and you were both so young when you were engaged. Added to that, rejection is so much harder to take when you're that young—by the time you're in your mid-twenties you've usually experienced a bit more of it, so it doesn't knock you quite so hard! And the person who rejected you assumes a much greater importance over the years than if the affair had just dwindled out naturally. Duncan needs to see you again, Kimberley. To see that you're not superwoman, that you're normal—just someone he used to know.'

It had the air of being a rehearsed speech. Kimberley was quite astonished, and couldn't help admiring the American girl's guts, but she felt bound to ask, 'You're taking a bit of a risk, aren't you, Caroline? What if it backfires on you?'

Caroline smiled. 'I'm a gambler—and I don't take unnecessary risks. Oh, my—here he comes.'

Kimberley automatically straightened her back, as though she were a soldier on parade, watching while Duncan wended his way towards his fiancée, a butler carrying a tray of champagne glasses following closely behind.

He hadn't seen her; she was concealed by the stoles and wraps which hung from the oversized coat-stand, and she had ample opportunity to observe him.

It was amazing how much two years had changed him, and in that time he had gone from boy to man. It shocked Kimberley to see how much he had changed, if only because it emphasised how very young he must have been when he asked her to marry him. He was dressed conservatively, in a well-cut suit, and his hair was short and neatly combed. He had the preppy look of someone who had been influenced by their environment—as obviously he must have been influenced by the country he had chosen to live in. His eyes rested fondly on Caroline, and the look shining from them told Kimberley everything she needed to know.

She stepped forward, a genuine smile on her face. 'Hello, Duncan,' she said quietly.

There was a moment's silence. She noted every emotion which passed in quick succession over his face. Part recognition, surprise, bewilderment and then, heart-warming, but heart-rending too—because she didn't think she really deserved it—a wry smile, which became wider. He put his hands on her shoulders, kissed both cheeks, and stood staring down at her. 'Kimberley,' he said. 'You're looking good.'

'So are you.' There were so many things she wanted to say to him, things she knew must remain unsaid—because if she told him she was sorry it would resurrect it all, and wasn't the past best left buried?

But it was as though Duncan could discern her mixed feelings, because he looked down at her, a glint of amusement in his eyes—such warm, uncomplicated eyes when you compared them to those of his older brother.

'Kimberley,' he said quietly. 'Would you understand if I said thank you—for doing me the biggest favour of my life?'

Kimberley nodded, a lump in her throat, knowing exactly what he meant. 'I would. And thank *you*, Duncan—for being so big about it.'

There was a rustle behind them. 'Have you met Caroline?' He was eager, proprietorial, as his beautiful fiancée stepped forward and he bent to place a brief but possessive kiss on her mouth.

'I have.' Kimberley smiled. 'She invited me. I do hope you didn't mind?'

Caroline was smiling the reassured and victorious smile of the woman who has got her man. 'Of course he doesn't mind, Kimberley—he doesn't mind a thing I do! Let's all go into the other room. And, Duncan— you must dance with Kimberley. I'll bet you have *heaps* to talk about!'

In the event they didn't; they survived on niceties but Kimberley knew that that had not been the purpose of the dance. The public show of unity, Caroline's smiling approval of their dance all served to show the assembled guests that there were no deep yearnings from the former partners. No broken hearts which hadn't healed. Everything was all right.

But not for long.

Kimberley became aware that they were being watched, and she didn't need to be psychic to know by whom. Some sixth sense had alerted her to his presence as soon as he'd entered the ballroom.

It was evident from the little buzz of whispered excitement that the most eligible bachelor had just walked into the room. Kimberley saw women actually preening themselves—saw bosoms being thrust out and stomachs sucked in. Saw women tossing extravagant curls around their heads like tempestuous young fillies.

She looked up into Duncan's face, and had opened her mouth to say that she wanted to go and find her mother when a deep voice, which was about as welcome as a heat-wave in the desert, penetrated her consciousness.

'Why, Duncan,' came the sardonic admonishment, 'I'd be careful if I were you. If you leave that beautiful fiancée of yours on her own much longer then someone might just whisk her away.'

Duncan dropped his hands from Kimberley's waist immediately, and looked around. 'Sure. Thanks, Harrison. I'd better go find her. Nice to see you again, Kimberley,' he said absently, and set off in search of Caroline.

'Excuse me,' said Kimberley, and made to push past him, but he stopped her with an arm of steel.

'You're not going anywhere.'

'Let me go,' she said desperately, as just the touch of him started that familiar aching.

The deep velvet voice was tinged with anger—restrained but unmistakable anger. 'But surely you want to dance with *me*, Kimberley? Or is it just Duncan that you want to turn those big blue eyes up at? What the hell do you think you're playing at?'

'As a matter of fact Caroline came to my house today and asked me to come. She wanted to make sure that Duncan only had eyes for her, which, as anyone can see, he patently has.'

'Oh, really?' he mocked.

'Yes!' she answered impatiently. '*Really*! And now can you go away and bore someone else with your nasty suspicious mind? And damn well take your hands off me—'

But he ignored her protests, pulling her into his arms to lock her against the warm and beckoning sanctum of his broad chest. His arms went about her waist, as lightly as Duncan's had done, but oh, the difference took all her breath away. She was aware of the weight of each long finger as it rested at the narrow indentation between her ribs and the gentle curve of her hips. The butter-soft silk, which had seemed such a good idea at the time, now mocked her with its insubstantiality—for it felt as though he touched her skin instead of her dress.

Her breath came short and painfully from her lungs, catching the back of her throat to dry her already dehydrated lips as he drew her body closer, so that she could feel the solid length of each strong, muscular thigh as it moved enticingly against hers.

'Harrison...' It was meant to be a plea; it sounded like a prayer.

He gave a soft, low laugh. 'Yes, I know. So let's show them, little temptress. Which brother you want so much it's nearly killing you.'

If her brain hadn't been so befuddled by his proximity then warning bells would have sounded at those cold, clipped words, but the words had been accompanied by his completely enfolding her waist in his arms, and by his head falling to rest on hers.

The magic of dance could bewitch you into believing what you wanted to believe, and this dance was more bewitching than any other, thought Kimberley as she drifted in time with him to the music. For within the outwardly decent boundaries of what constituted a slow dance there were many variations, which ranged from the innocent to the sensual...and this dance was profoundly, shockingly sensual. But not just sensual—Harrison danced with such skill that for a moment there even seemed to be tenderness mingled with the voluptuous pleasure of his touch.

Or perhaps, thought Kimberley, she was confusing tenderness with propriety—they were, after all, in the middle of a dance-floor, exciting the interested looks of most of the county set—so he could hardly touch her with the undisguised passion he normally demonstrated towards her.

She tried to tell herself to leave, yet she was reluctant to move her head from his shoulder, where the material of his jacket rubbed softly against her cheek. She forced herself to straighten up, but that was even worse—she would have to confront those narrow grey eyes which gleamed with some unspoken message.

'Are you going to let me go now?' she whispered.

'No.'

'I'll struggle.'

'Try.'

'Scream, then.'

'I'll kiss you.'

'Oh, Harrison—why are you doing this?'

'Why do you think?' he asked softly.

She closed her eyes to shut out that speculative grey gleam. She tried to imagine how she would behave if Harrison were some tiresome executive she was dealing with. Reason might work.

She opened her eyes again, wondering what it was she read in the spark of those enigmatic eyes—was it humour, or challenge? Whichever—it made no difference. She put on her calmest voice. 'You're a very attractive man, Harrison—'

'I'm glad you've noticed.'

He'd deliberately misinterpreted her. 'What I mean is that there must be countless women in this room who are dying to dance with you—do you really have to resort to these caveman-like tactics?'

'It seems that with you I do,' he said softly, and his eyes glittered. 'Besides, I don't want to dance with anyone else. Just you.'

She forced herself to remember that the words meant nothing. This was just a different approach to settling that 'unfinished business' he'd spoken about. And it seemed that reason was totally ineffective against such a determined and single-minded man as Harrison. Plain speaking might work.

'Well, I don't want to dance with you,' she said decisively, marvelling to herself that lying could be this easy. 'So can we please stop this nonsense right now?'

With her question she gave a little shake of her head, and as she did so a lock of hair tumbled free and fell on to her mouth—which was sticky with scarlet gloss—and stayed there.

Immediately he lifted a finger and pulled it away from her lips, staring at her for a long moment with hard and brilliant eyes, and suddenly his whole demeanour altered. The soft, languid grace which had characterised his dancing up until then disappeared, and instead she saw him tense, his body become rigid, and as it did so his face acquired a taut and flinty look to it.

'You're absolutely right,' he said harshly. 'This ''nonsense'', as you so sweetly put it, has been going on for too damned long.' And, so saying, he clasped her hand firmly in his and led her off the dance-floor, through the crowds of dancers, past the curious eyes of the onlookers and out into the hall.

Kimberley looked around her wildly, waiting for someone to challenge him, stop him—to quit behaving as if it were perfectly normal for a man to drag a girl behind him as if they were still living in the Stone Age.

But no one did anything other than smile indulgently as Harrison led her through a series of rooms, until at last they were in the library.

She supposed she could have stopped him herself; she didn't ask herself why she hadn't until afterwards, and by then it was too late. She could have stopped him at any time, especially once they entered the realms of total fantasy, when he pulled aside a crimson velvet curtain to expose a wooden panel which, when touched, slid silently aside to reveal a spiral staircase. He pulled her inside before the panel slid shut to enclose them.

It was ridiculous, crazy—like something out of the adventure stories she'd read as a child—but still she kept her hand meekly in his, saying nothing, not even when the staircase terminated in a room at what was obviously the very top of the house.

And she couldn't even pretend surprise when she saw that it was a bedroom.

CHAPTER FOUR

KIMBERLEY snatched her hand out of Harrison's, and this time he made no demur, just let her.

She stared up at him, dark and tall and forbidding in the stark black dinner jacket and the slim-cut tapered trousers. His dark hair was very slightly ruffled—had she done that? she thought suddenly. Hadn't her fingers crept up to run themselves luxuriously through his hair during that dance? His eyes had an almost luminous brilliance as they studied her, waiting for her next move—but grey was essentially a cold colour, she reminded herself, and Harrison's eyes were well suited to his nature.

She realised that she had been expecting him to take her into his arms, confident that once he had begun to touch her there would be no argument from her about what he had in mind—and it was pretty obvious just *what* he had in mind. After all, you didn't bring a woman into a room with a huge double bed and little else if you wanted to talk about the weather!

'You're smiling,' he observed. 'What's amused you?'

'You have,' she answered coolly.

'Oh?' A black eyebrow lifted elegantly upwards.

'I had expected a little more subtlety from you. Does it usually work—this approach?'

'And what approach is that?' he asked softly.

'Dragging a woman into the nearest bedroom.'

'It isn't the *nearest*,' he pointed out infuriatingly. 'But it's the one where I can guarantee we won't be disturbed.'

His words, deep and sensual, full of some sweet, sexual promise, sent a reluctant shiver down her spine. 'You're assuming a lot, aren't you?' She was amazed at how calm, how controlled she sounded, just as if she was the kind of woman who was frequently being propositioned like this.

'Am I? Don't you like the room?'

Dark woods and crimson hangings, a bedcovering of gold and deep bright hues; it looked medieval— and so did Harrison, she realised, for he had unknotted and removed his bow-tie and was now in the process of draping his jacket over the back of a chair. Positively medieval, she thought, her mouth drying as she stood watching him. But it wasn't the clothes that made him look that way, it was that whole masculine and arrogant stance—the total lack of pretence. He wanted her, and…and…

'Would you have preferred the women's magazine guide to seduction?' he queried. 'The romantic, candle-lit dinner followed by the stilted offer of a nightcap? The soft music and the grappling on the sofa?' He smiled. It was a cold smile. 'Such a bore, don't you think?'

'You cynic,' she said disbelievingly.

'But no hypocrite,' he parried softly.

The most unbelievable thing was that she was actually continuing the conversation, actually enjoying the mental sparring in a perverse sort of way, instead of turning round and fleeing from him. 'Do you do this sort of thing very often?'

Her cool query seemed to surprise him. 'Never.'

'So what makes me different?'

Only one tiny fragment of her mind acknowledged what she wanted him to say—that he loved her, that she was the only woman in the world for him. But of course he didn't say it. Because, in his own words, he was no hypocrite. Nor a liar.

'You know why,' he said softly. 'Because you're a fire in my blood which refuses to be dampened. You know that. It can't go on like this. *I* can't go on like this any more. We have to have this one night together.'

One night. That was all he offered. No, he was certainly no hypocrite. She shook her head and made to turn away, but then he did touch her, catching her lightly by the shoulders to turn her to face him, and she revelled in the feel of him, almost as much as she reluctantly thrilled to the burning brilliance of his eyes.

He stared down at her, the intensity which hardened his features making his face seem like granite come to life. 'Tell me you haven't thought of me these last two years, Kimberley, and I'll call you a liar,' he whispered softly. 'Tell me you haven't tossed in your bed at night, reliving that very first kiss and wanting me to kiss you again but this time not to stop. I want you, Kimberley—God, help me—I want you as I've never wanted a woman before.'

She recoiled even as she was enthralled by the stark

statements. Hating him, yet wanting him, too. 'But I don't even like you...' she said brokenly.

His eyes hardened into slivers of grey metal. 'I know that. You've made that abundantly clear. But liking has nothing to do with us—or this. *This*...' And he shuddered as his mouth sought hers.

It was the end—or the beginning, whichever way she cared to look at it, and she couldn't even pretend that he'd forced his lips on hers because he hadn't. She had turned her face up to his eagerly and of her own volition, entranced by that raw and harsh entreaty.

He kissed her hard, passionately—not even bothering to disguise the depths of his ardour—and she kissed him back in kind, opening her mouth to him like a flower to the morning sun. She knew one brief moment when she tried to tell herself that it was not too late. That if she pulled away now and walked out of that door he would not stop her. But she knew she would not walk away, for he had spoken nothing but the truth to her. She *had* thought about him, tossed in bed, dreamt of him and wanted him, like this.

And what was he offering her? Very little. One night—nothing more. To damp the fire in his veins; to free him from the curse of wanting her. So might it not do the same for her? Leave her free to lead a normal life, instead of existing in the self-imposed isolation she'd sought because Harrison had haunted her mind and her senses for so long?

He broke away and, incredibly, he was smiling. A sweet, soft smile, more insidiously enticing than the hard, heated pressure of his body, and Kimberley found herself smiling back, forgetting everything but the pleasure of the night to come.

'You're so beautiful, Kimberley,' he whispered softly. 'So very beautiful, with your hair as black as the night itself and your face pale as a moonbeam.'

But she had to put a stop to this; he was telling her everything she wanted to hear, but she was in danger of reading more than he intended into his soft words of seduction. She wound her arms around his neck, pressed her body sinuously close to his, her mouth against his ear. 'Isn't that starting to sound like the women's magazine guide to seduction?' she whispered huskily, echoing his own words of earlier. 'And didn't you say you found that boring?'

For a moment she felt him stiffen and grow rigid beneath her touch, and then it was gone and he pushed her away from him, his face a series of hard, unreadable planes and shifting shadows, the eyes now less brilliant than opaque. 'Boring?' His hand slid round to the back of her dress and slid the zip down in one fluid movement. 'Sweetheart, the last thing you're going to be tonight is bored.'

The dress pooled around her ankles with a silken whisper, but Kimberley's heart beat a little faster—not at the exultant look of pleasure which hooded his eyes as she stood before him wearing nothing but her underclothes but at the almost cruel indefinable note in his voice as he made that last statement.

A small sound escaped his lips as his gaze devoured her, and, strangely, she wasn't shy. She liked it. Liked seeing that hungry, almost awestruck look on his face. He was, she realised, with a sudden flash of insight, as much at her mercy as she was at his. Uncaring of her semi-nakedness, she stood before him in her scarlet silk and lace until he took her into his arms.

She felt that he was quite fierce with excitement—kissing her on a long sigh, his hand moving up to unclip her hair so that it spilt in streams of black satin over her pale shoulders. With slow, sure fingers he massaged her back, gradually moving his hand round—but taking forever to reach her breast. And then it was her turn to make a helpless little throaty assertion, to shudder as his fingers traced tiny circles closer and closer to the nipple, until they both grew impatient with the costly bra, and he moved his hand round to her back, unclipped it with a single movement, so that her breasts fell out and against him, and the soft mounds were crushed against his chest.

He moved her away from him, studied both the pale, swollen globes so that they tightened almost unbearably under his lingering scrutiny, then bent his head and began to suckle at one tingling erect nipple. A sharp dart of pleasure pulled deeply at her womb.

'Harrison!' she whispered helplessly. Stop this, she wanted to say, though she was powerless to say it as she glanced down at his dark head at her breast. She hadn't known... No one had told her... That it was going to be this intimate, this beautiful...this special.

He kissed her while he removed his own clothes, one by one. Instead of feeling embarrassed, as his magnificent body was gradually revealed, Kimberley felt instead a mixture of heady pleasure and anticipation—for hadn't she lived this scenario in her dreams, a thousand times over?

He kissed her while he unbuttoned his shirt, and she helped him take it off, eager to feel the silk of his bare skin against her fingertips, and as she slid her hands down to rest against the hair-roughened chest she heard him make a small sound of delight as he deepened the kiss still further.

His ardour fuelled hers, so that she let him push her down on to the softness of the silken rug.

He kissed her from mouth to breast, over and over again. His lips found her eyelids, her cheeks, her shoulders, the tiny warm, soft crook of her elbow, and each of these he kissed, anointing her with the soft caress of his mouth.

She saw the brilliance in the grey eyes as he knelt over her, before his mouth began to explore her body, to seek out every centimetre as if he were paying homage. His tongue found the dip of her navel and her head fell back as he began to trace a wet path to her panties. And then she waited, her apprehension only surpassed by her breathless anticipation of what he was going to do next.

He hooked his fingers at the edge of the flimsy little garment and tore the delicate scarlet lace apart with a gentle ripping sound, and the thought of his scant disregard for the expensive piece of underwear sent her trembling anew with excitement.

She saw him smile as the discarded garment fell unnoticed to the floor and his gaze fell to the lush, creamy bloom of her naked body. She gasped with shocked excitement as he pushed her thighs gently apart with his fingers and dipped his head to kiss the soft fuzz of hair.

'No,' she begged him, but her body was trembling with delight.

'Oh, yes,' he whispered, before his tongue found that aching, delicate spot and he started to lick her with slow, pleasurable sweeps of his tongue, over and over again, until she realised that he was taking her down a path from which there could be no return.

'No!' she said again, on a broken note of protest, but it was already too late, and she moved with disbelief as she felt waves of pure pleasure tantalise her, rock her, until they finally engulfed her and she exploded against his mouth, sobbing as he caught her and pulled her into his arms.

She felt helpless, hopeless, vulnerable, shaking in his arms as her climax subsided, and he soothed her by stroking her all over again, until the delicious warmth began to build up once more, and Kimberley began to play with his nipples, to suckle them exactly as he had hers.

She looked up once and stole a glance at him. He had his eyes closed, a look of such exquisite rapture on his face that she grew bolder, her fingers moving down to touch him as intimately as he had touched her, and her breath caught in her throat with the pleasure of her first touch... Oh, it was enchanting to be able to touch him like this.

She felt him shudder beneath her fingers as she experimentally began to stroke him, waiting until he grew more and more aroused, then, wanting to taste him as he had tasted her, she bent her head, took the potent fullness of him in her mouth… She heard him give a groan of pleasure before she felt herself being gently but decisively moved away, and he scooped her up to lie on top of him.

'No,' he said firmly.

'Oh,' she protested.

He laughed. 'Did you happen to read up a textbook about every man's ideal fantasy woman? Because, if so, I think maybe you might have skipped a chapter, my sweet. I don't want any substitute—not this first time. I've dreamt about this far too long to want anything other than the real thing, Kimberley. You.'

'But you did it to me,' she pointed out. 'So why not?'

He looked very definitely surprised at her persistence. She could read a mixture of things in his eyes—arousal, amusement, and—yes, definitely—he was a little bit *shocked*!

'That wasn't supposed to happen,' he said wryly, circling her proud nipple with one long finger. 'You just happen to be *very* responsive…' And his mouth found hers.

But only to you, she thought as she felt his nakedness beneath her, remembering other men who had tried to arouse her, who she hadn't even been able to bear kissing her.

'Oh, God, Kimberley!' he sighed as he tightened his arms around her naked waist. 'You're so gorgeous. *Gorgeous*.'

She could feel the tension and excitement growing, could feel herself growing dizzy with the pure delight of the touch she'd craved for so long. She could scarcely believe that this was happening to her, that she was lying in a tangled and naked heap with Harrison. Her heart soared as he kissed her until the blood thundered in her ears, and she felt as though she would die unless he took her. Daringly she shifted her body slightly, so that she was lying directly over him, and now only one movement, one tiny little movement, was separating them from the ultimate intimacy.

'Let's go to bed,' he whispered urgently, but for answer she pushed her hips provocatively against his. Through her passion-glazed eyes she saw his own snap open, and a helpless look crossed the rugged features as he realised the fight was up.

'You witch,' he whispered softly against her mouth. 'You beautiful little witch.' Then he swiftly turned her over on to her back, all masculine arrogance and domination as he thrust into her with sweet, wild power.

Kimberley awoke in the bed, and as soon as she regained consciousness she remembered exactly where she was. Lying over her thigh was an unaccustomed weight…Harrison's leg—and the rhythmical sound she could hear beside her was Harrison's breathing.

She lay stock-still, holding her breath, afraid that he might be able to sense by instinct alone that she was now awake. Because—she had to face it—he had guessed just about everything there was to know about her body during that long night of lovemaking. To think that she'd been a complete and utter novice before they'd started—now she felt fully qualified to be able to rewrite the Kama Sutra—and throw in a few extra chapters besides!

Her heart quickened. She had never dreamt that it would be so...so wonderful, blissful, heavenly—every single superlative in the English language, in fact. She'd actually lost count of the times he'd made love to her. And each time it seemed to become more special, more intense, the kisses deeper, gentler. She had found herself wanting to murmur sweet nothings into his ear, to tell him that he was the most wonderful man in the world, that she adored him. She wanted to invent silly names for him. She wanted to make him boiled eggs for breakfast! She was in love!

Oh, Kimberley! What have you done? Her glorious, glowing happiness disintegrated like an ice-cube dropped into a glass of boiling water. Just because *she* had become unbearably affected by last night it didn't mean that Harrison had. He had said 'one night'. Just because he had been so sweet and gorgeous and sensational during that one night it didn't mean that he was about to start prowling around jewellers' or estate agents' windows, or flicking avidly through Tupperware catalogues!

She had to think calmly.

And then she nearly screeched aloud as she remembered her car.

Her car!

Her scarlet sports car was at present sitting in the drive outside Brockbank House, drawing bold attention to the fact that she hadn't gone home last night and advertising to even the least discerning just how she had spent the last few hours.

She suppressed a groan as she glanced over to the bedside table where the luminous dial of Harrison's watch was just visible. It was four a.m.

Far better if she crept out and took the car back home to London now. If anyone saw her she could say she'd had a bit to drink and had slept it off. She would have to hope they wouldn't ask where.

The alternative was falling back to sleep and meeting up with Mrs Nash, Duncan and Caroline over the kippers and kedgeree.

And Harrison.

She glanced again at his naked sleeping form. Dragging herself away from him was going to be sheer hell, but it had to be done. If he'd decided that one night was enough she would be saving face by disappearing now, rather than having to undergo the humiliating experience of him saying goodbye to her in the morning—and meaning it.

Some dark emotion, as brutal as a physical assault, made her skin break out into an icy sweat. Had he meant it literally when he had said 'one night'? And if he had could she possibly bear it? She bit her lip very hard. There was no alternative—she would *have* to bear it. She swallowed as she determined that if he wanted nothing more to do with her, even though she might be breaking up in a million pieces inside, externally at least she would maintain her pride and her dignity. She certainly wasn't going to beg him to see her again.

Very carefully Kimberley wriggled out from beneath Harrison's leg and rolled over to the side of the bed, holding her breath to hear whether he'd wakened.

He hadn't.

She slid off the bed and shivered as the cool night air hit her naked flesh, and she narrowed her eyes in search of her discarded clothing.

Silent as the night itself she put her bra on and pulled the black dress over her head, before slipping her bare feet into her shoes. She would carry her stockings and suspender belt and... In the darkness she blushed as her gaze fell on the ripped panties, and as she bent to pick them up, her fingers quickly closing around the tiny crumpled ball of scarlet lace, she couldn't help giving a grimace of regret. To have him make love to her was one thing, but had she really needed to respond quite so uninhibitedly? Surely it couldn't be *right* for a virgin to feel intensely turned on by having her underwear torn off her?

'Send me the bill,' came a flat, drawling voice, and Kimberley glanced over at the bed to find a pair of very cold, speculative grey eyes watching her every move. Something in the harsh set of his face immediately made her frantic thoughts alight on his statement with confusion.

'Bill?' she demanded. 'What are you talking about?'

He put his hands behind his head and continued to subject her to that coolly impartial scrutiny. 'Send me the bill,' he repeated indifferently. 'For your underwear. I have to tell you that I'm not usually in the habit of ripping the clothes from a woman's body, but

I'm afraid that you really do bring out the worst in me, Kimberley.'

It was the most damning testimony to their night together. And Kimberley was stung and hurt and horrified that she had had the naïvety to imagine that he might have woken to contemplate some sort of future with her.

She gave him the kind of empty smile she would have conferred on the lowest form of life. 'The feeling is entirely mutual,' she said coldly. 'I hate you, Harrison.'

'Not half as much as I hate myself, my dear. But, as I told you, what we have between us has very little to do with liking,' he added bitterly.

Cheapened and ashamed, she moved away, sick to the depths of her heart.

'Oh, Kimberley?'

She stilled, some foolish little hope flickering into doomed life inside her. 'What?' She turned to look at him, and the arrogant indifference on his face told her everything she needed to know.

'I'm afraid that you didn't really give me the chance to discuss this last night,' he said matter-of-factly. 'And... Let me see—how can I put this without being offensive? In view of your *eagerness* to consummate the act, I assume you've already taken care of contraception?'

She froze, wanting to sob, to scream.

To die.

She stared at him. What the hell? She had already told him the ultimate lie; she had told him that she hated him. One more wouldn't hurt.

'Naturally,' she answered coolly, and left.

Left the room and, finding her handbag on a table in the hall, left the house and ran out, cold and despairing as she let herself into her tiny scarlet sports car, and drove to London as if the devil himself were pursuing her.

CHAPTER FIVE

KIMBERLEY lay on the bed perfectly still, waiting for the sickness to pass.

Outside the cherry tree, with its glorious snowy blossoms, danced in the light breeze of the perfect late April afternoon.

Morning sickness, she thought woozily, she could have coped with—this late-afternoon sickness did not fit in at all well with her timetable! Fortunately James, her boss, had been surprisingly accommodating—letting her evolve her own flexi-hours so that she started work at six in the morning and knocked off at between three and four, when the sickness usually started.

The doctor had told her that the nausea and vomiting she'd been having would probably ease off by the time she entered the second trimester, but she was nearly five months pregnant and it showed no sign of abating.

She remembered back to when she'd first discovered she was pregnant.

She had arrived back in London, sick and despairing over the disastrous incident with Harrison and feeling as though she'd lost every last vestige of pride. She knew that she could never see him again. But Christmas had been looming, and she couldn't possibly have left her mother in the lurch.

So, the following week, having mentally girded herself for a possible encounter with Harrison, whom she had assumed would stay on with his mother for Christmas, Kimberley had returned to Woolton. But he had not been there.

Harrison had returned to France the day after the party, according to her mother.

And, in a way, the finality of his abrupt departure had helped; she had known that there were no more false hopes to be cherished.

It had been a week after Christmas when Kimberley had experienced her first fears, and within a day—although she'd had no experience of such matters—she had known that she was pregnant.

She had found out for sure at the weekend and had spent almost all of the two days lying in bed, looking up at the ceiling while her mind had tried to take in the enormity of this event, which was going to change the whole pattern of her life.

She had decided within the first day that she was not going to tell Harrison. There wouldn't have been any point. He wouldn't have wanted to be troubled with the repercussions of his famous 'one night'— especially when that one night had been nothing but the settling of an old score with a sexual chemistry which had been too strong for either of them to resist.

She had doubted whether he'd want anything to do with a child born to a mother he despised, and so the only point of telling him would have been to try to get some kind of maintenance from him—and she certainly wasn't going to grovel around asking for his money.

If she needed money she had enough of her own. But she wasn't going to need any money, because she had also decided something else that first weekend—that she was going to have her baby adopted.

The doctor had been surprised. Adoption was a fairly radical step, he'd told her—traumatic for the mother, to have to go through nine months of pregnancy then have to give the baby up. He had advised her that in these times a woman had a choice. But the choice which he had offered her had been one which she had passionately rejected without giving it more than a second's thought. She could not have killed her child—Harrison's child.

The doctor had gently asked whether she'd thought of keeping the baby herself, had said that society accepted single mothers these days.

She had thought about it, of course she had. But wouldn't keeping the baby be worse in the long run? Was it fair to bring a child up with one parent out of choice? A parent, moreover, who would need to work long hours to be able to support a baby? Wouldn't the child become a typical 'latchkey' kid, with all the inherent disadvantages? Ferried from pillar to post, dumped on childminders she wouldn't really know—perhaps wouldn't even trust?

She would do the best for her baby; she would have a happy and healthy pregnancy and then she would give the child up for adoption. Give it away to some nice, loving, childless couple who would be able to offer him or her so much more than she could.

And, apart from the doctor, James was the only person she'd told. The others at work and the girlfriends she met up with at her health club would find out soon enough, when she started to show. There was no point in telling anyone else, especially not her mother—for wouldn't it only break her heart to discover that she had a grandchild on the way then to have to say goodbye to that grandchild forever?

James had been super—utterly supportive and pleased that she would be going back to work.

There were only two things which Kimberley had insisted upon. The first was that James never talked to her about the baby. Talking about the baby only seemed to make him or her more real, and she knew that the more real it became the harder it would be for her to have to give it up. The second was that she didn't want *any* baby paraphernalia—no tiny mitts or bootees—for exactly the same reason.

Kimberley dozed on and off for an hour, until the sickness had gone, then got up and had a shower to try and wake herself up. She had dressed in leggings and a sweatshirt and switched on the TV, deciding idly that now that the sickness had passed she really ought to start thinking about getting something to eat, when there was a sharp ring on the doorbell.

Because it was still light, and because she hadn't got round to it, she hadn't put the chain on, and she opened the door without a thought, the blood draining from her face as she found herself staring at Harrison.

He was dressed formally in an amazing oatmeal-coloured suit, which looked like an Armani, but his hair was untidy and his silk tie had been loosened.

His eyes were glittering as they surveyed her but

she could read nothing in his face. Absolutely nothing.

'May I come in?' he asked coolly, but there was a strange quality to his voice, an odd edge—something she should have recognised, but failed to do so.

The pounding of her heart had diminished enough for her to draw a deep breath—the intake of oxygen she needed—and answer him in the same cool fashion. 'What for? I doubt whether we've got anything that's worth saying to each other.'

His mouth twisted with derision. 'Quite. Talking was never our strong point, was it, Kimberley?'

The sensual implication behind his silky insult made hot colour flare at her cheeks and she began to close the door, but, like a character in a detective film, he inserted one elegant foot in the doorway, preventing her from doing so.

'What do you think you're doing? Get your bloody foot *out* of my door! This minute!'

The foot stayed where it was. 'I told you that I wanted to come in—'

'And I told you—' Her mouth dropped open as he moved her away from the door, let himself in and closed it softly behind him.

Kimberley began to panic as he walked down the hall and straight into the sitting-room as though he were an invited guest. All kinds of thoughts and fears were rushing to assail her—like, He couldn't possibly *know*, could he?

Well, could he?

He was looking around the room, at the vivid peacock-blue silk curtains and the matching cushions, which had been slung all over the deep, comfy rose-pink sofa. In a tall blush-coloured vase was an enormous spray of gypsophila, studded with pinks, breathtaking and fragrant. 'Hmm.' He gave a little nod. 'Elegant, but cosy. Exquisite taste, Kimberley. But then I always knew you would have.'

She neither wanted nor needed his approbation—so wasn't it rather pathetic that his obvious approval of her home should please her so much?

'What are you doing here? I thought you lived in France?'

'I did. But I've moved.'

'To—to—England?' she asked shakily.

He gave a cold smile. 'The very same—to London, to be even more precise.'

Kimberley's eyes widened. 'But why?'

Those mesmeric grey eyes glittered. 'I find that I have pressing—business—in England. Why else?'

The effort of trying not to alert his suspicions to her condition was nearly killing her. 'I still don't know why you're here—what the hell do you want?'

He gave a nasty smile, put his face mockingly close to hers, and her heart accelerated out of control as she thought that he was about to kiss her. 'That depends what's on offer,' he said, slightly unsteadily, and Kimberley realised what it was about him which was different—he'd been drinking.

Oh, he wasn't drunk—somehow she could never imagine Harrison out of control, nor losing touch with that formidable intelligence—but he had obviously drunk just enough to be reckless. She could see that from the dangerous glitter in the grey eyes, and suddenly she felt frightened. He must *not* find out. He mustn't.

'You've been drinking!' she accused.

He sat down in one of the chairs, unasked. 'Yeah,' he agreed. 'It's true. Drinking to forget the coldest little bitch I ever had the misfortune to meet.'

'Have you just come here to insult me?' she enquired politely, some instinct telling her that if she failed to react then he would leave her. And she needed him to leave her, just as soon as was possible, because she had just found that it was quite possible to hate someone very much indeed and yet to want them to pull you into their arms and never let you go.

'I've come to see how you are.' He laughed, and the sound of it sent a chill down her spine; it was an angry, bitter, empty little sound that tore at her soul. He stared at her consideringly, his head to one side. 'And now I've seen. You look terrible,' he said. 'Awful.'

'Thanks very much.' They were on dangerous ground here. He spoke the truth—she *did* look terrible—but he mustn't know the reason why.

She had been physically sick every afternoon for more than four months, so that instead of gaining a little weight in the first stage of her pregnancy she had lost it instead. And the sudden weight-loss was reflected in the sickly pallor of her cheeks. Even her raven hair had lost its usual glossy sheen, and she knew that the black leggings and white sweatshirt only emphasised her colourless appearance. The doctor had told her that lots of women lost weight in pregnancy, that there was no reason why the baby should be harmed, and that she wasn't to worry.

But of course she worried.

'I've seen you look better yourself,' she answered him tartly.

'Have you? When was that? When you left me, naked and wanting you, creeping out like a thief in the middle of the night? Had your conscience got the better of you, Kimberley? Did it sicken you to remember what we had done?

Lies, glorious lies. Her salvation lay in lies. Behind them she could hide her hurt. She shrugged her slim shoulders. 'Let's just put it this way—it happened, and it's best forgotten, wouldn't you agree?'

He smiled a cynical smile. 'And if I don't?'

Ignoring that, she stared down at him, hating the way that her heart lurched at the sight of him in her house, his long legs sprawled out with careless elegance. 'Do you want some coffee?' she said pointedly. 'Before you go?'

'No, I don't want any coffee. You know what I want. *You!*' he said deliberately, and his eyes narrowed and darkened with all the physical manifestations of sexual promise.

Her body responded as if she was on automatic pilot, her face flushing as her veins began to be flooded with the fierce heat of wanting him.

Did he see her weakening? Was that why he took the opportunity to reach up and pull her down on to the sofa beside him? For a minute she reacted on that same automatic pilot, her body softening and burgeoning as it came into contact with the hard sinews and magnificent muscular strength of him.

'I can't stop wanting you, Kimberley, do you know that? No matter what I do, the wanting won't go away—is it the same for you? Is it?'

As he spoke his mouth was kissing softly at her neck, his hands moving to brush lazily over the firm swell of her breasts and she felt them grow heavy with desire. She found that her body was pliant—soft and welcoming—as he pushed her back against the scatter-cushions, kissing her with the fervour and the hunger of a man who had never kissed before.

She went under like a drowning woman, the elemental fire of his desire transmuting into a white-hot and incandescent passion as she let him kiss her. She felt flooded, exhilarated, all reason leaving her as his mouth continued its deliciously rapacious plundering. Her hands were on his shoulders, pushing distractedly at his jacket, her palms flattening out over his chest. His small sigh of pleasure against her mouth was like pouring paraffin on to a blaze already nearly out of control, and Kimberley let her hand fall on to his lap, revelling in the hard throb as her fingers lightly brushed his arousal.

He said something shockingly profound beneath his breath and he moved his hand beneath her sweatshirt to stroke his way slowly up her bare midriff towards her breasts, and Kimberley froze.

They'd only spent one night together, and yet she knew that Harrison was better acquainted with her body after one night than another man would have been after thirty years. Every curve, every crevice, every centimetre he had explored with his hands and his mouth and the tensile length of his arousal. Some time during that long, wonderful night Kimberley had suspected that if he had had the means to do so he would have lain her heart and her soul and her body bare, too—such had seemed his desire to possess her totally and completely.

True, at almost five months a slight swell of the belly would have been normal, especially in a woman as slim as Kimberley, but her loss of weight meant that in fact she barely showed at all. But the difference was noticeable to *her* eye, and would be, she suspected, to Harrison's, too. And, quite apart from anything else, she had gone up a bra size since she'd become pregnant—at times she even had to go to bed wearing a bra, her breasts were so aching and swollen. He would surely be able to detect *that*?

She sat upright, and pushed him away. She had to get him out of here. And quickly.

He gave her a quizzical look, a satirical dark eyebrow raised. 'So what happened to make you change your mind?' he enquired, as if it didn't matter one iota to him. But she could see from the sharp lines of tension on his face that it was as painful as hell for him to stop now. And for her, too. But it was imperative that reason take precedence over the desire of a man who cared nothing for her.

'Changed my mind? You arrogant bastard! I hadn't made it up in the first place!'

'No? That's not the message I was getting.'

'Whatever message I send out you only ignore it and then damn well interpret it the way that *you* want to!' she accused him, knowing that it was unfair—and untrue.

'Oh, come, come, Kimberley,' he chided. 'That intelligence of yours does not marry very well with crass hypocrisy.'

She averted her eyes from the darkly handsome and mobile features. 'I'd like you to go now. Please.' She tacked the nicety on to the end, thinking that it might appeal to some deeply buried chivalrous streak in his nature.

It didn't.

'I'm not leaving until I've said what I came here to say.'

'I can hardly wait.' She stood up, wanting to put distance between them, going to stand by the window. The daylight had almost gone now, the white of the cherry blossom looking unnaturally bright in the gathering gloom of the dusk.

His eyes were watchful. 'I have a proposition to put to you.'

'*Another* proposition?' she enquired icily, remembering when he'd used those words on another occasion. 'Not more money, surely?'

'No,' he said heavily. 'Not more money.'

'Go on—I'm listening.'

'I want to see you,' he said huskily.

Violins threatened to start playing, but she put them on hold. 'See me?' Then, stupidly, or perhaps not so stupidly, because she needed to know just what he was suggesting, she asked him, 'What for?'

He gave his cool imitation of a smile. 'Whatever you like. Theatre. Dinner. Picnics at weekends. You know—the things which men and women usually do together.'

'And bed, presumably? You're forgetting bed.'

His eyes darkened in a predatory and feral gleam. 'Oh, no, Kimberley,' he said softly. 'I'm certainly not forgetting bed.'

For the first time she became fiercely grateful that she *was* pregnant, because the baby was protecting her from her own foolishness, in a way. For could she honestly put her hand on her heart and say that if she hadn't been pregnant she wouldn't have been tempted to go along with his cold-blooded request? And have her pride trampled into the ground and end up with a heart even more broken?

'Sorry,' she said indifferently, 'I'm not interested.'

There was a momentary bleakness which hardened his autocratic features, and it affected her far more than it should have done; he obviously wasn't used to having his propositions turned down. She would never know whether he would have tried to kiss her again in order to change her mind—probably not, she decided—because the doorbell rang.

He stood there, unmoving and cold, as if he'd been hewn from purest marble, and Kimberley went to answer the door, wondering who it was, and how she was going to get rid of Harrison before she broke down in front of him and gave it all away.

It was James. Carrying roses. Red roses. He grinned. 'Just saw these and—' He stopped when he saw the warning look in Kimberley's eye, and in a brainwave she knew how she could get Harrison out of her life for good.

'Oh, darling!' she cried expansively, and she took the roses from James's arms and planted a kiss on the side of his surprised face as she linked her arm through his. 'They're absolutely beautiful! But you shouldn't have done—you spoil me!'

She heard a soft footfall behind her and then, blinking a little, she turned, as if she'd completely forgotten all about the dark, towering man with the set face who stood in the doorway of the sitting-room, watching them. 'Come and meet an old friend of mine. Harrison—this is James Britton, my boss. James—I'd like you to meet Harrison Nash.'

The atmosphere was as brittle as peanut-crunch. Harrison gave something masquerading as a smile and took James's hand, giving him a terse nod. 'A short acquaintanceship, I'm afraid. I was just leaving.' He gave Kimberley a strange, fleeting look. 'Goodbye.'

He said it as though he meant it, and although this had been what she'd wanted, Kimberley suddenly felt an overwhelming sense of blind panic. 'I'll see you out,' she said desperately.

She followed him out to the front door, alarmed by the forbidding set of his shoulders, tempted—unbearably tempted—to tell him the truth. But, when he turned around, the disdain and scorn which were clearly etched on his face stopped her.

'Your *boss*?' he queried sardonically. 'You're sure as hell doing a great job for industrial relations!' His mouth twisted in distaste. 'Tell me, does dear James know that you were touching me up minutes before his arrival? He must either be exceptionally trusting or exceptionally stupid. Or both.'

The accusation stung her, hurt her more than words could express. 'How dare you?' she said between gritted teeth. 'I won't have James insulted!'

'It's *you* I'm insulting. *Sweetheart*.'

'Get out!'

'Don't worry. I'm going.' And he dropped his mouth to hers, briefly and brutally, that one kiss openly displaying all the contempt he felt for her. 'Thanks for the memory,' he said bitterly, and walked out.

James came to find her and said nothing for a moment as he took in her trembling lips, the tears which were spilling from her blue eyes like water from a dam whose floodgates had finally been opened. He put an arm around her, warm and comforting, and turned her face into his shoulder, letting her cry and cry until there were no tears left.

'It's all right,' he told her. 'It's all right.'

She raised her tearstained face to his and shook her head distractedly. 'No, it isn't,' she whispered. 'It's never going to be all right.'

'He's the father, isn't he?'

There seemed no point in denying it, and she didn't think she had the strength to deny it—besides which she'd uttered enough lies that afternoon to last a lifetime. 'Yes.'

'I didn't realise you even *knew* Harrison Nash,' said James drily. 'Are there any other bosses of multinational companies you're keeping under your hat?'

'I—oh, *James*!' Kimberley gripped her abdomen, her eyes filling with tears again.

'For God's sake—what? Is everything all right?'

But in spite of the tears she was now smiling—a smile which threatened to split her face in two as she stared at James.

'What is it?' he repeated.

'I felt it!'

James frowned. 'Felt what?'

'The baby,' she said, on a note of wonder. 'James, the baby just *moved*!'

CHAPTER SIX

THE doorbell rang and Kimberley waddled to answer it, feeling like a whale—beached or otherwise! Only four weeks to go—four weeks which seem to stretch ahead of her like an eternity. She felt enormous. She *was* enormous!

After her early weight-loss she'd gone from strength to strength, and now had a bulge which her doctor joked would have made him bet on twins if he hadn't seen her scan for himself!

She peered through the peephole which James had insisted she have installed, blinking her eyelids in a mixture of horror and disbelief when she saw Harrison standing there.

She sagged back against the wall, biting her lip as she wondered what on earth he was doing here—but that didn't actually matter. What was important was that he left her alone. And what was vital was that he didn't see her.

The doorbell rang again—a sharp, impatient sound. Kimberley decided to ignore it, until she heard his deep drawl.

'It's all right, Kimberley—I know you're in. Your car is parked outside and your neighbour informed me somewhat peculiarly that you usually have a ''rest'' in the afternoon. I don't know whether that was her euphemism for describing what you and

James Britton get up to, and frankly I don't care. But whether he's in there or not, I'm not going anywhere until I've seen you.'

'You're the last person in the world I want to see! Go and take your horrible grubby mind and your nasty insinuations somewhere else!'

'Are you going to let me in?'

'No!'

'Then I may have to break this very attractive little door down. Pity about that.'

'Just *try*!' shouted Kimberley, bordering on hysteria now. 'And I'll have the law down here so fast—'

'Your mother sent me.'

This completely took the wind out of Kimberley's sails. 'My *mother*? Why would my mother send you?'

'She's worried about you.'

'But there's nothing for her to worry about!' Kimberley shut her eyes in horror, ashamed of her own deception, and yet there had seemed no other alternative at the time. She had rung her mother regularly, and written. But she had not been down to stay since the pregnancy had become impossible to disguise, even with the baggy and layered clothes she wore. She had told her mother that she was having to go to Paris some weekends. She had blamed pressure of work. And she hated living the lie. 'Why's she so worried?' Kimberley asked brightly. 'I'm fine.'

'Could the fact that she hasn't seen you for nearly four months have something to do with it?' he grated. 'Now, are you going to let me in or not?'

'No! I'll ring her tonight.'

His voice was impatient. 'I promised her I'd deliver a package to you in person.'

'Package?'

'It's your birthday present. From her. And there's a letter with it.'

'Can't you just leave it on the doorstep?' asked Kimberley desperately. 'I honestly don't want to see you, Harrison. Surely you can understand that?'

There was a short silence. 'Yes,' he said, in an odd and harsh-sounding voice. 'I can understand that. OK—I'll do as you ask and leave the package on the doorstep. But I gave her my word I'd speak to you, so promise me you'll go and see her?'

'I promise.' Now go, she thought. Please *go*.

Leaning back against the wall, her hands drawn protectively over the baby, she waited. And when she looked out through the peephole there was no sign of him.

Slowly and cautiously she opened the door, breathing quickly as she gingerly bent down to retrieve the brown paper package, since such movements were extremely uncomfortable in this late stage of pregnancy. She picked the package up and straightened herself, rubbing the small of her back with a weary hand, and found herself staring into a pair of disbelieving grey eyes as Harrison emerged from behind one of the cherry trees, now bloomless and covered with leaves.

She tried to make a dash for it, but she was too large and too cumbersome and he caught her wrist— not hard—but so firmly that she couldn't break free.

'Dear God,' he whispered in a strained voice. 'So

this is why. This—is—why,' he repeated slowly, then seemed to come to his senses, like a man coming round after an accident. 'Dear God,' he said again.

Kimberley swayed and might have fallen had he not caught her by the waist. She saw her neighbour staring over at them curiously, thought what a peculiar sight they must make.

'Are you all right?' Harrison grated.

'I want to go inside,' she said shakily as, blindly, she pushed the door open, hardly realising where she was going, hearing his footsteps behind her and the sound of his quickened breathing.

In that short walk into the sitting-room she'd managed to compose herself, to have ready the answers to the questions she knew he'd start to fire at her, when all at once a hot dart of fire squeezed at her womb. Breathless with the impact, Kimberley clung on to the back of the nearest chair. Beads of sweat broke out on her forehead.

Harrison's eyes narrowed; he was by her side in an instant. 'What's happening?'

Another iron band constricted her; she panted the way she'd been taught. The sensation dominated her entire world, so that she was scarcely aware of the man who stood before her, his face creased with concern.

'I think—I think it's the baby,' she managed to get out. But it couldn't be! She couldn't be having the baby now—she *couldn't*. Not when she still had four weeks to go. She wrapped her hands tightly around her abdomen, glancing at her wristwatch as she did

so. Time them, she remembered. Time the contrac-
tions.

He was really the last person in the world she
should have wanted there, and yet, in reality, the sight
of his broad, strong body made her feel ridiculously
safe, and she could have wept, because his strength
and dependability were nothing but an illusion.

He was staring at her very hard as he took in her
pale, clammy face. 'What do you want me to do?' he
fired out briskly.

'Ring the midwife. The number's on the pad. I
need— *Oh*!' she gasped. Another. And stronger this
time. And only two minutes after the last.

For a moment he hesitated, moved over to take her
by the shoulders, grey eyes searching her face, and
then he said, 'Sit down,' and helped her gently down
on to the sofa before going to telephone.

Harrison stood by the telephone, listening intently
to the midwife. He glanced at his own wristwatch.
'Two minutes,' he said briefly into the mouthpiece.
'And they're regular.'

So he'd been timing them too, thought Kimberley,
and then another wave hit her and she shifted restlessly on the sofa, the sweat now drying icily on her
face.

Harrison was replacing the receiver. 'The ambulance is on its way. Tell me where your overnight bag
is!'

'In the bedroom.' She closed her eyes as another
hot, dark stab clutched at her.

Harrison returned moments later. His face was

guarded as he crouched down beside her. 'Do you want me to call anyone for you?'

'Like who?' she enquired faintly.

'Like your mother?'

'No,' she whispered, from between dry lips. 'She— doesn't know.'

'I see,' he said grimly.

'Harrison…' Her voice tailed off.

'What?'

'You won't tell her? Please don't tell her!' she begged as the pain swamped her again.

'Tell her? Why should I? It's nothing to do with me.' His grey eyes were penetrating as he stared down at her. 'Is it, Kimberley?'

'No.' She shut her eyes, afraid that her fears and her feelings might show. He hadn't asked. Amazing. But the baby was early, and perhaps he…he… thought. Tears threatened to well at the bitter thought. Why should he suspect that she was having his baby? He probably thought that he was only one of a long line of lovers in her life.

Forcing herself, she opened her eyes and looked up at him. 'Can I have some water, please?'

He frowned. 'I don't know whether you should.'

'Why not?'

'Well, if they have to give you an anaesthetic—'

'For God's sake!' Alarmed, Kimberley sat bolt-upright, her hair snaking wildly down her back. 'I'm only having a baby—why should they want to give me—?'

'Shh,' he soothed her. 'We'll compromise.' He disappeared into the kitchen and returned with a clean towel and a bowl of cool water, with which he proceeded to dampen her lips.

'Oh!' She smiled up into his eyes. 'That's good.'

He gave her a strange smile and nodded, but he didn't speak, just continued to dab at her dry lips every two seconds.

They heard the siren long before the ambulance screeched up outside the front door, and Kimberley tried and failed to stand up.

'Stay there!' ordered Harrison. 'They'll send a wheelchair for you.'

'Such a fuss,' she mumbled, until she discovered that the wheelchair was infinitely preferable to walking.

'She's going to be all right, isn't she?' demanded Harrison, and the ambulanceman gave him a reassuring smile.

'Don't worry, sir—she looks fit enough to me. In my experience it's always the father who goes to pieces! You'll have a healthy baby son or daughter before you know it, sir!'

She knew what conclusion they'd jumped to. She wanted to tell them that Harrison wasn't the father, but now they were putting a mask over her face, telling her to breathe deeply, and the sickly sweet smell of gas was making her feel disorientated, making the pain retreat, become bearable.

'Can you get in the back, please, sir?'

Harrison climbed in beside her, some dark and unfathomable emotion on his face as he stared down at her.

'What are you doing?' she asked in bewilderment.

'I'm coming with you,' he stated.

'Harrison—'

'You can't be on your own,' he said in a voice which brooked no argument. 'I'm staying.'

She stared up at that strong, beautiful face, found herself wanting to touch it, to tell him... Not just about the baby, to tell him that... She reached her hand out and he gripped it. 'Harrison,' she whispered, but then another contraction, stronger and more intense than any of the preceding ones, made her pupils dilate in pain, and the ambulanceman put a finger over his lips.

'Don't talk! Concentrate on your breathing,' he said urgently. 'And say a prayer that the traffic's quiet!'

The ambulance pulled away—the driver obviously had his foot down—and the journey all became a blur to Kimberley. She was aware of little other than the bands of contraction, which became fiercer and stronger and closer together. She was aware of gripping Harrison's hand, with her nails digging into his flesh so tightly that he should have winced, but he didn't wince, just gently smoothed the sweat-soaked strands of black hair which fell over her cheek from time to time. I must look absolutely awful, thought Kimberley fleetingly.

By the time they reached St Christopher's, Kimberley was past caring *what* she looked like, or even what was happening. They were bundling her on a stretcher and travelling upwards in a lift and then into a room which looked less like a ward than somebody's bedroom. It was all part of the new, relaxed policy towards birth, remembered Kimberley as Harrison helped lift her on to a flower-sprigged bed. She recognised one of the midwives she'd seen at her hospital appointments, who now began to examine her.

'Please,' Kimberley gasped. 'Can I have an epidural now?'

The midwife laughed. 'An epidural? Oh, heavens no, dear—it's far too late for that.'

'Too late?'

'Why, yes—the baby's on its way now. Keep breathing the way you've been taught, and any minute now I'm going to ask you to start pushing.'

Pain swamped her; someone wiped her brow and Kimberley looked up to see Harrison's darkly handsome face swimming into view.

'Harrison—' she said weakly, but he shook his head.

'Don't talk. Save your strength for the baby. It's all right—I'm here and I'm not leaving you.'

Oh, if only. The face swam away again. It was too late to tell him now. She felt a desire to push which consumed her… She saw the midwife's encouraging nod… Minutes later the baby was born and immediately gave a lusty cry.

'It's a girl!' said Harrison softly, bending his head to speak in her ear. 'A beautiful baby girl.'

And Kimberley burst into tears.

They laid the baby on her breast and Kimberley experienced the strangest, strongest sensation, of being physically exhausted and yet wonderfully, powerfully strong and triumphant.

'And Daddy can hold her in a minute,' smiled the midwife.

Kimberley said nothing, just stared down at the black little head which nestled against her. Too confusing to try to explain. Certainly not now.

'She's a fine healthy girl,' said the midwife. 'And a good weight, too—considering that she's early.' She smiled at Kimberley. 'Have you changed your mind about the adoption, now that you're back with the baby's daddy?'

The world spun on its axis.

Kimberley glanced up to find a pair of perceptive grey eyes, suddenly gone as cold as an arctic sky, boring into hers. He knows, she thought, with a sudden flash of insight. He knows he's the baby's father.

'Adoption?' he queried softly.

The midwife was beginning to look confused; perhaps things were not all they seemed with this striking-looking couple, she thought. Embarrassed, she turned away and began to wash her hands at the sink.

'Adoption?' he repeated, and there was a frozen look of rage on his face.

Words failed her. Literally. She gave a gulping speechless nod.

There was no way out. Not now. 'Yes,' she told him, lifting her chin defiantly. 'I intend to have the baby adopted.'

'I see,' he said, in a voice so sombre that Kimberley's skin turned to ice.

CHAPTER SEVEN

KIMBERLEY didn't know what she had expected to happen—but what she had *not* expected was that cold and terse little nod he gave her.

'I'll let you get some rest now,' he said abruptly. 'I'll be back later.'

It was like a sentence of death hanging over her head. Kimberley fed the baby, and they both slept. They gave her a cup of strong tea and a marmalade sandwich, then she had a wash, and the staff nurse washed and brushed her hair for her.

'Got to look pretty for your boyfriend,' she said to Kimberley confidingly. 'I can't keep the student nurses away—they're dying to see him again. What a hunk—are there any more like him at home?'

Kimberley tried to smile, and failed. Her lip wobbled precariously and the staff nurse nodded understandingly.

'Feeling a bit blue, are we? Don't worry, dear.' She plumped the four pillows into shape behind Kimberley's back. 'It's quite normal to feel like that afterwards.' She beamed down at the sleeping infant. 'Decided what to call her yet, have you?'

Kimberley swallowed. She had discussed this with her doctor. Apparently it didn't matter *what* name she called her baby, because the adoptive parents would probably change it. She stared down at the crib. So,

even though she might call her Georgia or Alicia—
two names she liked very much—her daughter might
instead grow up as an Anne or a Mary.

She must have dozed off, because when she awoke
it was to find Harrison there, at the end of the bed.
He was studying the child intently, an expression of
rapt preoccupation on his face, but he seemed to sense
that Kimberley's eyes had opened, for he glanced up
immediately and a coldly indifferent look chilled his
face.

'Harrison—' she began, but he stopped her with
one decisive shake of his dark head, an expression of
distaste curving his mouth scornfully.

'Save it.' He spoke tersely. 'I don't want any more
of your lies. She's mine, isn't she?'

'Harrison—'

'*Isn't* she?'

Dispiritedly Kimberley sank back against the pillows. 'Yes. She's yours.'

It was as though her spoken admission, even
though he had known it to be a fact, had shocked him
to the core. He stared first at Kimberley—and the look
of naked pain and anger and hatred in his eyes
scorched her to the very core—then shook his head
very slowly from side to side, as though he couldn't
really take it in.

'But you knew all along, didn't you?' she asked
weakly. 'Why didn't you say something?'

His mouth became a grim, harsh line. 'You may
have a low opinion of me, Kimberley, but I'm not in
the habit of debating paternity when a woman is in
labour.' A muscle began to work furiously beneath

one perfect cheekbone. 'Just tell me,' he said, in a strange, gritty voice, 'tell me that you aren't planning to have her adopted.'

She heard the plea in his voice, and she couldn't lie to him—but neither could she prevent her voice from shaking. 'I—yes,' she managed. 'Yes, I am.'

The look he gave her was one of pure contempt.

'My God,' he whispered in disbelief. 'I thought that my opinion of you couldn't possibly sink any lower, but I was wrong. It was bad enough when you traded my brother in because you fancied making a quick buck. But this…' He shook his head. '*This* defies all comparison. What right did you have, Kimberley, to deny me all knowledge of the fact that I was going to have a child? Have a *child*.' And his face softened marginally as his eyes strayed to the snuffling infant.

Kimberley was fighting for her life—her sanity. 'What *right*?' she demanded, not caring who heard her. 'You forfeited any *right* when you offered me that one night! A quick roll in the hay doesn't automatically guarantee your *rights*! If you recall, you couldn't wait to make sure that I'd actually used some contraception—and I'm ashamed to say that even the thought of it never occurred to me—'

'Because you were so hot for me,' he said insultingly.

She knew that his need to wound her was deep, and that it stemmed from discovering that she had kept the secret of his paternity from him, but knowing that didn't stop it hurting. 'Yes, I was "hot" for you—as you so delightfully put it. I'm sure that's nothing new, Harrison. You're pretty good in bed.'

He gave an angry snarl, his eyes sparked fire, but then, as if he was remembering just where they were, and that Kimberley had given birth less than four hours ago, he stopped himself from responding with what was obviously a huge effort.

'Why *should* I have saddled you with a baby from what was never supposed to be anything more than a one-night stand?'

He flinched, a muscle working frantically in his cheek. 'You too,' he answered coldly, 'have such a delightful way with words.'

She felt deflated. What was the point of all this?

'May I hold her?' he asked suddenly.

Kimberley nodded, feeling tears prick at the back of her eyes as she watched him bend down and cradle the tiny bundle, before lifting her up to lie her on his shoulder, placing the large and soft shawl tenderly around her shoulders.

He stood like that for a moment, completely unconscious of the striking picture he made, just gently rocking back and forth on his heels, and the baby gave a sigh. He was so tall, so strong—so powerfully masculine—and yet he was as gentle as a kitten with the baby. A student nurse stuck her head round the door and almost swooned, but his eyes narrowed by a fraction, he gave the tiniest shake of his head, and the nurse took the hint and scuttled off.

'But the end result is the same,' he said heavily, his eyes going reluctantly to Kimberley's, and she blinked away the glittering tears which sparkled at the ice-blue depths. 'What have you decided to call her?'

'Can't we talk about this some other time?' she pleaded.

He shook his head. 'I've certainly no wish to tire you out. I won't keep you long, and the whole business will be kept on a completely impartial basis.'

What on earth was he talking about?

'But I have to go abroad for a few days,' he continued, 'and we must get a few things settled before I go. Like her name.' And he smiled into the soft, downy black head.

Kimberley felt panicked. She had to tell him. She took a deep breath. 'It doesn't really matter what I'm going to call her,' she reminded him gently. 'Because I'm going to have her adopted.'

There was a strange, frightening look on his face as he enunciated the single word. 'Why?'

'Because I don't feel it would be fair—to keep her—'

'Fair to whom?' he interrupted coldly. 'To you— or to her?'

Kimberley tried to explain. 'What chance would she have? Brought up by a single mother who has to go out to work to support her? I'd have to work late some nights—what then? Stuck at some childminder's—her never seeing me, me never seeing her. And when I did I'd be too tired and—'

'You selfish little liar! How dare you even consider it?'

Kimberley exploded with rage. 'How dare *you*?' she demanded. 'You talk about rights—what *right* do you have as a man to try and take some ridiculously moral stance on what I should do? If you must know,

I thought I *was* doing the right thing by the baby. I thought two parents were better than one—'

'But she *has* two parents,' he pointed out.

Kimberley stared at him. 'Just what are you suggesting?'

'I'm not suggesting anything at the moment, I'm merely stating a fact. But one thing is certain, Kimberley—I will not have my daughter put up for adoption, and I'll fight you through every court in the land to stop you.'

There was a whimpering at his shoulder, which rapidly gave way to a shrill shriek emitted by the widest mouth on such a tiny little creature that Kimberley could imagine.

She held her arms out. 'Give her to me.'

The momentary hesitation on his face nearly killed her, but then he handed the baby over reluctantly, frowning slightly as he watched her suckle Kimberley immediately—the shriek becoming a blissful glug as the baby greedily drank the milk.

Harrison moved towards the bed. Towering over it, he was at an advantage, and his grey eyes burned their ice-fire into hers. 'I have to go abroad for a few days—there's nothing I can do about it.'

'It's of no concern to me.'

He shook his head. 'Oh, but it is, Kimberley,' he contradicted her. 'It concerns you very much. Don't even attempt to give the baby up. I shall instruct my lawyers to act for me at once—and don't think it's an idle boast when I tell you that you'll have no case against me.'

'Case?' What was he talking about? 'Just what are you planning to do?'

'I'll adopt her myself—that's my plan. As you don't want her. And one other thing—I want us to agree on a name before I go. I'm fed up with calling her "she" already.' There was a pause. 'Had you any names in mind?'

'Why consult *me*?' she whispered brokenly. 'I'm only her mother.'

'And mothers fight to *keep* their children,' he snarled. 'Not give them away.'

Kimberley bit her lip, not trusting herself to say anything.

'So. Names?'

'I like Georgia,' she said reluctantly. 'Or Alicia.'

'I like Georgia, too,' he said surprisingly. 'I like it very much.' The baby finished feeding and he was staring down at her, entranced. Quite instinctively Kimberley held her out to him.

Without being told, he winded her and changed her nappy; he was brilliant for a beginner, Kimberley conceded, then she watched as he laid her carefully down in her crib and tucked the shawl round her.

'Goodbye, sweet little Georgia,' he said softly, and as he straightened from planting a kiss on the soft little cheek he said something else softly, too. Very softly—but Kimberley heard it. 'Let's hope you don't grow up to be a lying little cheat like your mother.'

And he walked out of the room without a backward glance, leaving Kimberley shaken and close to tears, and on the brink of a truth which had nagged at her and refused to leave her since the first time Georgia had lain on her breast and a tiny little hand had curled itself tightly around her finger.

Her words had been empty, her thoughts wishful.

She would move heaven and earth to keep her baby.

CHAPTER EIGHT

KIMBERLEY and Georgia stayed in the hospital for five days. They told her that this was usual for first-time mothers, particularly as the baby had been early.

Kimberley had sent James out with a fortune to spend on baby clothes, delighting in the tiny garments he had brought back. She'd have to buy a pram, she knew, and a cot—countless things—but she'd wait until she was discharged and then go choose them herself.

Two days after Harrison left for France a giant pink teddy bear had arrived, with a card saying, 'To the most beautiful baby in the world. With love from Daddy'. And just the sight of it had filled Kimberley with an inexplicable fear.

She was packing her suitcase to go home when he walked into the room. She was crouched over her suitcase wearing a broderie anglaise cotton shirt, which buttoned down the front so that she could breastfeed, and it came to mid-thigh. She saw the reluctant darkening of his eyes as his glance roved over her semi-clothed state and felt colour scorch her cheeks as she registered his physical presence, the impact he always made on her. Her breasts tingled, and she felt as though her body had completely betrayed her—for surely it wasn't normal to ache and hunger for a man when you'd only just had his baby?

Over the past five days she'd had time to reflect on her behaviour, deciding that she had been wrong and cowardly not to tell him. Yet it had seemed the only thing to do at the time, and it was now far too late to make amends.

But sooner rather than later he was going to find out that she had no intention of letting Georgia be adopted, and if he was going to demand access, which she was certain he was going to do, then it would be infinitely preferable if their relationship was polite and civilised rather than as tempestuous as it had been up until now.

'Hello,' she said.

He stared at her swiftly, seeming to gauge her mood. 'Hello.' He glanced over at the crib. 'How is she?'

Kimberley smiled. 'Just perfect—though I'm biased, of course! She's—'

'I have a car waiting,' he said abruptly.

Kimberley blinked. 'What for?'

'To take you home, of course—or did you imagine that I would have you call a cab?'

Kimberley held her chin up—he was making it sound as though she had no one in the world to care about her. 'As a matter of fact, James is on his way to collect me.'

The face blackened. 'Then he'll have a wasted journey, won't he?' he snarled.

'Meaning?'

'You're coming with me, Kimberley—and that's that. Now, would you mind getting dressed?'

Feeling cornered, she gave a nod, biting her lip as

she did so. She mustn't keep antagonising him; he would make a cruel adversary. 'Would you mind turning your back?' she asked stiffly.

'A little late in the day for modesty, wouldn't you say?' came his harsh rejoinder, but he did as she asked, and Kimberley silently put on a lemon silk shirt and a grey pleated skirt with trembling fingers, amazed that the waistband of the skirt wasn't in the least bit tight.

'You can turn around again now,' she told him.

He narrowed his grey eyes as he watched her pull the brush through the thick black silk of her hair, seemingly fascinated by the movement as it spilled glossily down over her breasts.

A muscle worked in his cheek as he gestured towards the baby. 'Do you want to carry her, or shall I?'

And then, remembering the tender way with which he'd handled the baby, she managed a smile. 'You can carry her if you like.'

His mouth twisted; she was becoming used to that critical curve. 'Of course,' he mocked.

The nurses came in, an absolute gaggle of them, to say goodbye and to thank Harrison. Apparently he had not only left them chocolates, champagne, fruit and flowers, but had stuck a very hefty cheque into the Nurses' Benevolent Fund, with instructions that they use it for their Christmas dance. Whereupon he had immediately been invited to be guest of honour!

Kimberley watched all the laughing interaction with a growing uneasiness which she was reluctantly beginning to recognise as jealousy.

Outside she did not see the ridiculously expensive black car, but instead a discreetly gleaming green Bentley, complete with a chauffeur who held open the back door, and Kimberley climbed in, followed by Harrison holding on to Georgia.

There was a tiny baby-seat in place, and Harrison gently clipped the baby in.

Kimberley grew confused. 'Your car is different. I thought you drove a black car.'

'Not exclusively. This is one of several I own.'

'And I suppose they all have baby-seats?'

'The ones which aren't sports models do. Now. I had them installed last week—it seemed practical.'

Kimberley swallowed. He'd talked about adopting Georgia, but that had been before—before she'd decided that she couldn't let her baby go. 'Harrison—'

He frowned. 'Let's not begin what is obviously going to be a difficult conversation in the car, Kimberley. In the circumstances, I feel it is more prudent to wait until we get home.'

'Prudent?' she demanded, angry at being spoken to in that admonitory manner, but even angrier at the way he was fast taking the upper hand. She turned her face to stare sightlessly out of the window—anything was better than having to be made aware of that daunting physical presence. And she was supposed to be adopting a civilised attitude towards him, she reminded herself. She might find it difficult, but she really ought to try. 'It's very kind of you to give us a lift home,' she said.

'My pleasure,' he answered, in a tone which made mockery of his words.

But the car was going nowhere near Hampstead. Instead she started to recognise signs for the south-west. 'Where are we going?' she asked suddenly.

'To Kew.'

'Why Kew?'

'It's where I live.'

'Harrison—I want to go home.'

'And that, too, is something we must discuss. But not now.'

He was quite emphatic in his refusal to say any-thing further, and he didn't utter another word until the car had drawn up outside some wrought-iron rail-ings in front of an enormous double-fronted house which stood in its own walled garden.

As he walked alongside her, carrying Georgia, she became aware that the garden was a scented para-dise—there were stocks and honeysuckle, tobacco plants and sweet roses, and, with the mellow brick of the wall acting as a backdrop, tall delphiniums and hollyhocks, too. She liked it; she liked it very much. Did he garden, or did someone do it for him? But even if he did employ a gardener he surely must have had some input in the creation of this country garden right in the middle of the city? Ironic, really. How little she really knew about the father of her child.

She followed him inside, but by this time she wasn't taking very much in—only that the ceilings were high and the rooms large and well-proportioned. In the spacious wood-panelled entrance hall stood a top-of-the-range pram, with a flaxen-haired doll smil-ing inanely at them from its depths.

Panic mounting, Kimberley turned to him. 'What

on earth is going on, Harrison? Why have you brought me here? And why are all these baby things lying around?'

He gave her a chilly smile. 'I brought the baby here because there was nothing for her at your house. Not a single item of clothing, not even a cot for her to sleep in. But then, I suppose as you had planned to hand her over to someone else just as soon as you could—'

Past feeling the pain of his censure, Kimberley caught his arm. 'I want to explain to you—'

'Frankly, I'm not interested in your explanations, but I will give you a chance to speak. After we get Georgia settled. She is, after all,' he emphasised, 'the important one.' But the look on his face suggested that she thought otherwise. And who could blame him? thought Kimberley wildly, seeing her actions through his eyes for the first time.

And waiting for them in the drawing-room was a girl of around twenty-three, with a cap of gleaming blonde hair surrounding a serene and smiling face. She was dressed in a brown and white uniform which stirred some vague memory in Kimberley's mind.

'Hello, Sarah,' smiled Harrison. 'We've brought the baby home, and I'd like you to meet Kimberley Ryan, her mother.'

Kimberley's heart gave a great leap of alarm and she looked up at Harrison, a question in her eyes.

'This is Sarah Hansford,' he said in a neutral voice. 'Who is to be Georgia's nanny.'

Georgia's nanny!

'I'm pleased to meet you,' said Sarah, and held out

her hand, but her pale eyes were not on Kimberley, or on Georgia, instead they were fixed very firmly and adoringly on Harrison.

Kimberley felt faint. How could he have appointed a nanny without consulting her? 'And is this your first job, Sarah?' she probed.

Sarah's eyes glinted, and she almost seemed to inflate herself before their eyes. 'Oh, no. I worked for a member of the royal family until I accepted Mr Nash's offer of a job.'

'I see.' Kimberley felt as though the world around her was going mad, as if she'd somehow managed to lose control of her own destiny.

'I'd like to talk to you, please, Harrison. Alone,' she added pointedly. 'I've fed Georgia, Sarah—I think you'll find she's ready for her bath before bedtime. Then I'll come up and settle her down for the night.'

Sarah took Georgia into her arms, and Kimberley couldn't fault the way she held the baby. But her next words filled her once more with an inexplicable dread. 'Oh, don't you worry about a thing, Miss Ryan. I'd prefer to adopt my own routine, if you don't mind. Nanny knows *best*—doesn't she, Georgia?'

Kimberley let her go. There was too much which needed to be sorted out. But once they had disappeared she turned to Harrison. 'Who is this girl?' she hissed as she watched Sarah carry the baby upstairs. 'I don't know her from Adam.'

'She comes highly recommended. She looked after a friend of mine's children for several years.'

Was he talking about the royal? wondered Kimberley faintly.

'She's excellent,' he continued. 'Firm, kind, with the sort of old-fashioned methods of child-rearing which I thoroughly approve of.'

He had thought everything through, Kimberley realised. With as much detail as a military campaign. 'And which methods are they?'

He shrugged. 'Regular meals, regular bedtimes. Firm handling with limitless love. How does that sound?'

'And how many other staff do you have?' she asked, imagining a legion of maids suddenly appearing.

'Just someone to clean and to garden, and Mrs Caithness prepares the food—although I use a firm of caterers for large functions, of course. But that doesn't really concern you, does it, Kimberley? I mean, it's not as though you're staying.'

Kimberley's head swam. 'Could we please talk now?' she asked desperately.

'Sure.'

'Don't you think that you ought to have consulted me about something as important as hiring a nanny?'

'Frankly, I didn't think that you'd be particularly concerned about it either way,' he said sardonically.

'Well, I w-would,' she stumbled, then closed her eyes quickly, lest he see the tears that glittered there.

But if he didn't see the tears then the tremor in her voice alerted him, made him look up sharply. He studied her face very closely for a long moment, and when he spoke his voice was quite gentle. 'You're very pale. Why don't you make yourself comfortable and we can talk?' He gestured towards a sofa. 'Would you like some wine?'

She would have loved some, but had grown so used to avoiding alcohol, avoiding smoke and smokers, and considering all the other responsibilities of pregnancy, that it was going to take a little time for her to relinquish them. 'I'd love some. But I wonder would a glass be OK—with me feeding Georgia?' she asked automatically.

Another quick glance, definitely tinged with surprise this time—as though he was taken aback at her solicitude. He looked as though he was on the brink of smiling, then appeared to change his mind. 'I'm sure that one glass won't hurt. Wait here while I fetch some.'

He left the room and reappeared moments later, carrying a bottle and two crystal goblets. There was silence as he opened it, and she found herself observing him unobtrusively while pretending to study a superb water-colour which hung over the fireplace.

He looked so tense, his face so grave and unsmiling. She found herself remembering that night of love, the rapture on his face when he'd told her that she was beautiful, and she'd given him that cold and, she'd thought, clever little reply. Another wall she'd built around herself.

Since the moment she'd met him she'd been constructing walls to protect her from being hurt by him. And every one of her actions had been badly misconstrued by him. She had always wanted him to think the worst of her, and he did. But she found herself wanting to defend herself on something as important as this—not so that he would think well of her, but so that he would trust her to bring up their child properly.

And it was therefore vital that she convince him she had *thought* that she had acted in Georgia's best interests in trying to conceal her from him. For it seemed the most awful kind of crime that a man—and not just any man—that Harrison should imagine that she had cared nothing for the child which had grown within her.

'Here.' He interrupted her reverie, handed her a glass of red wine and motioned for her to sit down. She perched down on the sofa but he remained standing, his face unreadable as he started to speak.

'I told you that I intended speaking to my lawyers, and now I have. They—' he began, but Kimberley began to tremble and she quickly put the glass of wine down on the small table. Still it slopped over the side, her hand was shaking so much.

'Please, Harrison, before you say anything more about lawyers, I want you to know that I've had a good chance to think things through, and—well, the point is that things have changed, or rather *I've* changed. And I don't want Georgia to be adopted.'

There was silence. He sipped his drink. 'I see,' was all he said for a moment or two. He took another sip of wine, before studying her with those clear grey eyes. 'And what brought all this on—this sudden change of heart? Or is it simply to prevent me from having her?'

Surely he knew? And hadn't he felt it too—that

overpowering surge of emotion at holding a child that you'd created in your arms? 'I just—didn't know that I'd feel this way about her. I think that I must have been very slightly mad to think I'd ever be able to give her up for adoption,' she finished quietly.

A slight inclination of the dark, elegant head was the only indication that he'd heard her softly spoken words. 'And just what are you proposing to do? How will you manage?'

'I've got to speak to James, see if he'll let me go back to work part-time—'

'And if he doesn't?'

'I'm kind of depending on him saying yes, but if he doesn't—well, then I'll have to rethink. But I'm young—adaptable. I've got a brain in my head. I'll take whatever work comes along to support us. It might be a bit of a struggle, but I'm prepared for that.'

'And isn't that the very scenario which turned you against single parenthood in the first place?'

Kimberley swallowed. 'You know it is. Perhaps now you'll realise that I *was* thinking of the baby's best interests. This way will be harder financially, but emotionally—there really is no alternative. Now I've got her—I can't let her go.'

He nodded his head, as if considering what she'd said. 'And what about me?'

She knew immediately what he meant. 'Oh, I have no intention of denying you access,' she told him quickly.

'That's *terribly* generous of you,' he said sardonically. 'What kind of access did you have in mind?'

'The usual,' she said bluntly.

'The *usual*?' he bit back. 'And what's that? Every other weekend? A few weeks in the summer?'

'I'm prepared to be more generous than that—' she began.

'Well, let me tell you that I am *not* prepared to accept any grudging bits of largesse you may condescend to bestow on me. If you had gone through with your plan to give her up for adoption, I would—as I told you—have been perfectly agreeable to adopting her myself.'

'But now I'm not going to do that, am I?'

'No. And, while I am not cynical enough to try and deprive a child of her mother, neither do I intend to be a part-time father. Which leaves us only one alternative.'

'Which is?'

'That she has two parents.'

A frown creased her forehead. 'But how—?'

'There's only one way.' He said it without expression. 'That you marry me.'

Kimberley stared at him. 'You cannot be serious.'

He reached forward, tipped some more of the wine into his glass, then came and sat down beside her, leaning back against the sofa and sipping his wine, watching her coolly, as though he had not just dropped a bombshell. 'Oh, but that's where you're wrong, Kimberley.' He smiled. 'I am. Deadly serious.'

'But—men don't have to marry women for that reason any more. Not these days.'

'I know they don't. But perhaps sometimes they should. Particularly in our case. Imagine the hurt we're going to cause our families, just for starters. Your mother has yet to find out that you have a child, and she is bound to want to know who the father is. Now, while you might be tempted to tell her yet another lie—'

'I—' She tried to interrupt, but he shook his head and refused to let her.

'I have no intention of letting Georgia's paternity remain a secret,' he continued, unperturbed. 'As I also have no intention of becoming a father on the very part-time basis which you wish to bestow on me. I want to be *involved* in her life. I want her to have stability—both emotional *and* financial—and I can provide that.'

Kimberley shook her head sorrowfully. 'But you seem to be forgetting our mutual antipathy and distrust—do you think that's going to provide much stability?'

His eyes glittered. 'That depends on how we set this marriage up.'

He was unbelievable! 'You mean, like setting a company up?'

'Why not? Any institution works best within a framework—provided that framework is not too constricting.'

'And what ''framework'' did you have in mind for our marriage?' she asked quietly.

'You shall have all the independence you require. The best nannies, staff—you can start back to work just as soon as you like.'

'That sounds exceedingly generous, Harrison. And just what would you get out of it?'

'I would expect you to play the corporate wife—within limits, naturally. But you would be required to host dinners, and weekends occasionally, at whichever house I happen to be staying in. There will be some travel—but that can be tailored to suit the needs of your career. What I require most, of course, is the opportunity to be a hands-on father, and marriage is the most sensible way for me to accomplish that.'

There was a subject which he had completely ignored, of course. Kimberley struggled to keep her voice steady as she asked the question. 'And is that it?'

'*It*?' He gave a cruel and suddenly ruthless smile, as though he'd guessed exactly what was on her mind. 'Could you be a little more specific?'

'You know exactly what I mean!' she said bitterly, the colour flooding her pale face.

'Do I?' he murmured, moving closer as with one finger he outlined each of her dark, bold eyebrows, as though he'd been painting them.

'Ye-es,' she said shakily, wishing that he wouldn't do that, and yet making no attempt to stop him because her skin was rejoicing in the sensual caress of his touch. Touch was dangerous. The slightest brush of his fingertip sent little shivers of sensation rippling from the point of contact to every single nerve-ending in her body.

'You have,' he murmured, 'such exceptionally fine eyebrows—so strong and so exquisitely shaped. Pre-Raphaelite, in fact. Almost as beautifully shaped as your lips, which are just crying out—aren't they, Kimberley,' he whispered, 'to be kissed?'

The temptation was overpowering; his face was so close, his mouth was so close...so very temptingly close. She stared into those eyes, now smoky with passion, with want, with need, and he must have read her own helpless surrender, for he bent his head to take her mouth softly in a kiss.

Kimberley's eyes fluttered to a close as she succumbed to that sweet, heady sensation, the melting flood of desire flooding her veins immediately, kick-starting her senses into glorious, forgotten life. And what had started as pliant submission vanished as she put her arms around his broad shoulders and kissed him back, with a hunger of such raw and sensual depth that she began to tremble uncontrollably.

He felt her give-away, blatant response to his kiss and he muttered something inaudible against her mouth and began to kiss her, as though her instant and unhidden hunger had driven him over the edge of reason and towards insanity, as if the cool, calculating man of a few moments ago had been vanquished forever.

His mouth was now on the slim, pale column of her neck, and he was pushing the thick silken ropes of black hair back over her shoulders impatiently, as if he wanted to expose more flesh. And more. He began to undo the buttons of her lemon shirt, each one slipping aside easily so that it slithered open, revealing her lush and swollen breasts. She watched while his eyes darkened, saw him urgently unclip the bra, barely waiting until her breasts came tumbling out, free and unfettered, before his head swooped to take one swollen and erect nipple possessively into the hot, passionate cavern of his mouth.

Kimberley almost fainted with pleasure, a small gasp escaping her lips, and he released her breast at once, looking up at her, his eyes hopelessly dazed.

'Am I hurting you?'

She shook her head; never in his arms could he hurt her—in that place he offered only pleasure of untold delight. 'Oh, no.'

'Do you like it?' he murmured. 'Shall I do it again?'

'Yes.'

'Like this?' he whispered as his mouth closed over the pointed peak once more.

'Just like that.' She made the throaty assertion without thinking. 'Oh, *yes*,' she breathed ecstatically. She just couldn't stop herself. Later she might despise herself, but for the moment she was at the mercy of the sweet command he seemed to exert over her body, and at the mercy of her feelings for him—her love and her need.

For she loved Harrison; she had loved him from the first moment he had taken her into his arms, and despite all her protestations that love had never really diminished. She had lain with him and borne his child, and right now—powerful and primitive—came the sweeping desire from deep within her to have this man who had impregnated her, to have him fill her with his need once more.

His mouth tugged and suckled at her again, and the dizzy darts of pleasure swam through her veins as thick and sweet as honey.

'Touch me,' he whispered against her breast. 'Kimberley. Touch me.'

The almost helpless appeal in his voice turned her on unbearably—and she had done this to him. She had the power to disintegrate that cool exterior, that hard ruthlessness he had demonstrated so often, and turn him into this man who was going out of his mind for her.

She touched his chest lightly, touched the nipples through his shirt, and he moved his hand up her leg beneath her skirt, his fingers running luxuriously around the lacy rim of her stocking-top.

'Now touch me as I'm going to touch you,' he ordered in a velvety whisper.

And she did. She let her hand stray down to find his hardness. And, oh, yes—he wanted her. He *really* wanted her. She moved her hips, inviting him to touch her where he'd promised, but instead he moved to lie on top of her, shaking his head, barely able to speak coherently.

'Not here. We'd better go upstairs to bed. Sarah might— '

Sarah? The unfamiliar name darted into the mists of Kimberley's befuddled mind, and just the mention of the nanny's name brought the uneasy situation back into sharp and distressing reality. She moved away, wriggling out from beneath him, and positioned herself at the end of the sofa, her face averted, burning with shame, afraid to look at him until she had her desire for him under control. Because she was in such a highly volatile state that one look from him and she would go under yet again.

She fumbled with her bra.

'Can I help?' There was hateful amusement in his voice, and this infuriated her more than anything. Any other man would have been angry; *she* was angry— and so het up that it hurt. Whereas he had himself firmly under control. She didn't bother to reply, just reclipped her bra and rebuttoned her shirt calmly, as though that were the kind of thing she did regularly.

'Now,' he murmured, 'just what were we talking about? Remind me.'

'Don't be obtuse, Harrison,' she bit back, goaded by his attitude.

He clapped his hand on to his forehead in mock brainwave. 'Eureka! I've remembered—we were debating the nebulous subject of "it". By "it",' he continued, still in that hateful, mocking voice, 'I assume you want to know whether I will require you in my bed at night? Well, I think we've just demonstrated very effectively what the answer to that is.'

She felt like slapping him in the face as hard as she possibly could, but she was in no position to play the shrinking violet, whose reputation he had besmirched with his words.

But he wouldn't talk to her as though she were…as though…. 'Don't you dare speak to me as though I'm some kind of whore, Harrison. I won't tolerate it.'

He laughed then, but it was a bitter, empty laugh. 'No? But I thought you had your price for everything, Kimberley—or perhaps you prefer to deny that, with the benefit of hindsight?'

She gave a heavy sigh as she remembered what she'd done. Oh, the impetuous behaviour of youth. A crazy stone thrown into the pond, and still the ripples reverberated down through the years. 'You're referring to the money you gave me to stay away from Duncan, I suppose?'

'That was, as I recall, the *only* time I offered you money. And rather a lot of it, too.'

The tension showed in the brittleness of her laugh. 'If only you knew the truth about why I accepted that money, Harrison!'

'Oh, I'd love to. Try me.'

'You'd never believe it in a million years...'

'Try me?' he invited again.

She shook her head. She was weak enough, and if he ever found out about her unrequited love for him it would make her weaker still. How he would play with her if he had any idea of the foolish love she'd harboured for him over all these years. She wondered whether he would ever forgive her for saying that she wanted Georgia adopted. She very much doubted it. And imagine how sweet he could make his revenge if he suspected the true depth of her emotional attachment to him.

'So we still haven't settled the subject of conjugal rights,' he persisted. 'But I'd like to reassure you that it's entirely up to you. I certainly shan't force you.' But the mocking tone spoke for itself—I wouldn't need to! 'Personally,' he continued, 'I would like to make it a marriage in the complete sense of the word.' And his eyes glittered like a stormy sea, sparkling with sexual anticipation, and she had to steel herself not to respond to their compelling light.

Because it could never be a 'complete' marriage,

she thought sadly. Complete marriages meant that there was love, too—and there was no love between her and Harrison. None on his side, anyway—and wouldn't it grind away at her self-respect if she submitted to him? Knowing that she was nothing but a body he found irresistible—and for how long?

'However,' he continued, 'I can quite understand if you find the idea of sleeping with me distasteful. If, for example, you require a little more *variety* in your sex-life than I can provide. But if that's the case, my dear Kimberley, then count me out. I have to tell you that I will not share you. I am not—' his eyes glittered again, but this time with menace, with an underlying threat '—a sharing kind of man. All I would ask is that you be discreet—I won't have our daughter's name sullied by her schoolfriends knowing that her mother is a tramp.'

Kimberley swallowed the bile which had risen in her throat. His regard for her really could sink no lower than it was at the moment.

'Your answer, my dear?' he asked mockingly.

She lifted her small chin proudly. 'You mean, to your very sweetly couched proposal?' she mocked him back.

'The very same,' he agreed gravely.

'It sounds worse than hell.'

'But that depends on your perception, surely?'

'And what's the alternative?' She twisted her hands together in her lap. 'To this farce of a marriage?'

There was a cruel smile. 'No alternative. Leastways, not one which you would find acceptable. If you refuse me, then we go to court and we have one hell of a custody battle on our hands. The costs,' he mused, with deliberate emphasis, 'could be astronomical. Do you think that you could afford to pay them, Kimberley?'

He knew she couldn't. He had her in every which way he could—and he knew that, too.

She stared angrily into the stormy grey eyes.

Some day, she vowed, Harrison Nash would live to regret what he was forcing her into.

CHAPTER NINE

'OH, KIMBERLEY, darling,' said Mrs Ryan wistfully. 'You look absolutely *beautiful*!'

'Do I?' Kimberley stared into the full-length mirror of her mother's bedroom to see a stranger, who looked exactly like her, all dressed up in her bridal finery.

'Mmm. Quite radiant—I can't wait to see Harrison's face!'

I can, thought Kimberley gloomily. The only thing I'm likely to see on Harrison's face is lust. Or contempt. Sometimes, in fact, she was cheered even to see *that*. At least it meant he was reacting to her with his mind rather than just his body.

In the past seven days since she'd been living with him—well, it wasn't exactly living *with* him, more like co-existing separately in the same house—she had barely seen him. He had been working all the hours that God sent. He played for an hour with Georgia early in the morning before he left for work, while Kimberley was still in bed, returning late in the evening, by which time she'd fallen back into bed, exhausted. But at least, she supposed, that cut down on the row situation.

She had been left alone with Georgia and the dreaded Sarah. Sarah who seemed to eat away at her

self-confidence, telling her that everything she did for
Georgia was wrong.

Her prim little face would light up with delight as
she imparted yet another snippet. 'Oh, *no*, Miss
Ryan—' she never missed an opportunity to rub in
Kimberley's single status '—we shouldn't breastfeed
on *demand*! Baby will start to rule the roost, won't
she? And that isn't good for her. Routine—that's
what babies like. Now, why don't you let me bath
her, while you go and put your feet up?'

Kimberley could have screamed, if she'd had the
energy to scream, but Georgia was a fractious baby
at night, waking several times regularly. This, too,
was Kimberley's fault, according to Sarah, because
she didn't give Georgia enough 'firm handling'.

It was all very well having a nanny, thought
Kimberley wearily one night, as she padded bare-
footed from her bedroom to the nursery next door,
but they didn't give a hand during the small hours of
the morning, when you were so tired you felt like
dropping. She had tried to catch up on sleep during
the day, but that was when sleep stubbornly refused
to come, her mind so bound up with the situation she
was in, with wondering why Harrison came in so late
every evening, whether the fact that she had not taken
him up on his offer to share his bedroom had anything
to do with it.

Well, at least Sarah wouldn't be able to look down
her nose at her for being an unmarried mother any
more, because today she and Harrison were getting
married, and in some considerable style, too.

Kimberley had thought it only appropriate—what

with Georgia and all—to have a quick ceremony in a register office somewhere in London.

'And I suppose you'd like to pick up a couple of witnesses off the street?' Harrison had snarled. 'Just to *really* devalue it!'

She had tried to be reasonable. 'Well, it's not as though either of us are doing it because we *want* to, is it?'

And a funny little cold expression had creased the handsome face. 'No, of course it isn't, Kimberley.'

He had argued that she had denied her mother her pregnancy, and that being an only child she ought to allow her to participate in the wedding. 'And I know my mother would like to watch us get married,' he had added. 'My brother and Caroline, too.'

Now that had made her feel odd. 'OK,' she'd agreed. 'You obviously want to get married near Woolton.'

'*In* Woolton,' he contradicted.

'But the nearest register office is in—'

'I don't want to get married in a register office, Kimberley,' he had said. 'I want us to get married in a church. The church at Woolton.' He must have seen her disbelieving expression. 'For Georgia,' he had added.

Of course. He would move mountains for that child. If only... She blocked the thought as she stared at her wedding ensemble. There were to be no 'if only's in her life, and the sooner she accepted that, the better.

She had refused point-blank to get married in white—not with a two-week-old baby. Her mother

had talked her into cream, however—and if she had
only known it, the cream silk brought out the faint
roses in her cheeks and warmed her pale skin where
white would have drained it.

It was a simple dress, with a scoop neck and cap
sleeves, and it came to just above the knee. She wore
cream court shoes and a cream hat. The hat was her
one big expense and her one frivolity, and it had cost
more than the dress and shoes put together! It was a
jaunty top hat in cream, from which floated a shoulder-length piece of tulle. She wore her shiny black
hair pulled back from her face in a soft pleat, and the
stark simplicity of the style suited her.

'You look so young,' said her mother wistfully.
'And so innocent.'

'Hardly innocent,' responded Kimberley drily. 'Not
with a two-week-old baby!'

'Little treasure!' said Mrs Ryan fiercely. 'And
don't you worry about that! Nearly everyone does it
this way round these days. It's how you feel about
each other that matters.'

Kimberley paused in the process of applying a light
coat of pink lipstick. She couldn't let her mother carry
on living in cloud-cuckoo-land about her and
Harrison; she really couldn't. 'Mother—about me and
Harrison—'

'I'm so lucky,' her mother almost crooned. 'To
have him for a son-in-law. I really *like* him.' Her still
exceptionally fine blue eyes sparkled with merriment.
'And I always suspected that there was something going on between the two of you—so did his mother.
Especially after the party at their house. That's why

I went to him to find out why you hadn't been in touch. Of course, I can't say that it wasn't a *shock* to find out that it was because you were pregnant, but still... All's well that ends well.'

And Kimberley knew that she would never be able to disillusion her mother about her true relationship with Harrison.

Her mother clipped a pearl hatpin in place. 'You're not having a honeymoon, then?'

'No.' Thank God. 'I'm feeding Georgia, and...' There was no reason to have a honeymoon in a marriage where there was no love involved.

'No matter,' said Mrs Ryan briskly. 'You're fortunate enough to be going back to a beautiful home— a lot of couples don't have that. There'll be time for honeymoons later. I just wish that your father was alive to see you.' She dabbed briefly at her eyes with a lace handkerchief, then pulled her shoulders back in a no-nonsense gesture. 'Come along, now, Kimberley—you don't want to be late for your own wedding!'

And in an attempt to cheer her mother up, and convince her that all was well, Kimberley was able to joke, 'But brides are *supposed* to be late for their own weddings, Mum!'

They walked the short distance to the church, and Kimberley was still smiling at something her mother had said to her when she walked into a church filled to bursting with flowers and saw Harrison waiting for her at the altar. Her heart turned over with love. He had chosen Duncan for his best man, and an intense and narrow-eyed look had come into his face when he'd asked her whether she minded that.

'I don't,' she'd answered. 'But Duncan might.'

But Duncan had not minded. In fact, he had been delighted, and so had Caroline, now his wife.

The buzz of conversation from the small congregation died down as Kimberley appeared in the nave of the church, and Harrison immediately turned round, his face impossibly grave and handsome, the suit he wore emphasising his height, the powerful breadth of shoulder, the long, elegant thrust of his legs. Sitting in the front pew to his right, his mother cradled Georgia, who was decked out for the day in an impossibly frilly white baby dress, bought especially from Harrods for the occasion by her father.

It was moving enough to have her mother give her away, but by the time Kimberley reached the altar and looked up into the serious grey eyes, then down again at Georgia's tiny head, her black hair almost hidden by the matching frilly bonnet, Kimberley was so choked up with emotion that she was unable to speak.

That was when Harrison took her hand and squeezed it, but this only made things worse, until he took a pristine white handkerchief from his top pocket and wiped at the tear which sparkled on her cheek, bending his head to whisper to her.

'You look very, very beautiful.'

And he said it in such a way that the words carried Kimberley through the ceremony. They came outside to a multi-coloured flurry of confetti and she heard some of the comments from some of the villagers who had come to stand at the back of the church to see the bride and groom.

'Why was she crying?'

'Hormones,' came the reply. 'She's only just had the baby.'

'Catch *me* crying, if I was marrying *him*!'

Some of the tension lifted now that the ceremony was over. Kimberley couldn't help it—she giggled, and Harrison looked down at her approvingly.

'That's better! Feel ready to face the reception?'

Not really. She would have preferred to have crept away, with him and Georgia. But perhaps it was better that they *were* going to the reception, since she was feeling very soppy and very vulnerable, and in that state there was no saying what she might do if she was actually left alone with Harrison. Her husband.

So they dutifully ate the magnificent feast of prawns and salmon and strawberries, all washed down with the finest vintage champagne, which Mrs Nash Senior had provided, and served in a marquee in the grounds of Brockbank House.

But, sitting next to Harrison, the baby nestled in the crook of his arm, Kimberley felt on a strange high, and it was nothing to do with the one and a half glasses of champagne she'd drunk. Something had happened to her there in the church, when he had wiped the tear away from her face. She had thought…thought… Thought what? That some deep spark of something approaching affection had flown from his eyes as he had stared down into hers? Or was she simply imagining that the gesture had been redolent of tenderness?

But his voice remained gentle when, after the speeches, he looked down at her with a smile. 'Want to go home now?' he asked.

Home. Her heart was going crazy as she met that soft grey stare. She nodded, her breath catching in her throat. 'I'd better go and get changed first.'

'Don't.' There was the glitter of sexual promise in his eyes as they skimmed over the way the cream silk clung to her full breasts like a second skin. 'I like it.'

Kimberley blushed like an eighteen-year-old. Crazy, *crazy* to let a silly little compliment affect her in this way. 'Thank you,' she said breathlessly. And then, because it seemed the safest thing to say, 'Georgia has been a poppet, hasn't she?'

He nodded. 'Personally, I think she's the best baby in the world, but—like you—I'm rather biased. Come on, let's say our goodbyes. Then I'll put her into the car.'

Fifteen minutes later they were speeding away, Georgia sound asleep in her baby-seat at the back. Harrison sat at the wheel of the large Bentley, Kimberley at his side.

He shot her a look. 'There. That wasn't too bad, was it?'

'No.' She stole a glance at him. 'Thanks.'

'For what?'

'For rescuing me in the church.'

His teeth gleamed white as he smiled. 'I've always liked rescuing maidens in distress.'

'Not much of a maiden,' she said wryly.

'No.' There was a pause. Then he said, in a kind of bitter voice, 'But you were, weren't you?'

Kimberley thought that she must have misheard him. '*What*?' she whispered incredulously.

'I was the first, wasn't I? Your first lover?'

'You mean you knew—all along?'

'Not all along.' She saw the hard mouth twist. 'No. Let's just say that it quickly became evident—'

'Harrison—you don't have to—'

'Oh, but I *do*,' he said bitterly. 'Why the hell didn't you tell me?'

She raised her brows. 'Do you think it would have made any difference?'

He gave her a quick, hard look. 'I'm not in the habit of seducing virgins,' he said. 'But I'd have been a damn sight more careful about contraception if I'd known.'

This hurt badly. It was as good as saying that they would not be here now if he had taken that simple precaution and hadn't she lulled herself, during the reception, into believing otherwise? Fool. Kimberley shut her eyes briefly, before opening them again. Don't get hurt, she willed herself. Or upset. Don't destroy what has been the most honest talk we've ever had with each other.

'But that night, even after you'd found out that I was a virgin, you still assumed that I was protected?' she probed. 'At least, that's what you said at the time.'

His hands tightened on the steering-wheel. 'I assumed that you would have told me if you weren't. Or, at least, that if you found yourself pregnant, you would have contacted me. When you didn't, I naturally took it for granted that we'd been—'

'Lucky?' she put in bitterly, before he could damn her with the word himself.

'I just wish you'd been a little more honest with me at the time.'

'I didn't think it was honesty that you were searching for that evening,' she told him candidly. 'You've always tended to make a lot of assumptions about me, haven't you, Harrison? For example, would you have really believed that I was a virgin if I'd told you?' she asked softly, and heard his long sigh.

'Probably not.'

She shrugged. That, too, hurt. It made her feel like some rapacious little tramp. 'Well, then, there's nothing more to be said, is there?'

'I rather think that there is,' he said quietly. 'I owe you an apology, for one thing.'

She forced a little laugh—it was the kind of brittle laugh she had heard other women use and she found it surprisingly easy to master. 'Forget it. Perhaps I should be flattered that you considered me so sexually experienced that it didn't occur to you that I might be otherwise.'

'As I think I told you once before—you seem to bring out the worst in me.'

'Oh, well, that's the way of the world,' she answered lightly. 'And, as I once told *you*—the feeling's entirely mutual.'

'I'm sorry,' he said simply.

She heard the self-recrimination in his voice, but she was honest enough to know that there had been no coercion on his part and she could not let him carry all the blame.

'Don't be. I love Georgia to bits.'

'And so do I.' His voice was very soft. 'And thank you, Kimberley.'

She paused in the act of removing her hat. 'What for?'

'For having her.'

She frowned. 'Meaning?'

'That there was always an alternative—which most people would perhaps have considered the more sensible option, given the circumstances.'

'Then it's a good thing I'm not most people,' she answered, but it was an effort to keep her voice steady, because that one very important compliment had gone a long way towards banishing some of the anger she felt towards him.

She saw him glance over at her again. 'What did you do with the cheque I gave you?' he asked suddenly.

Kimberley was astounded by his question, and apprehensive about his reasons for asking it. 'I cashed it,' she said.

'Yes, I know that—but what did you do with the money?'

'Why?'

He shrugged. 'Curiosity.'

'I spent it on expensive holidays and clothes,' she lied wildly.

'The truth!' he bit out tersely.

And now Kimberley was curious, too. 'And how do you know it isn't the truth?'

'Let's just call it a gut feeling.'

Kimberley sighed. 'I gave it away—to charity.'

'All of it?'

'Every penny!'

He nodded his head very slowly, as if he'd just worked out the answer to some ongoing and irksome problem. 'I should have guessed.'

'And why should you have?' whispered Kimberley, feeling that she, too, was on the brink of some tremendous discovery.

He shrugged. 'You have a particularly stubborn kind of pride, Kimberley—one which does not go hand in hand with accepting bribes.' Then he frowned. 'But why did you take it in the first place?'

To get him off her back, of course. But if she told him that he might draw his own conclusions as to why. Her mind cast around for a convincing alternative. 'Because I was angry with you—insulted that you thought you could buy me off. I thought I'd make you suffer—financially, at least. So I took your money from you and gave it away.'

Those intelligent grey eyes were too damned perceptive, she thought as she pretended to fiddle with the catch of her cream clutch-bag.

'But if you were simply angry with me then the most effective thing you could have done would have been to go ahead and marry Duncan.'

'But I couldn't marry Duncan. Not once I discovered that I was so…' She chose her next words carefully. 'Sexually attracted to you.'

He said nothing in reply, but she saw him give another small nod as he drove on, quite fast but very carefully. There was a more companionable silence between them as the powerful car ate up the miles, and she was aware that a truce, of sorts, had been unspokenly declared.

Kimberley felt an excitement growing within her. Didn't that conversation symbolise some kind of hope? His honestly spoken apology had warmed her—and his recognition that going ahead and having the baby on her own had not been the easiest option. And he had, it seemed, credited her with the integrity of not accepting his cheque simply for financial gain.

On such a basis was there not room for respect and liking to grow? And these, hand in hand with the dynamite of their sexual chemistry, wouldn't these be enough to become the foundations of a satisfactory marriage—if not the love-locked union her heart yearned for?

Should she allow their wedding-day to draw to its natural conclusion? Should she allow him to make love to her tonight? Kimberley gave a little shiver of excitement. Could she honestly say no to him?

It was almost seven when they arrived back in Kew, but as they drew up outside the large, imposing house all her old insecurities about him came flooding back. Kimberley felt a sudden sense of shyness as Harrison switched the engine off, wondering where they went from here, afraid to look him in the eye in case she discovered that the qualities she had attributed to him in the car had all turned out to be figments of her imagination. She was therefore ridiculously pleased when Georgia gave a little squawk of protest.

'She must be hungry,' she said hastily, and leapt

out of the car to open up the back door. 'I'd better feed her.'

He followed her, and when she turned and saw the grim set of his face her heart sank, but she felt a certain sense of relief too. She thanked her lucky stars that she hadn't allowed a false sense of security to lull her into doing something foolish, like letting him know how she felt about him. And, if she was being brutally honest, if she allowed their relationship to become properly intimate would she really be able to stop herself from telling him?

She remembered how she'd been that night of the party—she'd had to force herself not to smother him with soft and soppy words—and that had been just *one* night. Imagine every night. In his arms. The act of love. She'd be bound to slip up and tell him she loved him, and where would that lead her? A declared one-sided relationship would surely be doomed? She knew what happened to unrequited love; everyone did. The ones who loved lost all their self-respect, and the objects of their love eventually despised them for their devotion.

Waiting for them in the hall, her hands primly clasped in front of her waist, stood Sarah—her blonde hair gleaming, her brown and white uniform crisply pressed as she held her arms out for Georgia.

'Congratulations,' she said in her rather colourless voice, her eyes, as always, fixed steadily on Harrison.

'Thank you, Sarah,' he said, his deep voice warming in a smile, and Kimberley felt an acute stab of jealousy as Sarah gazed back at him.

'Mrs Caithness has laid out a cold dinner for two in the small dining-room, as you ordered, sir.'

Which was what a real honeymoon couple might have done, thought Kimberley—eaten a meal together and gone upstairs to make love.

But the difference was that this was all farce. And if she hadn't been so certain that she couldn't play-act indifference towards him—especially not tonight, after the heightened emotion of the marriage cere-mony—then maybe she might have gone through with it.

But, being forced to hide her feelings from him, she would simply have felt like a lamb being fattened up for the sacrifice.

She found herself staring into a pair of quizzical grey eyes. 'Well, Kimberley?'

A simple enough question, but she knew that it had many shades of meaning. He was asking her yes or no, and her answer had nothing to do with the meal he'd had prepared.

'I'm not hungry,' she answered coolly. 'And I must see to the baby.' And, so saying, she took Georgia from Sarah's arms and mounted the stairs towards the nursery, unable to miss the hostile fire which flamed in the depths of those smoky grey eyes or, indeed, the smug little smirk of triumph which Sarah flashed in Harrison's direction.

'But what shall I do with all the food?' she heard Sarah asking plaintively.

'Do what you want with it.' She heard his indif-ferent reply. 'I'm going out!'

And the last thing she heard was the front door closing behind him.

CHAPTER TEN

KIMBERLEY had realised the mistake she had made within hours.

The day following the wedding she stumbled blearily down to breakfast, Georgia having woken several times during the night, but even if she hadn't done it wouldn't have made any difference, since Kimberley hadn't been able to sleep. She'd spent a miserable night in her old room, lying awake and listening for the sound of Harrison returning home. But he hadn't returned home.

Just after midnight she had crept downstairs, thinking that perhaps he might have come in and fallen asleep in the drawing-room, but there had been no sign of him. Even though she'd eaten nothing since the reception she had felt too sick at heart for food, but she had been very thirsty, and something had made her look into the dining-room to see whether Sarah had removed the food. She had.

Kimberley had felt tears prickle the back of her eyes as she'd seen the beautiful spray of white roses, stephanotis and freesia in the centre of the table—it looked so very bridal. Had Harrison chosen that? she wondered. Kimberley had sighed, thinking what a mess everything was.

She had just been turning to go when she'd seen a slim silver-wrapped package lying at one of the two

142

places, and, her curiosity alerted, she had moved closer and seen that the small card attached to it bore her name.

She had hesitated for only a moment, then, with trembling fingers, she had torn the paper off. Inside had been a navy leather box stamped with the name of one of London's most exclusive jewellers. She had flipped the top off, and there—dazzlingly bright against the black velvet of the interior—had been a necklace of diamonds and aquamarines—starry and spectacular and utterly beautiful.

Kimberley had closed the box and held it over her heart. Why had he bought her such a gift? So costly and so exquisite. As a peace-offering? She'd closed her eyes, knowing that she had spoiled it all, and, after fetching herself a glass of milk from the kitchen, had crept miserably back upstairs to her room, the box still clutched in her hand, to lie awake, still listening for him.

And, apart from Georgia waking for her feeds, the night had been one of long silence.

This morning Harrison was sitting at the table in the dining-room, drinking coffee and eating eggs and reading the financial pages of the newspaper. He barely looked up when she entered the room.

'Good morning,' said Kimberley.

He barely glanced at her. The grey eyes were cold as a winter's sea. 'Is it?' he mocked.

Kimberley tried very hard to behave normally. She fetched herself some scrambled eggs from the silver tureen on the side, added a few mushrooms and a slice of toast, sat down and poured herself some coffee. Then she smiled at him, but met no answering response. His features might have been hewn from granite, they were so uncaring and so unresponsive.

She drew a deep breath. 'I—saw the necklace you left for me. It's very beautiful,' she said.

'Forget it,' he said dismissively.

'No, really—'

'If you'd prefer some other stones, then you can always exchange it,' he said. 'Or sell it,' he added insultingly.

Kimberley almost gasped aloud at the venom in his voice. He'd been cold with her in the past but never this cold. She had turned down his intimate supper last night, and his gift. Had he, then, she wondered with a sickening lurch of her heart, gone out to find solace in the arms of someone else? Clamping down the murderous jealousy which flooded hotly through her veins, she clenched her trembling hands on her lap beneath the heavy damask of the white tablecloth, where he could not see them. She had to know. She *had* to know.

She narrowed her blue eyes at him. 'You didn't come in last night,' she said, in a voice which was remarkable for its steadiness.

'That's right,' he drawled.

'May I ask where you went?'

'You may not.'

'Did you—did you sleep with somebody else?' she blurted out, then cringed at the total lack of pride inherent in her question.

'Why,' he drawled mockingly, 'should that concern you? You don't want me, do you, Kimberley? Or rather, you *do*—you're just not honest enough to admit it. Perhaps you like playing games; maybe it turns you on to dangle your sexual favours. But I'm not into games, and I'm not your plaything. Fight the attraction all you like—but don't for one moment imagine that you're going to condemn me to a life of celibacy.'

His brutal frankness took her breath away. She stared at that cold, handsome face, at the icy chips of his hard, cruel eyes, and at that moment she really and truly hated him, with a strength of feeling which left her speechless but which showed in the frosty glitter of her blue eyes.

'You—*brute*,' she accused him in a hollow whisper. 'You absolute brute.'

He actually laughed. 'What's that—cue for the brute to demonstrate his brutishness by pulling the fastidious Kimberley into his arms and taking her by force? That would solve your problem for you, wouldn't it, my dear, and salve your conscience? You could have all the pleasure without having been weak enough yourself to actually *admit* that you wanted it. Well, sorry, sweetheart—but I'm not taking the bait.' He pushed his chair back and rose from the table.

'I'm going away for a week on business,' he said harshly. 'And while I'm away you might like to consider when you want to go back to work. I don't imagine, given the current state of affairs between us, that you want to hang around the house any more than you have to.'

She stared at him incredulously. 'You mean you're

happy for us to live like *this*—constantly bickering and squabbling?'

His hard, cynical mouth twisted. 'Happy? Hardly the word I would use. No, Kimberley, I'm not happy. But you're the one who has chosen to live like this. Remember that. And don't try leaving while I'm away. At least, not with Georgia. I told you—I want my daughter, and I'll do anything to keep her.'

Kimberley swallowed. 'Very well,' she said steadily. 'I'll be here when you get back.' And she couldn't damp down the desire to try and hurt him as much as he had hurt her. 'And, as you seem to have acquired yourself a bed-partner, I'll have to start looking around myself.'

His eyes darkened. 'Not in this house, you won't,' he threatened.

'No. I won't do that. I'll just stay out all night, as you did.'

A muscle worked angrily in the side of his face. 'And I suppose that dear James is to be the lucky recipient of your desires, is he?' he ground out.

And two could play at this game, Kimberley decided. 'That really has nothing to do with you,' she answered coolly.

He stared at her for a long minute, passion and fire and fury making the grey eyes smoulder, and she thought that he *was* about to stride across the room and start making angry love to her. Then he abruptly made a curse and turned his back on her. But at the door he paused, and when he turned around again his face was perfectly composed.

'Oh, I meant to tell you. The evening after I arrive

back, I've decided to hold a party here. It'll give some of my friends a chance to meet you, since you refused to allow any of them to come to the wedding. They've been asking me why I'm keeping you hidden away.' His mouth twisted. 'If they only knew.'

She lifted her head proudly. 'And presumably they don't?'

'No. And I'd like to keep it that way.' He paused. 'I want you to be my hostess.'

He made it sound like a whore, but she bit back her angry reply. She was going to have to come up with some kind of solution to what was promising to be an intolerable living situation, and much more anger and recrimination between them was not going to solve anything.

And all this bitterness seemed to stem from her refusal to dine with him last night.

Why?

It couldn't just be the physical thing. It just couldn't. A man like Harrison could have just about any woman he wanted. And he had done, she thought, with angry desperation. Last night. And he would go on doing so, just as long as she held him at arm's length.

If only she had the strength to leave here, to see if he really would fight her in the courts for Georgia's custody. Surely as a mother she held most of the cards?

But she didn't have the strength, and she wasn't at all sure that the reason had anything to do with the costs or publicity incurred by a court case.

He was regarding her quizzically. 'So you'll be at the party?' he enquired softly.

'Yes, Harrison,' she echoed on a sigh. 'I'll be at the party.'

CHAPTER ELEVEN

IT WAS a Friday afternoon, exactly seven days later, and Kimberley was sitting in the magnificent yellow drawing-room, which overlooked the beautiful gardens at the back of the house, when she heard the front door slam shut.

'Hello?' came the deep sound of Harrison's voice.

She took a huge, huge breath. She had had a lot of time on her hands for thinking during those seven days—she had decided what her strategy was going to be, and she was going to stick to it. The time for conciliation was long overdue.

'I'm in here,' she called.

She heard his footsteps moving towards her, and then the door opened and he stood there looking down at her, where she was curled up on the tartan sofa, a magazine by her side, Georgia at her feet, asleep in her tiny chair.

She stared back at him, trying not to feast her eyes on him. As always, just the sight of him did strange things to her heartrate; it was as though he electrified the whole atmosphere of a room just by being in it.

He'd left in a suit, but now he wore jeans. The jeans were very old and faded, and fitted so snugly to his buttocks and thighs that they might have been sprayed on. A white T-shirt was tucked into the jeans, and it clung lovingly to the muscles which rippled in his upper chest and arms. His hair was ruffled and he needed a shave. He looked, she realised, much younger than his thirty-three years—and unbelievably sexy.

The week he'd been gone had seemed like an eternity. She had missed him like hell, although she had wondered how it was possible to miss someone you fought with the whole time.

She, too, was wearing jeans—black jeans with a black T-shirt—and her thick black hair cascaded freely down her back. She hadn't been expecting him back this early, and had planned to change into something a little smarter, but now she was glad she hadn't done. She would have felt a fool. She saw his eyes flicker to the swell of her breasts, felt them tingle into life.

On the other hand, she thought, this T-shirt was awfully clingy, and maybe that hadn't been such a good idea either. Kimberley crossed her arms over her chest protectively, and she saw the sardonic curve of his mouth.

His eyes softened as he looked down at his daughter, fast asleep and sucking her thumb in her little baby-chair. 'She's grown,' he observed, shaking his head a little. 'Incredible. Only a week, and she's changed.'

Her heart turned over at the tenderness written on his face, and she nodded. 'Yes. She's put on weight,' she said proudly, wondering whether this was the shape of things to come. Polite little platitudes about their daughter—just about their only neutral ground, really.

He was frowning. 'Something's different.'

She waited.

'She doesn't usually sleep down here.'

'No, that's right.' Because Sarah had insisted that she always take her nap in her nursery.

He looked around the room. The bright pink teddy he'd sent from France was sitting on the sofa next to an orange rabbit his brother and Caroline had bought for the baby. They clashed like crazy, but Kimberley was certain that Georgia loved them. People said that babies didn't recognise things until they were six weeks old, but she didn't believe them—not babies as intelligent as Georgia, anyway!

Harrison smiled when he saw the teddy. 'And there are more of her toys down here than usual.'

Another of Sarah's edicts. Kimberley could just hear her prim little voice. 'We don't want the house looking like a kindergarten, do we? Not for Mr Nash coming home!'

'Where's Sarah?' he asked, suddenly and perceptively.

She could justify exactly what she'd done, but her heart beat faster all the same. 'I've fired her,' she said calmly.

He looked at her as though he'd misheard. 'You've done *what*?' he demanded.

'I've fired her.'

'Would you mind telling me why?'

'Sure. I didn't agree with her way of bringing up babies.'

He raised his eyebrows. 'And you're the expert, I suppose?' he enquired sarcastically. 'On babies?'

'Yes, I am, actually, Harrison—with this particular baby, certainly. Besides, I've been reading books on the subject all week. Four of them, actually.'

He was staring at her in bemusement. 'Four books and she knows more than a girl who spent two years training?'

'Yes!' she snapped, conciliation forgotten for the moment. 'I *want* to demand-feed, and I *do* want to pick her up when she cries. And what I *don't* want is to hide away all signs that she exists. She happens to live here, too—and I don't believe that babies shouldn't be seen and shouldn't be heard! But, more than that—and I'm sorry if this offends you Harrison—I didn't happen to like Sarah. I thought she was prim and smug and narrow-minded, and not particularly intelligent. And if you think that I'm going to let someone like that bring my daughter up, well— I'm not, basically.' She paused for breath, wondering how he'd take it.

'Wow,' he said softly. 'That's some speech!'

'And I mean every word of it.'

'I can see that.'

'And you don't mind?'

He shrugged the broad shoulders. 'It isn't me it will affect, is it? It's you. So, tell me, are you planning to replace Sarah with someone who isn't prim and smug and narrow-minded? Or had you intended to take her into the office with you?'

And now it was time for her next bombshell. 'I'm not going back to the office.'

'*What*?' he asked in disbelief.

'I'm taking some time off—to bring Georgia up.'

'But your career is very important to you,' he pointed out.

'So is she,' she said quietly.

'And what are you going to do all day? Bake bread?'

She found herself giggling, still high with the excitement and amazement of it all—of discovering that this was what she really *wanted* to do. 'I might,' she said. 'As well as making play-dough. There will also be long walks and finger-painting—'

He held his hand up, but there was a glint of amusement lighting his eyes. 'Enough! I get the idea. And if it's what you want—'

'It is.' She saw him frown. 'If it bothers you that I won't be earning—'

The beautiful grey eyes narrowed, and the amused glint became a distant memory. 'I don't give a damn about that,' he said roughly.

And then, perhaps because they had exhausted the subject of Georgia, he moved away, his shoulders tense. 'You haven't forgotten the party, have you?'

In truth, she'd scarcely given it a thought. 'No, of course not,' she said stiffly.

'I've organised for our guests to arrive at seven-thirty for eight tomorrow evening. The caterers will be here most of the afternoon. Does that suit you?'

Kimberley swallowed. She hated that formal tone he could adopt, as though she were someone he'd just met at a cocktail party and not the mother of his child. 'Perfectly,' she answered coolly. 'Can you give me a rough idea of numbers?'

'There will be about fifty,' he said curtly. 'But you

won't need to do anything. I've had my secretary send out invitations—she's arranged everything through the office.'

'How nice,' said Kimberley nastily. 'I'm surprised that you didn't ask *her* to be your hostess for you.'

'I damn well wish that I had done!' he ground out, then, with an effort, he seemed to gain some ascendancy over his temper, so that when he spoke again it was very slowly—as though he were explaining something to a simpleton. 'I thought that you'd be too tired, and too tied up with the baby to want to go to the trouble of organising a party.'

It was as though he'd retreated from her, thought Kimberley. She might have been some servant or some underling from the way in which he addressed her.

'And is it to be formal?' she asked.

'Black tie,' he told her. 'And now, if you'll excuse me, I must go and change.'

'Will you—?' She forced herself to ask it. 'Will you be in for dinner tonight?'

He shook his head. 'I'm eating out. I thought that you'd probably prefer it.' And he left the room without another word.

Kimberley watched him leave, her neck and back held stiff and proud, determined that he shouldn't find out that she had asked Mrs Caithness to leave them something easy for supper—something which she could heat up herself. She had planned, or rather hoped, for a companionable meal together. But it seemed that she was being given no chance to achieve that.

*   *   *

The following evening she was as nervous as a schoolgirl going to her first ever party as she got ready. Would his friends, naturally curious to meet her, see that he was unhappy? And would they understandably blame her for that unhappiness?

After she'd fed Georgia, bathed and changed her and settled her down in her cot for the night, Kimberley turned her attention to her appearance.

She spent ages deciding what to wear, eventually choosing the most dramatic outfit in her wardrobe. To hell with it! She'd had it made up on a business trip to Hong Kong, and had never seen anything like it in England. The tiny chemise top and long, flowing skirt were in vibrant turquoise silk—material as soft as a sigh, which fluttered against her breasts and long legs. The matching matador jacket and wide cummerbund were in a patterned silk brocade in the same turquoise teamed with jade-green and swirls of kingfisher-blue.

Her hair was fixed into a dramatic topknot, kept in place with two silver combs studded with tiny turquoise chips. She did her make-up dramatically too— with kohl pencil outlining her almond-shaped ice-blue eyes and a bold sweep of a deeper blue eyeshadow emphasising their unusual pale colour. Even her lips looked fuller than usual after she'd carefully painted them with coral gloss.

She stepped back from the mirror, satisfied with her appearance, but slightly in awe of the sophisticated image which stared back at her. But at least from the look of her no one would have any idea that inside she was as nervous as hell about meeting Harrison's friends.

She had had nothing to do with the preparations; Harrison and his secretary had seen to all that. And how! There were people to serve the drinks and people to take the guests' coats. The food would be cooked and served by professional caterers. They had even arranged for a florist to arrange blooms in every one of the five reception rooms.

'And what do you want me to do?' Kimberley had asked him over lunch.

'Just be there,' he'd said briefly, but his face had been so cold that she'd wondered if he wanted her there at all.

But when she came down the staircase, to find him waiting for her in the entrance hall, his eyes narrowed as he took in her appearance, and something in the humourless upward tilt of his mouth made her wonder if she was completely overdressed.

'Is this OK?' she asked.

'Perfectly OK,' he answered, his voice becoming less of a whisper, more of a threat. 'That is if you don't mind every man in the room wondering whether the body underneath all that silk could possibly be as exquisite as it promises. But perhaps that was your intention—to have every hot-blooded male under the age of ninety lusting after you.'

'You're hateful,' she mumbled, and was half inclined to run back upstairs and seek refuge in her little black dress when there was a loud peal on the doorbell.

'Smile, Kimberley,' he ordered softly. 'And let's play newlyweds.'

Soon all the staff hired for the evening were hard

at work, and within half an hour all the guests had arrived and were being served with champagne and canapés in the drawing-room.

Although it was early September, the weather had been so glorious that the newspapers were calling it another Indian summer, and the large French windows at the back of the house had been opened on to the garden.

Harrison introduced her to a stream of people, including his secretary, Anne Lyons—and Kimberley despised herself for the relief which flooded over her when she discovered that not only was Anne a Mrs but a grandmother too! There were men Harrison had been to boarding-school with, and others he'd known at various stages of his climb up the corporate ladder. There were people from the States, and from Europe, too. Most of them with partners.

And there were women on their own, as well. Women who smilingly took Kimberley's hand and congratulated her—some more genuinely than others. Including a strikingly statuesque young model in her early twenties called Tania who Kimberley recognised immediately—she'd broken all records for the number of magazine covers her face had graced that year. Close up, the girl was even more stunning than she appeared in photographs, with waist-length hair the colour of a glossy brown conker and the most amazing long-lashed violet eyes.

Kimberley could sense the model's antagonism towards her immediately, although it was reasonably well-hidden by the huge flashing smile with its perfect teeth. But as the evening wore on Kimberley could see something in the way the younger woman monopolised Harrison—or maybe it was him monopolising her.

And suddenly she knew.

The glass of champagne she had raised to her lips remained untasted as realisation, stark and brutal, made itself clear to her. She knew by the way Tania darted him her saucy smile, and by the way he jokingly pretended to pull her hair, bending his head to listen to something she said. Something in their body language spoke volumes, and she knew with a blinding instinct which ripped at her heart like a newly sharpened sword that there had been intimacy between them.

Had been?

Her world blurred out of focus as she realised that the past tense might be inappropriate.

That night he'd stayed out—had he stayed with Tania? This week he'd been away—had his 'business' been spurious? Kimberley closed her eyes and almost swayed, terribly afraid that she might do something really stupid, like faint.

And then, delicate as some beautiful wraith, Tania suddenly appeared by her side, looking down at the full glass of champagne which Kimberley was clutching like a lifeline.

The violet eyes glittered like costly amethysts. 'Hey, you've been nursing that glass all evening! Not in the party mood?'

Kimberley shook her head. 'I'm a little tired,' she answered, trying not to sound as though her world was threatening to crumble around her.

As if of one accord, they both looked to where Harrison stood, saying something to a group of people, effortlessly dominating not just the group who were listening to him with rapt attention but the entire party. He stood out among every other man there—and what woman wouldn't want him? thought Kimberley with a sinking heart.

'He's mine, you know,' came the softly spoken threat beside her, and Kimberley stared at Tania in amazement, certain that she had misheard what the model had said.

'I'm sorry?'

'No, you heard right,' said Tania nonchalantly. 'I was just warning you off.'

'But I'm married to him,' said Kimberley quietly. 'Remember?'

'Are you?' the girl challenged, her bottom lip pouting in a way that should have looked truculent but instead managed to look very, very provocative. 'You don't act like you're married. Harrison's so uptight, he looks as though he might snap—and you've hardly talked to him all night.'

'I'm married to him,' said Kimberley again, her voice dignified. But her hands were shaking.

The beautiful violet eyes were suddenly made ugly by the expression in them. 'Yeah, you're married to him. Know why? Because of the baby. And because possession is nine-tenths of the law, and a father who has never even lived with his daughter doesn't have much say. Harrison figures that pretty soon your life will be so miserable you'll be glad to walk away—and this way he'll have clout in court, when it comes to custody.' She smiled. 'Then he'll come running to me,' she finished on a soft threat.

Kimberley managed somehow not to flinch, then, very deliberately, she turned her back on the model and walked to the end of the garden, a smile fixed to her face, afraid to stop moving in case she broke down and made the most appalling scene.

She found herself the seclusion of the rose-bower, hiding in its sweetly scented shade, letting her cheek rub against the velvety petals of a late pink bloom while she willed her thundering heart to slow down and the dizzy, sick feeling at the pit of her stomach to go away, so that she could put her troubled thoughts into some kind of order.

From here she could watch, unobserved, as Tania picked her way across the lawn and joined Harrison's group, immediately convulsing into a fit of giggles at something he was saying. And Kimberley knew that she could no longer carry on ignoring the situation she was in.

Things between them were fast becoming unbearable. Harrison had laid the rules down at the very beginning. A marriage without its physical side meant that he would look elsewhere. And could she bear that?

Never.

She loved him; indeed, she had always loved him. There had never been anyone else, and she knew herself well enough to know that there never would be.

He, on the other hand, seemed to despise her when he wasn't lusting after her body.

But...

Again her mind flew back to the day of the wedding—his gentleness towards her in the church, the conversation in the car, which had cleared the air, paved the way for a tentative truce. And perhaps, if it hadn't been for her highly emotional state and the sight of Sarah standing waiting for them, she might have done the most sensible thing and had supper with him and gone to bed with him—and they could have started off the marriage so differently.

It was not what she wanted; the question was whether it would be enough.

She stared through the gathering darkness at the tall and lithe form of him, head and shoulders above all the other men—and in more ways than just stature. She remembered the way he'd stayed with her during labour, his compassion in refusing to let her face that on her own. And he had done that knowing that she had kept his child a secret from him.

The question was—did she have the courage to show him that she wanted him, that she was prepared to change?

And then she saw Tania affectedly sweeping her hair back off her brow—her tiny black velvet mini-dress barely skimming her pert little bottom—and Kimberley's heart hardened.

Harrison was *her* man, and she knew how much he wanted her. She knew that in his arms she had a strange kind of power over him—as much as he had over her.

And tonight she had the perfect opportunity to show him, to show his friends—to show scheming little wannabes like Tania—that Harrison was spoken for.

She drank the glass of champagne quickly, and as the rush of the dry cold bubbles went fizzing throughout her bloodstream she strolled back through the garden.

She knew that people watched her—it was perfectly normal that they should watch the hostess, the woman who had married their friend—and she knew the precise moment when Harrison's grey eyes joined theirs, knew by the prickle of the tiny hairs at the back of her long neck and the shiver of anticipation which crept up her spine. Very deliberately she stared back at him, then raised her empty glass in toast.

Unselfconsciously, heady with the excitement of what she was planning to do, she stood alone, proud and beautiful as a statue, allowing her glass to be filled with mineral water and sipping it. And her eyes never left Harrison's handsome and mobile face.

She knew that he carried on speaking but that his thoughts were elsewhere—on her. She must only have stood there on her own for seconds, and yet time and time again she was aware of his eyes raking over her, questioning, probing.

In a couple of minutes two men and their wives joined her, complimenting her on the party, and she was chatting easily to them when, out of the corner of her eye, she saw Harrison move away from his group and come over to join them.

'Hello, darling,' she murmured.

It was a term of affection she had never used before, exactly the kind of thing which a newly married woman might say to her husband, and yet, not surprisingly, he frowned, and she saw the light of challenge fire in the back of the magnificent grey eyes.

She met the challenge full-on, her blue eyes widening with an unmistakable message, and she heard the soft inrush of his breath, felt the immediate flowering of her body as she saw his eyes darken with the same message he must have read in hers.

She wanted to leave the group and she wanted to take her jacket off, since tiny beads of sweat had formed on her forehead, but she didn't dare. She knew that her nipples were as erect and as excited as if he were actually caressing them, but she remembered, too, his earlier words, about her outfit enticing others. She didn't want him to think that. This was for him— all for him. No one else.

She didn't say anything; she didn't have to. Every fibre of her being spoke the message for her. She didn't know for how long they stood there, just that the need to have him touch her had grown so overpowering that she knew she would have to do something soon, or die.

She saw the tense lines of his face, the corded bunching of the muscles at his neck, and knew that he felt it too. She put her arm through his and rested her head against his shoulder. 'Can I talk to you for a moment?' she murmured, so that only he could hear, but the sultry tone of invitation was evident.

He tensed. Seemed to hesitate. But only for a moment. 'Please excuse us,' he said smoothly to the two couples, who were tactfully carrying on their conversation, seemingly unaware of the sexual currents which were fizzing and sizzling between the two of them.

As soon as they were out of earshot he dipped his head to speak softly into her ear. 'Shall we go for a walk around the garden?'

'No,' she said, in a low voice.

'But you wanted to talk?'

'Not here,' she said urgently, desire threatening to overwhelm her while her courage threatened to flee. 'Inside!'

He heard the note of raw hunger which deepened her voice to a husky whisper, took one look at her tense, white face, her eyes looking huge and dark in contrast, and unlinked her arm, placed her hand very firmly in his, and took her towards the house.

She was unable to speak, but Harrison paused now and then to exchange a word with their guests. To an outside observer they might just have been doing the kind of thing which party-givers always had to do, no matter how much help they had—checking that everything was running smoothly—but Kimberley thought she saw Tania start when she observed the feral glitter in Harrison's eyes as he led her inside the house after what had been the longest walk of her entire life.

He led her straight into his study, then let her go and turned to face her, his face as non-commital as a judge's.

'Well, Kimberley?'

He wasn't, she realised, going to give her any help at all. She swallowed convulsively.

'You said that you wanted to speak to me,' he observed coolly.

He gave the impression of having little time, or patience, and Kimberley made up her mind. There was no way she could back out of this now.

Casually she strolled over to the door, locked it, and put the key on his desk.

He raised his eyebrows but still said nothing.

She thought of what some women might do in this situation—a slow and seductive striptease, which would send him out of his mind—but she scotched that idea immediately. Her heart was thundering so loudly in her chest and her hands trembling so much that she knew there was only one thing in the world she could do, and she went over to him, raised herself up on tiptoe, put her arms around his neck and kissed him.

There was an infinitesimal second when rejection seemed a very real possibility, when the hard, sculpted lines of his mouth remained passive beneath the soft caress of her lips. But it was no more than the briefest fragment of time, and he reached his arms out to encircle her slender waist, deepening the kiss so sweetly and so provocatively that Kimberley melted under the onslaught.

They explored each other's mouths as though it was the first time they had ever kissed—and in a way perhaps it was, thought Kimberley, through the hot mists of passion and desire. For in that kiss was a new understanding—born of mutual need, mutual honesty and, for Kimberley at least, commitment. And not just a commitment that she would end up in his bed that night, but much more than that—a commitment that she would give the marriage a real go. And who knew what would happen if they both did that?

His mouth never leaving hers, he slipped his hand beneath the turquoise silk of her chemise to find her unfettered breast, cupping it in his hand and smiling against her mouth as he felt her helpless sigh. Her heartrate accelerated as she felt desire pool, then escalate out of control, so that she was pulled helplessly along, caught up in its powerful current.

So it was like being doused with ice-water when he suddenly raised his head and stared down at her shocked, mutinous face, a regretful look in the grey eyes. 'Kimberley,' he said, mock-seriously, 'you are very, very beautiful, and I want you very, very much, but I'm afraid that we'd better postpone this until later, or I'm not going to be in a fit state to go back to our guests.'

For answer, she raised her mouth greedily to his, running her hands deliberately down the white silk of his dress shirt, feeling him move with impatient frustration as she brushed further down, over the flat hardness of his stomach, and even further, where he was harder still...

He tore his mouth away, his words clipped and indistinct, barely recognisable. 'Kimberley, you realise what's going to happen in a minute if you don't—?'

'Yes,' she murmured.

He ground the words out with an effort. 'I'm going to have to take you right now—'

Her breathing was laboured. 'But you're not taking, Harrison,' she managed softly. 'I'm giving.'

He gave a small groan as he cupped her buttocks and gathered her roughly against him, his hands pulling the dress up her long legs impatiently, until it was gathered in rucks over her hips, so that only the tiniest scrap of her satin and lace panties covered her.

Very deliberately he pushed her back against the wall, his fingers moving to find her flowering moistness, and she gave a startled little moan of pleasure.

He caught her mouth again, murmuring something that sounded sweet and indistinct, and she felt him unzipping himself. She whispered her pleasure into his mouth, with soft little cries. His urgency was evident, since he didn't even bother to remove her bikini pants, just impatiently moved the fabric aside and thrust into her with such power that she was sure that consciousness slipped away from her for a second.

She noticed that he had stilled, and she looked up at him, gazing with wonderment into his dazed grey eyes.

'Oh, God, Kimberley,' he said, in a voice which verged on desperation. 'You feel so good.'

'Do I?' Her eyes closed, to hide her longing for softer words than these.

'Mmm.' He moved inside her slowly and she felt colour scorch over her cheeks. 'So *tight*.'

'Do I really?'

'Mmm. You know you do.'

'I thought— *Oh*!' She clung frantically to his shoulders as he thrust against her.

'What?' he murmured provocatively.

'That it would be different—after the baby.'

'It is,' he said softly, still with those great slow sweeps which filled her completely. 'It's even better. But then perhaps it's because it's been so long…'

And suddenly she wanted to shatter his control. She didn't want him to move with that perfect provocation, which showed his consummate skill as a lover. She moved her hips urgently against his, changing the speed.

His eyes flew open. 'Don't—' he warned.

'Don't, what?'

'Don't do—' But he never finished the sentence, for he caught her rhythm and transmuted it into something which defied all description, so that if he was no longer in control then neither was she. She felt the heat building and building, until it became exquisitely unbearable, and the universe shattered and Kimberley found herself sobbing as he lost himself in the same dark whirlpool of fulfilment, her name torn from his lips in a shout which didn't sound at all like Harrison's voice.

They stayed like that, locked in that intimate embrace for a minute or two, and she felt his shoulders shaking. She realised that he was laughing.

'What,' she demanded, 'is so funny?'

He lifted her chin up and stared down into her eyes, his mouth quirking with sensual humour. 'I've never been seduced by a woman before.'

'And did you like it?' she whispered, reaching up to kiss his neck to hide her face, afraid that the lovelight shining from her eyes might blind him.

'What do you think?'

'Want to do it some more?' she murmured.

He gingerly pulled away from her. 'Later, you beautiful and tempting minx.' He looked her up and down as he adjusted his clothing and helped to smooth her skirt down into place.

'You look quite normal, considering...' he mused. 'Your cheeks are a little flushed, of course, and your eyes are very bright. You are, you know, Kimberley, a rather amazing woman.' And he lifted one of her hands to his lips and gently kissed it, and Kimberley felt overwhelmed with love.

'Oh, Harrison,' she said foolishly, breathlessly, her heart still thundering in her ears.

'We'd better get back to the party,' he said softly. 'We can talk later.'

'I really ought to go upstairs and shower,' she said wryly.

'No, don't.' He bent his head to plant a kiss on her mouth. 'Stay exactly as you are, so that every time I look at you I can remember what we've just been doing, and imagine what I'm going to do to you once everyone has gone.'

And he unlocked the door, took her by the hand and led her back to the party.

CHAPTER TWELVE

'So WHAT brought all that on?' Harrison asked as Kimberley came down the stairs. The silk of her long skirt was still vaguely crumpled, and she wondered whether anyone had noticed.

All the guests had gone, all the party debris was cleared away, and the staff had departed too. Kimberley had gone up to check on Georgia, and was about to join Harrison downstairs for a nightcap. If the truth were known, she didn't really want a nightcap—or rather, she didn't want to sit down analysing her wild behaviour of earlier that evening, when she'd taken him into his study and seduced with the single-mindedness of a concubine.

She sat down opposite him and met his steady grey stare reluctantly.

'And don't say "All what?", when you know perfectly well that I'm referring to that extraordinary little scene of a couple of hours ago, which is threatening to put my blood pressure up into dangerous heights just by thinking about it.'

'Harrison, please,' she beseeched, but there was no mercy in his speculative smile.

'Don't go all coy on me, Kimberley,' he murmured. 'I think I rather prefer you taking the initiative.' He got up and poured out two small glasses of calvados and handed her one. 'I repeat—what brought it on?'

A new honesty, she had decided—or rather, as much honesty as their relationship could stand. She knew that the knowledge of her unrequited love would bring about the destruction of their already tenuous relationship in its wake, but there was no reason for him not to know about Tania.

'I spoke to Tania,' she told him, in a colourless voice. 'Or rather—she spoke to me.'

He sipped his drink. The grey eyes were as cool as a glacier. 'Oh?'

'Yes.' Her voice sounded bright. 'She told me—well, lots of things, really.'

'Care to let me in on a few of them?'

'Just that she wanted you. And that we didn't look married. And then I remembered what you said about me not condemning you to a life of celibacy, and I knew what I had to do.'

Some light died in his eyes, leaving them forbiddingly cold. 'You mean—seduce me? In order to stop Tania getting her hooks into me? That was very territorial of you, Kimberley.'

She turned towards him, exasperated now—and confused. 'Well, that was what you wanted, wasn't it?'

His mouth was unsmiling as he rose to his feet with seductive intent written all over his face and moved towards her. 'Yes,' he agreed, a new note to his voice—and she wasn't sure that she liked it very much at all. 'That's what I wanted.'

She stared up at him in bewilderment as he took

the glass from her hand and put it down, then swept her up into his arms, as if he'd been auditioning for a remake of *Gone with the Wind* and carried her up the staircase and into her bedroom.

It was as though he was reasserting his authority and dominance after what had happened earlier—for if she had held the power in their earlier encounter then he certainly had it now, as he slowly but ruthlessly stripped the clothes from her body.

It seemed to be a deliberate demonstration of how he could bring her trembling to the brink, time and time again, until she was half weeping with desperation, and she opened her eyes to see him pulling the black bow-tie off with impatient disregard.

And while he undressed he still touched her, stroked her, every single inch of her, as he efficiently removed the rest of the clothes from his body, keeping her at such an incredible fever-pitch of excitement that by the time he entered her with such magnificent power she climaxed immediately, and tears slid down her cheeks as her body contracted sweetly and helplessly around him.

He must have tasted her tears, for he stopped that delectable thrusting and gathered her in his arms, soothing her and comforting her. 'I'm sorry,' he said into her hair.

She felt an unbearable sorrow scoring jagged fingers over her; she didn't know why—she didn't think she wanted to. 'What for?' she whispered.

'For always wanting to punish you,' he said, a strangely sad note in his own voice, too, and

Kimberley's heart cried out for the love which eluded them, and she put her arms tightly around him.

'I can think of a lot worse kinds of punishment,' she whispered as he began to move again, taking her with him on another incredible but unbearably poignant journey into paradise.

Afterwards, he heard her sigh against his shoulder.

'What is it?'

'You make me feel—'

'What?'

She knew that she could only hint at the depths of the feelings he evoked in her. 'So—helpless, when you make love to me.'

'Do you think that I don't know?' he demanded, and his voice was savage. 'That it isn't the same for me, too?'

They slept then, exhausted, and when she awoke, some time in the night, Harrison had gone.

Things were very different between them after that. Better, but not perfect.

To the outside world they must have presented a united family front. When Harrison came home from work he played with the baby. Then, after she'd been bathed and fed, he and Kimberley would eat dinner together. At weekends, if it was fine, they took her to zoos and parks, even though she was much too young to appreciate it. On wet days they explored museums.

And at night Harrison made exquisite love to Kimberley in her big double bed. But he was never beside her in the morning.

And he remained an enigma to her; still she had

no idea how that razor-sharp mind of his worked. She had imagined—foolishly, perhaps—that the intimacies they shared every night might have brought them closer together, but the tenderness she unaskingly sought still eluded her.

In fact, she thought bitterly, waking one morning to find the rumpled sheets and her tender, bruised breasts and lips the only indication that Harrison had been there last night, making love with him seemed to have had the opposite effect from the one she'd wanted. If anything, Harrison seemed as distant as ever he'd been. If anyone had told her, years ago, that she would have been able to tolerate such a marriage she would have laughed in their faces.

But, amazingly, it was enough for her, and she counted her blessings rather than focus on the fact that what she wanted from Harrison was impossible, that he would never love her as she loved him.

But she had Georgia—she was blissfully happy in her role of mother. And if she couldn't have as much of Harrison as she wanted, well, she would just enjoy what she *did* have.

Until one night, when her world threatened to come crashing around her ears.

Harrison had just returned from Paris after a few days, and Kimberley had missed him unbearably.

Both picked without appetite at their supper, and when they went to bed—much earlier than usual—she was so eager and so hungry for him that she almost tore the clothes from his body, and he seemed to catch alight from her passionate fire immediately. They had never made love like it before. It surpassed every other time—and Kimberley hadn't thought that was possible.

Afterwards, she was reluctant to let him go. Often he made love to her again, straight away, and then he would leave—go back to his own room, leaving her alone and bereft. She'd never asked him why, because she didn't want to hear his answer; deep in her heart she suspected that Harrison was one of those men who considered sleeping together all too intimate, too constricting.

But this time, as he made to pull himself out of her arms, she shook her head.

'Stay,' she murmured sleepily, her voice still slurred with pleasure.

She had wanted the closeness of falling asleep in each other's arms, but to her consternation he had obviously thought she'd meant one thing and one thing only, and he started to make love to her again.

Quickly her doubts were vanquished as the familiar feeling began to seep its way into her body. His hands worked their usual magic, and his kisses elicited a soft trembling which shivered down her body.

Then, just before he entered her, he said the most extraordinary thing. 'Pretend something for me, Kimberley.'

He was an imaginative lover, and she naturally assumed that he wanted her to enact some fantasy for him. 'Anything,' she murmured, her lips at his neck, revelling in the sweet taste of him. 'Anything you want.'

There was a pause. Then, in the oddest voice, he said, 'Pretend that you love me, just for tonight.'

Kimberley stiffened in horror.

What kind of game was he playing with her? Had he guessed? And was he going to torment her with the knowledge that he had known all along of the humiliating inequality in their relationship?

He released her from his embrace contemptuously, and, even though she could see that he was still help-lessly aroused, he moved away from her, sat on the side of the bed and began pulling his jeans back on.

'I want a divorce,' he said abruptly, and Kimberley almost fainted. She had known that her love for him would be treated with scorn, but she hadn't dreamed that it would provoke such utter revulsion.

'What?' she whispered, in a hollow voice.

'You heard me. I want a divorce.' He turned and saw her frowning face. 'Oh, don't worry. I'll be ex-tremely generous.'

Kimberley felt her heart lurch. So Tania had been right all the time. She had said he would go back to her. What was it? Something about possession being nine-tenths of the law, and that he would fight for Georgia. 'But what about the baby?' she asked quickly. She saw his non-comprehending frown. 'Are you going to fight me for her?'

His eyes hardened in response. 'Oh, don't worry— I won't contest custody of Georgia. I won't try and take her away from you. I never meant to, anyway— that was all an elaborate ploy.'

Now he wasn't making sense. What elaborate ploy?

'But I will want reasonable access,' he continued.

Kimberley nodded like an automaton. 'Of course,' she said stiffly, as though her heart weren't shattering into a million tiny pieces. She had to know. 'Is there someone else?' she asked, amazed that she could sound so cool at a moment like this.

'What?'

'That you want—to—to marry?' Not quite so cool now.

He made an impatient little noise. 'No, Kimberley, there's no one else.'

'Then—' She swallowed as he frowned. 'Would you mind telling me why?'

He stared at her as though she had just done something as fundamentally stupid as putting her hand in a fire. 'Twisting the knife, are you?' he enquired sardonically, and then he shook his head in resignation, spoke almost as if to himself. 'Oh, why not? Perhaps you deserve your moment of triumph.'

Moment of triumph? What on earth was he going *on* about? Kimberley was now even more confused, and in a way she was grateful for it, because her churned and puzzled thoughts were preventing her from taking in the unthinkable. That Harrison wanted a divorce.

'I want a divorce,' he said slowly, as if recognising some great truth, 'because I can no longer tolerate living in this kind of marriage.'

Kimberley stared at him, her eyes blank. Of course. 'Oh. I see.'

'I thought that it would work. I hoped… Oh, what the hell! There isn't any use in raking it all up again.'

She tried to be adult—brave. To retain what little dignity she had left. 'I do understand—honestly, I do.

I think...' She hesitated painfully. 'That there has to be love for it to really work.'

He gave her a cold, empty smile. 'Exactly.' And he walked out of the room.

She lay in miserable silence for a time, almost relieved when she heard Georgia cry; at least feeding the baby would take her mind off things.

She fed the baby and changed her, and was just going back to her bedroom when she heard the sound of drawers being opened and slammed closed in Harrison's room. She pushed the door open and looked in, to find that he was throwing clothes haphazardly into a suitcase.

She met his hot, dark look of rage.

'Get out!' he snarled.

'What are you doing?'

'What does it look like?'

'Where are you going? You've only just got back.'

'I'm going,' he ground out, 'to a hotel. If you'd leave me in peace to do my packing.'

'You don't have to go to a hotel.'

'Yes, damn you—I do!'

'But I can take Georgia back to my house tomorrow—' she began, then stopped when she saw the look of black fury on his face.

'And doesn't it occur to you, you heartless little bitch, that it might be traumatic for me to live here once you've gone?'

He meant, of course, without Georgia. 'You'll have to get used to it,' she said, but it hit her hard to think how much he'd miss the baby he adored.

'Skip the patronising!' he gritted. 'And get out! If

I want to stay in a hotel I don't need your permission to do it!'

And every adult and reasonable feeling she'd had died a sudden death as white-hot jealousy hit her like a sledgehammer. 'Why?' she taunted. 'So that you can meet Tania there? Tonight?'

His face, angry before, became positively murderous. 'Do you really think that I'm just going to leap straight from your bed and into Tania's arms?' he demanded.

'Well, you certainly couldn't wait to leap out of my bed night after night, that's for sure!' she said. 'So why shouldn't I think that?'

'Because I'm not interested in Tania—I never have been!'

'That's not what she thinks!'

'Tania's muddled thought-processes are really not my concern,' he said, in a bored, tired tone. 'Or yours. So why don't you do us all a favour, Kimberley, and go back to your own room?'

'You arrogant, horrible, hateful bastard!' she screamed at him. She flew at him, grabbing him by the arms, shocked at how hard and unforgiving the clenched muscles felt beneath her hands.

He didn't move, or react, just stood there with a contemptuous look all over his beautiful, arrogantly handsome face. 'I thought we'd agreed about being honest with one another? If it's sex you're after, Kimberley, then you only have to ask—'

And she burst into floods of tears, ran out and down the corridor, flinging herself on the bed and soaking her pillow within seconds.

'I'm sorry,' came a heavy voice from the doorway.

'Go away!'

'I seem to spend my whole time being foul to you...'

'So—so why do you do it?' she sobbed helplessly.

'You know why.'

'No, I don't.'

'Because we always hurt the ones we love,' he said bitterly, and Kimberley's tear-drenched eyes snapped open and she sat up, staring at him scornfully.

'Don't ever say that to me, Harrison,' she said quietly. 'Insult me if you have to, or hurt me—but never tell me lies. Not about that.'

He gave an ironic laugh. 'Oh, how I wish it were a lie, Kimberley. How uncomplicated my life would have been if I'd never had the misfortune to fall in love with you.'

Her eyes widened to kitten-like proportions. 'What are you talking about?' she said, in a strangled whisper.

'I was doomed,' he said, his mouth twisting with the memory, 'the moment I saw you.' A strange, frightening light flared from the depths of the cold grey eyes. 'How do you think it felt for a man to look on the woman his brother was going to marry and to want her for his own?'

'*What*?'

'Oh, I tried to fight it,' he said bitterly. 'And I managed for about ten seconds. And then I kissed you.'

Colour flooded her pale cheeks as she remembered

the passion and the fervour, still so vivid, even after
all this time.

'When you responded the way you did, an ugly,
jealous and possessive streak sprang to life in me. I
couldn't bear to think of you kissing other men like
that—my *brother* like that.'

The torment on his face was indescribable. 'But I
never kissed anyone like that,' she said. 'Except you.'

He nodded. 'Oh, yes, I realise that now. The trouble
is that it has taken some time for me to understand
and accept that what happens between us physically,
while being very rare and quite amazing, has nothing
to do with love—at least, not on your part.'

This really was fascinating. And very promising.
Kimberley held her breath, surreptitiously pinched her
wrist. Still there.

'I couldn't let you marry him. When I offered you
the money and you accepted it, I felt both defeated
and elated. My worst fears were realised—the woman
I'd fallen in love with was nothing but a mercenary
little tramp—but oh, some day, some day I would
make her mine.'

Charming! She thought that he looked as though
he was about to stop talking. 'Go on,' she urged.

He gave a humourless laugh. 'Why not? As I said
earlier, perhaps you deserve to hear the truth. Where
was I?'

'You were—' she found the glorious words ridiculously difficult to say, '—going to make me yours.'

'Yes.' Then he spoilt it completely by adding, 'Oh,
I convinced myself that it was just your body I was
after.'

Great!

'And I couldn't have you until Duncan had found someone of his own, of course. I didn't want to hurt my brother any more than I could. And I was right about that, as I'd known all along that I would be— Caroline is far more suited to him than you ever would have been.

'I'd planned to come to London to find you, after I'd been to Woolton, when fate played right into my hands with your mother's injured ankle. And then I saw you again, incongruously scrubbing a floor at Brockbank, that black hair spilling all the way down your back, those blue eyes lit with ice-fire, and I knew then that I'd been deceiving myself all along. That I wanted so much more than just your body. I wanted everything.

'The engagement party was my idea. Duncan and Caroline agreed, and it seemed the only way I could entice you anywhere near a social function that *I* would be attending. I'd planned to woo you, to court you. I certainly hadn't planned to take you to straight off to bed...' His voice tailed off in self-recrimination. 'But when I did I thought that I'd found paradise—only to wake up to find you getting dressed, about to creep away without a word, with a look of such distaste on your face that seemed to sum up exactly how you felt about what had happened.'

Kimberley blinked. Had the dream not *come* true— but been reality all along?

'Harrison,' she said softly.

He glared. 'What?'

'I love you.'

He froze, his eyes unmoving as they stared into hers.

'The reason I had such a look of disgust on my face after our night together was that I felt slightly appalled that in my virginal state I had enjoyed having my clothes literally torn off me. I wasn't sure that you'd respect me for that.'

His eyebrows disappeared completely into the thick abundance of his dark hair. 'Not respect you?' he murmured. 'You were every damned fantasy I'd ever had, come startlingly true.' His eyes narrowed. 'Will you please repeat what I thought you said a moment ago?'

She smiled, the happiness beginning to well up inside her. 'I love you, you stupid man—I've always loved you! And I'd have told you a darned sight sooner if you hadn't given such a good impression of seeming to loathe me.'

Was it something in her eyes, or in her voice, or in what she said which really convinced him? She never found out. But she knew the exact moment that he believed her, because he gave a slow, slow smile. 'Loathe you?' he echoed, on a groan. '*Loathe* you? Oh, my darling, darling Kimberley.'

And he moved and so did she, and they were in each other's arms, kissing, hugging, speaking only in half-sentences, all of which began with 'darling' or 'sweetheart'.

They ended up lying in each other's arms, staring into each other's eyes and hugging each other tightly, as if they could never bear to let each other go.

'Why else do you think I accepted your wretched

money?' she demanded. 'Because I thought you hated me, and I knew how much I loved you. I thought that if I was only a mercenary little gold-digger in your eyes you'd never want to see me again!'

'That would,' he said wryly, 'be rather like reaching the summit of Mount Everest and not feeling proud of it!'

'You should write that down!' said Kimberley admiringly.

'You are also,' he said, 'the only woman who could make me so wild for her that all thoughts of contraception just flew out of the window.'

'Not even Tania?' said Kimberley nastily.

He moved to lie on top of her, and the sensation of that hard, lean body sent her senses singing. 'Listen to me,' he said, very gravely. 'My affair with Tania is all in her head.'

'Don't say you couldn't have had an affair with her?'

'Of course I could. I could have had affairs with lots of women. The whole point is that I didn't want to.'

Her eyes narrowed. 'Not at all?'

'Not once. Once I'd seen you...I'm afraid that was it.'

'And if I hadn't had Georgia—?'

'I would still have coerced you into marrying me.'

'And just how would you have gone about that?'

'Oh, I'd have thought of a way, don't worry,' he said with infuriating confidence. 'I was so convinced that we were twin souls, you see. And I was right.'

'Are you always so sure that you're right?' she queried dreamily.

'Mostly. But I thought that I could happily live with you, even if you didn't love me. In that I was hopelessly, hopelessly wrong. I vowed that I'd never spend the night with you until you told me you loved me.'

'Tonight's the night, then,' she murmured, her eyes sparkling with anticipation, but then she grew serious, shivered. 'How close we came to losing it all,' she whispered.

'Don't.' And he kissed her with a tender passion she had only ever dreamed of.

Soon he would make love to her again, and this time neither of them would need to hold anything back, but for the moment she was happy to be held, revelling in the closeness they now shared.

The joy of what lay before them was almost too frightening to contemplate, and they grinned at each other.

'I love you,' they both whispered, at exactly the same moment.

Now, that's *harmony*, thought Kimberley in delight, as she gave herself up ecstatically to his kiss.

MILLS & BOON®

Makes any time special™

Mills & Boon publish 29 new titles every month. Select from...

Modern Romance™   Tender Romance™

Sensual Romance™

Medical Romance™   Historical Romance™

MAT2

0701/05

Wedding Fever

Matrimony on their minds!

Available 6th July

*Available at branches of WH Smith, Tesco, Martins, Borders, Easons,
Sainsbury, Woolworth and most good paperback bookshops*

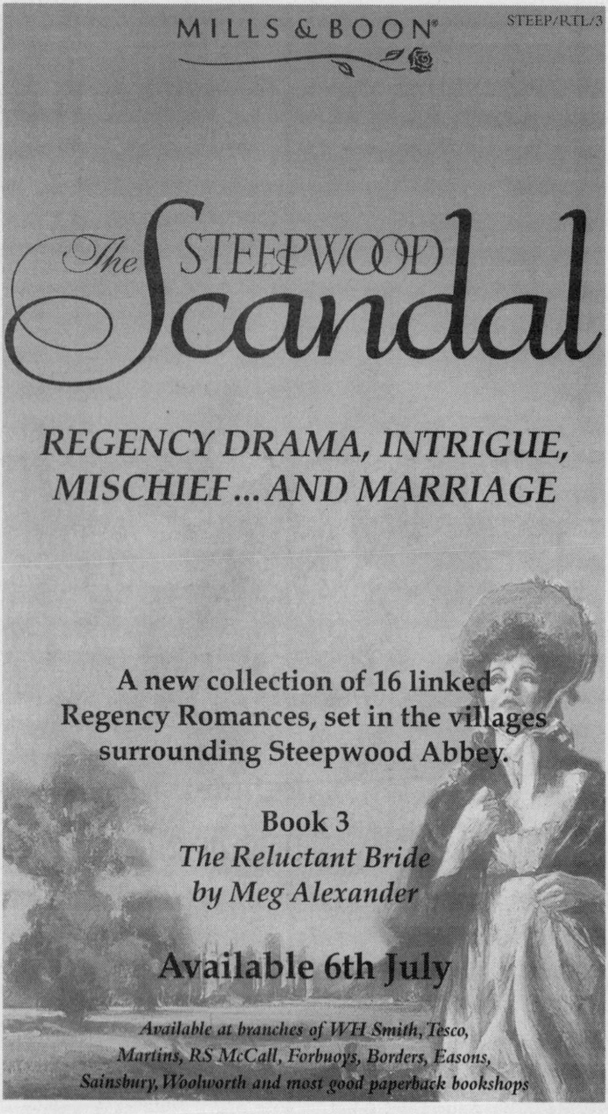
MILLS & BOON®
STEEP/RTL/3
The STEEPWOOD Scandal
REGENCY DRAMA, INTRIGUE, MISCHIEF... AND MARRIAGE
A new collection of 16 linked Regency Romances, set in the villages surrounding Steepwood Abbey.
Book 3
The Reluctant Bride
by Meg Alexander
Available 6th July
Available at branches of WH Smith, Tesco, Martins, RS McCall, Forbuoys, Borders, Easons, Sainsbury, Woolworth and most good paperback bookshops

Modern Romance™
Eight brand new titles each month
...seduction and passion guaranteed
Available at most branches of WH Smith, Tesco, Martins, Borders, Easons, Volume One/James Thin and most good paperback bookshops
GEN/01/RTL2